# SYSTEMS ENGINEERING
## MATHEMATICS

# PRENTICE-HALL SPACE TECHNOLOGY SERIES

*C. William Besserer and Floyd E. Nixon, editors*

ALEXANDER and BAILEY   *Systems Engineering Mathematics*
BAZOVSKY   *Reliability Theory and Practice*
ELLIS and LUDWIG   *Systems Philosophy*
LLOYD and LIPOW   *Reliability: Management, Methods, and Mathematics*
KOLK   *Modern Flight Dynamics*
SAMARAS   *Theory of Ion Flow Dynamics*
SCHLESINGER, et al.   *Principles of Electronic Warfare*
STILTZ, ED.   *Aerospace Telemetry*

PRENTICE-HALL INTERNATIONAL, INC.
*London • Tokyo • Sydney • Paris*

PRENTICE-HALL OF CANADA, LTD.

PRENTICE-HALL DE MEXICO, S.A.

# SYSTEMS ENGINEERING
# MATHEMATICS

*J. Eugene Alexander*

*J. Milton Bailey*

MARTIN MARIETTA CORPORATION
MARTIN COMPANY
ORLANDO, FLORIDA

PRENTICE-HALL, INC.

*Englewood Cliffs, New Jersey*

*1962*

Library of Congress Catalog Card Number 62–14912
Printed in the United States of America
88144-C

# PREFACE

System design requires engineers and physicists familiar with a wide variety of scientific disciplines. This book was written to provide a foundation in systems engineering by emphasizing the similarity of the mathematics describing elementary physical problems in electrical, mechanical, fluid, and thermodynamic engineering. The development of the mathematics begins with the physical laws themselves, so that the only prerequisite is a knowledge of differential equations.

The book is intended as a college text. However, the treatment of parallelism throughout makes the book a useful industrial reference, since an engineer trained in any of the fields covered can use his own particular education as the basis for understanding the other fields. It can also be used by mathematicians in industry. In fact, the first class taught from the manuscript was one from industry with about 50 per cent mathematics majors.

Several approaches can be taken in teaching the book in colleges. If the students have had Laplace transforms, Chap. 2 can be omitted. Then Chaps. 3 through 6 might constitute a three-hour, one-semester course. Chapters 7 through 11 might then make up the second semester. Chapters 9 and 10 can be omitted if time precludes covering all the material. Chapter 11, which is a detailed example, could serve as the basis for a one-hour design seminar. Obviously the individual professor will want to tailor his own course to his own curriculum, but the suggestions point out the flexibility of the book as an instructional aid.

The authors have tried to incorporate many practical examples taken from their experiences in industry. Where numerical values are given they are typical of those found in similar industrial problems.

J. EUGENE ALEXANDER
J. MILTON BAILEY

*Orlando, Florida*

# ACKNOWLEDGEMENTS

The beginning of our interest in and knowledge of systems engineering is due to Page S. Buckley of E. I. duPont de Nemours and Company, Inc. and the late Professor Donald P. Campbell of the Massachusetts Institute of Technology. We will always be grateful for the start they gave us. In particular, Mr. Buckley materially influenced the contents of Chaps. 3 and 10 and Professor Campbell, Chaps. 6 and 9. At the same time P. D. Schnelle of duPont was helping us translate the theory into practical applications.

We wish to thank the Martin Company for assistance in preparing the manuscript. We are indebted to Dynatronics, Inc., and Mr. R. C. Nichols of that company for use of the automatic telemetering tracking problem of Chap. 11. The Southern Bell Telephone and Telegraph Company in the person of Mr. J. L. Layne furnished typical distributed parameters for various telephone exchanges. AiResearch Manufacturing Company of Arizona, Division of The Garrett Corporation, has given us permission to use the information on the gas turbine discussed in Chap. 9 and control valves discussed in Chap. 7.

We wish to thank the following individuals of the Martin Company for their assistance: Warren B. Koch, M. E. McCoy, Edna Stevens, Frances Smith, Walter C. Nelson, Cliff S. O'Hearne, Ross S. Dutton, Stanley Kuca, James G. Johnston, Corinne Mear, Jane Beaty, Mary Foster, Marie Clugston, Cyril W. Coad, and Dave L. Sweitzer.

Lastly, we wish to thank the Prentice-Hall staff and the series editors, C. W. Besserer and F. E. Nixon, for their help in making a finished book from the manuscript.

# TABLE OF CONTENTS

# SYSTEMS ENGINEERING
# MATHEMATICS

# CHAPTER ONE

# INTRODUCTION

## 1.00 SYSTEMS ENGINEERING

Designing the complex systems of today requires many specialists. A missile system takes the composite knowledge of experts in aerodynamics, electronics, propulsion, hydraulics, and many other fields. To tie together the work of the individual specialists, someone must have a broad technical background and more than a speaking acquaintance with the various technical disciplines involved. This need is met by the systems engineer.

How does an engineer obtain the necessary breadth? The best approach is to use the tools of his own particular technology as the jumping-off point. The similarities among the behaviors of different systems should be related to what he already knows. One of the best keys to these similarities lies in the mathematical statements of the physical laws describing these disciplines. The same mathematical forms are used over and over. Specifically, linear differential equations with constant coefficients are widely used in electrical, mechanical, fluid, and thermodynamic problems. The coefficients and dependent variables represent different quantities. The independent variable, time, appears in all of them.

The similarities do not stop with the mathematical forms, however. The special case of Newton's second law of motion — force is equal to mass times acceleration — is the basis of the derivation for the application of moment of inertia in rotational systems and for the concept of inertance in fluid systems. Hooke's law for rectilineal springs can be converted to rotational springs. The dynamic equations of hydraulic and pneumatic systems have the same coefficients and the same variables. The differences are in the methods of calculating the coefficients.

Another similarity appears in the forms that disturbances take. A rectified a-c wave has a ripple on it, and the waveform can be expressed as a Fourier's series. Compressors have the same type of ripple in their outputs and they also can be described by a Fourier's series. To reduce the magnitude of the ripple and increase the ripple frequency, multiple phases are used in both the electrical and hydraulic systems. An example of how these disturbances affect a system occurred at the inlet to a chemical reactor. A thermocouple was sensing wide changes in temperature at a fairly regular frequency. One of the first thoughts was that the variation might be due to inadequate peripheral mixing of the various streams. Analysis of the compressor output and the hydraulic impedances showed that the temperature variation was due entirely to the pulsating nature of the compressor output flow. Both the magnitude and frequency of the temperature variation were calculated within small percentages of the measured values.

The purpose of this book is to organize the similarities so that a mechanical, electrical, chemical, aerodynamic, or hydraulic engineer can easily transfer his knowledge to fields outside of his specialty. To make the transition more meaningful, examples with typical numerical values are given. Most of the examples are taken from actual industrial problems.

## 1.10 DIFFERENTIAL EQUATIONS

The dynamics to be discussed are described for the most part by linear differential equations with constant coefficients. The general form of this type is

$$A_n \frac{d^n x}{dt^n} + A_{n-1} \frac{d^{n-1} x}{dt^{n-1}} + \cdots + A_1 \frac{dx}{dt} + A_0 x = f(t) \qquad (1.10\text{-}1)$$

It is of order $n$ because the highest-order derivative is $n$. It is linear because none of the derivatives of $x$ or the function $x$ itself is multiplied by any other function of $x$ or its derivatives. The $A$'s are constants.

The classical method for solving this type of differential equation can be demonstrated with the second-order equation given in Eq. (1.10-2).

$$3 \frac{d^2 x}{dt^2} + 4 \frac{dx}{dt} + x = t \qquad (1.10\text{-}2)$$

The solution obtained by this method contains two parts — the complementary solution and the particular solution. The complementary solution is obtained by treating the process of differentiation as an operator $D$ and setting the right-hand side equal to zero.

$$(3D^2 + 4D + 1)x = 0 \qquad (1.10\text{-}3)$$

The auxiliary equation is then written as

$$3m^2 + 4m + 1 = 0 \qquad (1.10\text{-}4)$$

which can be factored to

$$(3m + 1)(m + 1) = 0 \qquad (1.10\text{-}5)$$

The roots are

$$m = -\tfrac{1}{3} \text{ and } -1$$

The complementary solution is then

$$x_C = C_1\epsilon^{-t/3} + C_2\epsilon^{-t} \qquad (1.10\text{-}6)$$

There are two constants of integration because the equation from which the solution stemmed is second order. The number of constants is always equal to the order of the differential equation, although some of the constants may be zero. In dynamic problems these constants are usually found in terms of initial conditions, that is, the value of the function and its derivatives at time zero.

The particular solution to Eq. (1.10-2) can be obtained by noting that

$$x_p = At + B \qquad (1.10\text{-}7)$$

will make the left-hand side be of the same form as the right-hand side. Using this form of $x$ in Eq. (1.10-2),

$$3A \cdot 0 + 4A + At + B = t \qquad (1.10\text{-}8)$$

Therefore, $A$ must equal 1 and $B$ must equal $-4$, so

$$x_p = t - 4 \qquad (1.10\text{-}9)$$

Combining Eqs. (1.10-6) and (1.10-9),

$$x = x_C + x_p = C_1\epsilon^{-t/3} + C_2\epsilon^{-t} + t - 4 \qquad (1.10\text{-}10)$$

The constants $C_1$ and $C_2$ can now be determined if two initial conditions are specified. Suppose that $x$ and its first derivative are both zero at time zero.

Then

$$C_1 + C_2 = 4 \qquad (1.10\text{-}11)$$

$$-\frac{C_1}{3} - C_2 = -1 \qquad (1.10\text{-}12)$$

which are obtained by setting $x$ and $t$ equal to zero in Eq. (1.10-10) and by setting $dx/dt$ and $t$ equal to zero after taking the derivative of both sides of Eq. (1.10-10). The values of $C_1$ and $C_2$ are

$$C_1 = \tfrac{9}{2}, \qquad C_2 = -\tfrac{1}{2},$$

and Eq. (1.10-10) becomes

$$x = \tfrac{9}{2}\epsilon^{-t/3} - \tfrac{1}{2}\epsilon^{-t} + t - 4 \qquad (1.10\text{-}13)$$

for the specified initial conditions.

In Chap. 2 the Laplace transform method for solving linear differential equations with constant coefficients is given. In most cases it is the simplest method.

## 1.20 SYSTEM EXAMPLE

As an example of a system that involves differential equations of this type representing the application of several engineering disciplines, let us consider the control system of a missile that is command-guided from the ground in the $x$ and $y$ coordinates but derives its altitude commands from an internal pressure-sensing device. The system is shown in Fig. 1.20-1. The missile is fired and acquired by the tracker. The tracker

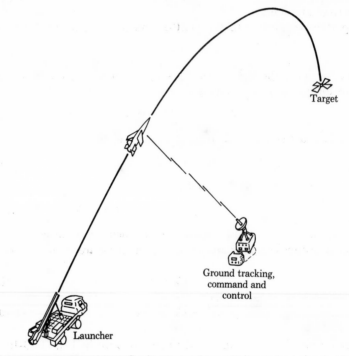

**Fig. 1.20-1** Surface-to-surface missile system.

moves mechanically to follow the missile, so part of the system response is dependent on the mechanical characteristics of the tracker. A ground computer calculates position and velocity of the missile, and appropriate commands are sent to the missile over the radio link. The commands go through electrical compensation networks, so the transfer functions of electrical circuits are involved. When the commands are received in the missile, they are translated into required control-fin movements. The fins are hydraulically actuated, so the response of hydraulic elements enters the picture. The altitude control system is pneumatic. To prevent the electronic components in both the missile and ground equipment from getting too hot, heat removal paths must be provided, so thermodynamic calculations are part of the system design. In examining only a few of the functions of this system, we have seen applications of all the disciplines with which this book is concerned — electrical, mechanical, hydraulic, pneumatic, and thermodynamic.

## 1.30 NOMENCLATURE

In a book that covers many disciplines, it is impractical to avoid using the same symbol to represent more than one quantity. In many cases, however, there is an analogous relationship among the quantities denoted by the same symbol. For example, $R$ stands for resistance in electrical, mechanical rectilineal, hydraulic, pneumatic, and thermodynamic equations. Some exceptions exist. $\gamma$ is used both as the ratio of specific heats and as the exponent of velocity for the general relation between rectilineal resistance, force, and velocity. In most cases, standard symbology for the particular engineering field is used.

In general, lower-case letters represent variables in the time domain while upper-case letters represent variables in the Laplace domain. Since the lower-case $t$ is reserved for time, torque is denoted by a capital $T$ in both the time and Laplace domains. The letter $s$ represents the Laplace operator in all time-to-Laplace-domain transformations. In Chap. 10 transformations are made from the $x$ or distance domain, and $p$ is used as the operator to emphasize that it is *not* a time-domain transformation.

Derivatives are indicated either as $(df/dt)$, $\dot{f}$, or $f'$. For the dot and prime notation the number of dots or primes indicates the order of the derivative.

## 1.40 PROBLEMS

Solve the following differential equations:

1.  $2\dfrac{dv}{dt} + v = 6 \sin t$

    where $v(0) = 0$

2. $6\dfrac{d^2x}{dt^2} + 24\dfrac{dx}{dt} + 18x = t$

   where $x(0) = 1$ and $\dot{x}(0) = -2$

3. $\dfrac{d^2q}{dt^2} + 2\dfrac{dq}{dt} + q = 5$

   where $q(0) = 0$ and $\dot{q}(0) = 0$

4. $\dfrac{di}{dt} + 4i + 5\displaystyle\int i\,dt = \sin 2t$

   where   $i(0) = 0$   and   $i'(0) = 0$

5. $\dot{x}_1 + 2x_2 = 4$,   $\dot{x}_2 - 3x_1 = 0$

   where   $x_1(0) = 0$   and   $x_2(0) = 0$

# CHAPTER TWO

# THE LAPLACE TRANSFORM

## 2.00 DIFFERENTIAL EQUATIONS

The following chapters will stress the similarity of physical systems by showing that the differential equations that characterize their behavior are analogous. In every case, the differential equations will be a special type called *linear differential equations with constant coefficients*. This type is unique among the class of differential equations in that it is the only subclass whose elements have known solutions. The fact that there is no general method of solving every differential equation severely restricts the characterization of a physical system. If the engineer characterizes a system with a nonlinear equation, he is faced with the problem of solving the equation. If he characterizes the system with a linear equation, the response might not adequately represent the system. However, a large number of physical problems can be adequately described by a system of linear differential equations with constant coefficients.

This applies especially in the field of electrical engineering, since electrical elements such as capacitors or resistors closely approximate linear behavior over wide ranges. For this reason, such differential equations appear often in electrical problems, and the analogies between other systems and electrical networks will be stressed in the following chapters.

In this chapter, a valuable tool for solving such equations will be developed. Since it is not our aim to develop operational mathematics, we will not delve too deeply into the mathematics of this tool but rather summarize its properties and show how it can be used in engineering problems.

Before discussing this problem some motivation is desirable. For an example let us consider a second-order equation:

$$\frac{d^2y}{dt^2} + a\frac{dy}{dt} + by = c \qquad (2.00\text{-}1)$$

The solution can be found by classical techniques and is

$$y = k_1\epsilon^{P_1 t} + k_2\epsilon^{P_2 t} + \frac{c}{b} \qquad \text{when} \qquad \frac{a^2}{4} \neq b$$

The first two terms of the right-hand expression are the transient solution and the exponents $P_1$ and $P_2$ are determined from the equation

$$P_1, P_2 = -\frac{a}{2} \pm \sqrt{\frac{a^2}{4} - b}$$

The two constants of integration $k_1$ and $k_2$ are determined by the initial conditions of the system Eq. (2.00-1) characterizes. If $P_1$ and $P_2$ have negative real parts, the last term of the solution of Eq. (2.00-1), $c/b$, is the steady-state solution, which is often written

$$y_{\text{s.s.}} = \lim_{t \to \infty} y(t) = \frac{c}{b}$$

However, if $P_1$ or $P_2$ has positive real parts, there is no limit to $y(t)$ and the solution is not bounded. For physical systems it is very important to know the value of these exponential coefficients since they determine the time response of the system. Moreover, if they are positive, the system is not bounded. This tool which we will develop called the *Laplace transform* will allow us to tell the nature of these exponents and the steady-state term. As an extra bonus the initial conditions are taken into consideration and appear automatically in the solution. With tongue in cheek, we can say that the Laplace transform is an "idiot-proof" method of solving a linear differential equation with constant coefficients.

## 2.10 THE LAPLACE TRANSFORM

In any textbook written primarily for engineers, as opposed to mathematicians, there exists the problem of a suitable starting point in developing a mathematical concept. Since there are many suitable books available on the mathematical development of Laplace transforms, our approach is to state the transform and then develop its use in the solution of differential equations. The Laplace transform is defined by the formula

$$\mathcal{L}[f(t)] = \int_0^\infty f(t)\epsilon^{-st}dt = F(s) \qquad (2.10\text{-}1)$$

$\mathcal{L}[f(t)]$ is the Laplace transform of the function $f(t)$. Since the variable of integration is $t$, the final function will be in the $s$ or Laplace domain and is written $F(s)$ where $s$ is a complex number $\sigma + j\omega$.

From the definition of the transform, it follows that, if $a$ is a constant,

$$\mathcal{L}[af(t)] = aF(s) \tag{2.10-2}$$

and

$$\mathcal{L}[f_1(t) + f_2(t)] = F_1(s) + F_2(s) \tag{2.10-3}$$

Since we are interested in differential equations, it is logical to determine now the Laplace transform of the terms of such equations and the types of inputs commonly encountered. First consider the exponential

$$f(t) = \epsilon^{-at}$$

From the definition

$$\mathcal{L}[\epsilon^{-at}] = \int_0^\infty \epsilon^{-at}\epsilon^{-st}\, dt$$

Thus,

$$\mathcal{L}[\epsilon^{-at}] = \int_0^\infty \epsilon^{-(s+a)t}\, dt = \frac{\epsilon^{-(s+a)t}}{-(s+a)}\Bigg]_0^\infty$$

Since the variable of integration is $t$, the equation now becomes

$$\mathcal{L}[\epsilon^{-at}] = \frac{1}{s+a} \tag{2.10-4}$$

Note that if the exponential coefficient were positive, the identity would be

$$\mathcal{L}[\epsilon^{at}] = \frac{1}{s-a}$$

Another transform follows directly from Eq. (2.10-4). By Euler's formula

$$\sin \omega t = \frac{\epsilon^{j\omega t} - \epsilon^{-j\omega t}}{2j}$$

From Eq. (2.10-3),

$$\mathcal{L}[\sin \omega t] = \mathcal{L}\left[\frac{\epsilon^{j\omega t}}{2j}\right] - \mathcal{L}\left[\frac{\epsilon^{-j\omega t}}{2j}\right]$$

Hence

$$\mathcal{L}[\sin \omega t] = \frac{1}{2j}\left[\frac{1}{s-j\omega} - \frac{1}{s+j\omega}\right]$$

and

$$\mathcal{L}[\sin \omega t] = \frac{\omega}{s^2 + \omega^2} \tag{2.10-5}$$

When $f'(t)$ is the first time derivative of $f(t)$, Eq. (2.10-1) becomes

$$\mathcal{L}[f'(t)] = \int_0^\infty f'(t)\epsilon^{-st}\, dt$$

This can be integrated by parts as follows: Let $dv = f'(t)\,dt$ and $u = \epsilon^{-st}$. Then $v = f(t)$ and $du = -s\epsilon^{-st}dt$. Hence:

$$\mathcal{L}[f'(t)] = \epsilon^{-st}f(t)\Big]_0^\infty + s\int_0^\infty f(t)\epsilon^{-st}\,dt$$

The first term of this expression, $\epsilon^{-st}f(t)\Big]_0^\infty$, points out a restriction upon the type of function for which the Laplace transform exists. For the present, suppose

$$\lim_{t\to\infty} \epsilon^{-st}f(t) = 0 \tag{2.10-6}$$

Then

$$\mathcal{L}[f'(t)] = -\lim_{t\to 0} \epsilon^{-st}f(t) + s\int_0^\infty f(t)\epsilon^{-st}\,dt \tag{2.10-7}$$

The first expression of Eq. (2.10-7) is the initial value of the function and will be written $f(0^+)$. The integral is by definition the Laplace transform of $f(t)$ and thus

$$\mathcal{L}[f'(t)] = sF(s) - f(0^+) \tag{2.10-8}$$

The second derivative, $f''(t)$, can be found from Eq. (2.10-8) as follows

$$\mathcal{L}[f''(t)] = \mathcal{L}\left[\frac{d}{dt}f'(t)\right]$$

Hence        $$\mathcal{L}[f''(t)] = s\mathcal{L}[f'(t)] - f'(0^+)$$

and          $$\mathcal{L}[f''(t)] = s^2F(s) - sf(0^+) - f'(0^+) \tag{2.10-9}$$

This procedure can be extended to any order derivative. Returning to Eq. (2.10-6), it is seen that were this restriction not met, the transform would not exist. A function satisfying this restriction is said to be *of exponential order*. (A function not of exponential order is $\epsilon^{t^2}$). One other restriction is that $f(t)$ be piecewise (sectionally) continuous.

Consider now the Laplace transform of the definite integral, i.e. $\int_0^t f(t)\,dt$. By Eq. (2.10-1),

$$\mathcal{L}\left[\int_0^t f(t)\,dt\right] = \int_0^\infty \left[\int_0^t f(t)\,dt\right]\epsilon^{-st}\,dt$$

Integrating by parts, let $u = \int_0^t f(t)\,dt,\qquad dv = \epsilon^{-st}\,dt$

Thus

$$du = f(t)\,dt,\qquad v = -\frac{\epsilon^{-st}}{s}$$

Hence

$$\mathcal{L}\left[\int_0^t f(t)\, dt\right] = -\frac{1}{s}\left[\left\{\int_0^t f(t)\, dt\right\}\epsilon^{-st}\right]_0^\infty + \frac{1}{s}\int_0^\infty \epsilon^{-st} f(t)\, dt$$

By definition

$$\int_0^t f(t)\, dt = \phi(t) - \phi(0^+)$$

where

$$\phi(0^+) = \lim_{t \to 0} \phi(t)$$

Hence

$$\mathcal{L}\left[\int_0^t f(t)\, dt\right] = -\frac{1}{s}\left[\phi(t)\epsilon^{-st} - \phi(0^+)\epsilon^{-st}\right]_0^\infty + \frac{1}{s}\int_0^\infty \epsilon^{-st} f(t)\, dt$$

Now by definition

$$\int_0^\infty \epsilon^{-st} f(t)\, dt = F(s)$$

Thus performing the indicated manipulations

$$\mathcal{L}\left[\int_0^t f(t)\, dt\right] = \frac{F(s)}{s} \qquad (2.10\text{-}10)$$

The value of the definite integral of bounded functions is always zero for infinitesimal increments and hence in classical differential equations, one generally uses the indefinite integral to allow for initial conditions. But in the type of physical problems that engineers encounter, the indefinite integral is confusing since the engineer is interested in the response of a system between some initial time $t = 0^+$ and some final time $t$. However, the Laplace transform of the indefinite integral can be obtained in a logical manner from Eq. (2.10-10). First, the indefinite integral can be expressed as a constant $k_0$ plus the definite integral, i.e.,

$$\int f(t)\, dt = k_0 + \int_0^t f(t)\, dt$$

where $k_0$ for the problems with which this book is concerned is the value of $\int f(t)\, dt$ at the initial time $t = 0^+$. Then

$$\mathcal{L}[\int f(t)\, dt] = \mathcal{L}[k_0] + \mathcal{L}\left[\int_0^t f(t)\, dt\right]$$

and using Eq. (2.10-3) and (2.10-10)

$$\mathcal{L}[\int f(t)\, dt] = \frac{1}{s}[\int f(t)\, dt]_{t=0^+} + \frac{F(s)}{s}$$

Thus if the initial conditions are zero, the definite and indefinite integrals have the same transform.

A common driving function in physical circuits is the unit step function shown in Fig. 2.10-1, written $u_{-1}(t)$ and defined as

$$u_{-1}(t) = 1, \qquad t \geq 0$$
$$u_{-1}(t) = 0, \qquad t < 0$$

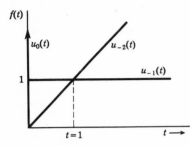

Its Laplace transform is

$$\mathcal{L}[u_{-1}(t)] = \int_0^\infty u_{-1}(t)\epsilon^{-st}\,dt = \int_0^\infty \epsilon^{-st}\,dt$$

Hence

$$\mathcal{L}[u_{-1}(t)] = \frac{1}{s} \qquad (2.10\text{-}11)$$

**Fig. 2.10-1** Unit step, unit ramp, and unit impulse.

The unit ramp function is the integral of the step function and is written $u_{-2}(t)$. Its Laplace transform is

$$\mathcal{L}[u_{-2}(t)] = \int_0^\infty t\epsilon^{-st}\,dt = \frac{1}{s^2} \qquad (2.10\text{-}12)$$

The derivative of the unit step function is the unit impulse written $u_0(t)$. It is illustrated in Fig. 2.10-1. This function is of infinite height and infinitesimal width which by definition has unity area; i.e.,

$$\int_0^\infty u_0(t)\,dt = 1 \qquad (2.10\text{-}13)$$

The Laplace transform of the unit impulse is then

$$\mathcal{L}[u_0(t)] = \int_0^\infty u_0(t)\epsilon^{-st}\,dt = 1 \qquad (2.10\text{-}14)$$

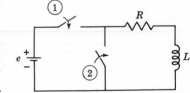

A differential equation can now be solved and serves to illustrate the usefulness of the Laplace transform. Consider the simple $R\text{-}L$ circuit shown in Fig. 2.10-2. Switch 1 is energized until the steady-state current flows through the resistor.

**Fig. 2.10-2** $R\text{-}L$ circuit with initial conditions.

At this time, switch 1 is de-energized and switch 2 is energized. The instant of switch 2's closing is taken as zero time. The characterizing equation is found by Kirchhoff's laws and is

$$0 = Ri + L\frac{di}{dt} \qquad (2.10\text{-}15)$$

where the initial condition is

$$i(0^+) = \frac{E}{R} \tag{2.10-16}$$

The first step is to find the transform of each term in the differential equation; i.e.,

$$0 = \mathcal{L}[Ri] + \mathcal{L}\left[L\frac{di}{dt}\right] \tag{2.10-17}$$

From Eq. (2.10-2),

$$\mathcal{L}[Ri] = RI(s) \tag{2.10-18}$$

where $I(s)$ is the quantity to be determined. From Eqs. (2.10-2), (2.10-3), and (2.10-8),

$$\mathcal{L}\left[L\frac{di}{dt}\right] = L\left[sI(s) - \frac{E}{R}\right] \tag{2.10-19}$$

Substituting Eqs. (2.10-18) and (2.10-19) into Eq. (2.10-17),

$$0 = RI(s) + LsI(s) - \frac{LE}{R}$$

Rearranging terms,

$$\frac{LE}{R} = (R + Ls)I(s) \tag{2.10-20}$$

and thus

$$I(s) = \frac{LE}{R[R + Ls]} \tag{2.10-21}$$

In Eq. (2.10-20) a reason is found for using the Laplace transform. The differential equation in the variable $t$ has been transformed into an algebraic equation in the variable $s$. Furthermore the initial condition automatically enters into the expression for $I(s)$. Rearranging Eq. (2.10-21) one obtains

$$I(s) = \frac{E/R}{s + R/L} \tag{2.10-22}$$

From Eq. (2.10-4), the time function whose Laplace transform is that of Eq. (2.10-22) is

$$i = \frac{E}{R}\,\epsilon^{-(R/L)t} \tag{2.10-23}$$

Of course, using the Laplace transform in solving a simple first-order equation is analogous to using a sledge hammer to crack a peanut. However, in higher-order differential equations, the transform technique is far superior to the classical technique.

Several theorems will now be developed which are useful tools in obtaining the Laplace transform of functions utilizing known transforms. The theorems will be stated and the proof outlined. Interested readers should review the conditions under which an integral exists and under which the order of integration of a double integral can be reversed. In every case, it will be assumed that $f(t)$ and $F(s)$ exist and that

$$\mathcal{L}[f(t)] = F(s)$$

## 2.20 TRANSFORM THEOREMS

1. *Final Value*

THEOREM

$$\lim_{s \to 0} sF(s) = \lim_{t \to \infty} f(t)$$

*Proof:* From Eq. (2.10-8),

$$\int_0^\infty f'(t)\epsilon^{-st}\, dt = sF(s) - f(0^+)$$

Since

$$\lim_{s \to 0}\left[\int_0^\infty f'(t)\epsilon^{-st}\, dt\right] = \int_0^\infty f'(t)\, dt = f(t)\Big]_0^\infty$$

and

$$\lim_{s \to 0}\left[\int_0^\infty f'(t)\epsilon^{-st}\, dt\right] = \lim_{s \to 0}[sF(s) - f(0^+)]$$

then

$$\lim_{t \to \infty} f(t) - \lim_{t \to 0} f(t) = \lim_{s \to 0} sF(s) - \lim_{t \to 0} f(t)$$

and

$$\lim_{t \to \infty} f(t) = \lim_{s \to 0} sF(s)$$

EXAMPLE: Find the final value of the time function whose transform is

$$F(s) = \frac{1}{s + a}$$

*Procedure:* Using the final value theorem

$$\lim_{s \to 0} \frac{s}{s + a} = 0$$

This can easily be checked since the time function is

$$f(t) = \epsilon^{-at} \quad \text{and} \quad \lim_{t \to \infty} \epsilon^{-at} = 0$$

A word of caution is due here, as this theorem is valid only if a final value exists. As an example, suppose $F(s) = 1/(s - a)$. Application of the final-value theorem gives the same results as $F(s) = 1/(s + a)$. However, $f(t) = \epsilon^{at}$ and $\lim_{t \to \infty} \epsilon^{at} = \infty$. (For conditions on the existence of a final value, see Sec. 2.30.)

2. *Initial Value*

THEOREM

$$\lim_{s \to \infty} sF(s) = \lim_{t \to 0} f(t)$$

*Proof:* From Eq. (2.10-8),

$$\int_0^\infty f'(t)\epsilon^{-st}\,dt = sF(s) - f(0^+)$$

Taking the limit of both sides of the equality,

$$\lim_{s \to \infty} \int_0^\infty f'(t)\epsilon^{-st}\,dt = \lim_{s \to \infty} [sF(s) - f(0^+)]$$

but

$$\lim_{s \to \infty} \left[ \int_0^\infty f'(t)\epsilon^{-st}\,dt \right] = 0$$

hence

$$\lim_{s \to \infty} sF(s) = \lim_{t \to 0} f(t)$$

EXAMPLE: Find the initial value of the function whose transform is

$$F(s) = \frac{1}{s + a}$$

*Procedure:* Applying the theorem, one obtains.

$$\lim_{s \to \infty} \frac{s}{s + a} = 1$$

As a check, $f(t) = \epsilon^{-at}$ and $\lim_{t \to 0} \epsilon^{-at} = 1$

3. *Multiplication by s*

THEOREM: Multiplication by $s$ in the Laplace domain is analogous to differentiation in the time domain if $f(0^+) = 0$.

*Proof:* From Eq. (2.10-8),

$$\mathcal{L}[f'(t)] = sF(s) - f(0^+)$$

If $f(0^+) = 0$, the theorem is proved. The proof then consists of determining the conditions under which this is true. Consider $sF(s)$ as a ratio of two polynomials in $s$; i.e.,

$$sF(s) = \frac{q(s)}{p(s)} = \frac{s^n + a_1 s^{n-1} + \cdots + a_n}{s^m + b_1 s^{m-1} + \cdots + b_m}$$

Hence

$$\lim_{s \to \infty} sF(s) = 0, \qquad m > n + 1$$

Thus, from the Theorem 2 (initial value), $\lim_{t \to 0} f(t) = 0$. Therefore,

$$\mathcal{L}[f'(t)] = sF(s)$$

EXAMPLE: Knowing that $\mathcal{L}[\sin \omega t] = \omega/(s^2 + \omega^2)$, find $\mathcal{L}[\cos \omega t]$.

*Procedure:* Since $\lim_{t \to 0} [\sin \omega t] = 0$, the differentiation theorem holds and

$$\mathcal{L}[\omega \cos \omega t] = \frac{s\omega}{s^2 + \omega^2}$$

Thus

$$\mathcal{L}[\cos \omega t] = \frac{s}{s^2 + \omega^2}$$

4. *Multiplication by t*

THEOREM

$$\mathcal{L}[tf(t)] = -\frac{dF(s)}{ds}$$

*Proof:* By definition

$$\int_0^\infty f(t)\epsilon^{-st} \, dt = F(s)$$

Taking the derivative with respect to $s$, one obtains

$$\frac{d}{ds}\left[ \int_0^\infty f(t)\epsilon^{-st} \, dt \right] = \frac{dF(s)}{ds}$$

Hence,

$$-\int_0^\infty tf(t)\epsilon^{-st} \, dt = \frac{dF(s)}{ds}$$

and

$$\mathcal{L}[tf(t)] = -\frac{dF(s)}{ds}$$

EXAMPLE: Knowing $\mathcal{L}[u_{-1}(t)] = 1/s$, find $\mathcal{L}[t]$.

*Procedure*

$$\mathcal{L}[t] = \mathcal{L}[tu_{-1}(t)]$$

Hence

$$\mathcal{L}[t] = -\frac{d}{ds}\left[\frac{1}{s}\right] = \frac{1}{s^2}$$

5. *Division by s*

THEOREM

$$\frac{F(s)}{s} = \mathcal{L}\left[\int_0^t f(t)\,dt\right]$$

*Proof:* This theorem has been developed and proved in Eq. (2.10-10).

EXAMPLE: Knowing $\mathcal{L}[u_{-1}(t)] = 1/s$, find $\mathcal{L}[t]$.

*Procedure:* Since $\int_0^t u_{-1}(t)\,dt = t$,

$$\mathcal{L}[t] = \frac{1}{s} \times \frac{1}{s} = \frac{1}{s^2}$$

6. *Division by t*

THEOREM

$$\mathcal{L}\left[\frac{f(t)}{t}\right] = \int_s^\infty F(s)\,ds$$

*Proof:* By definition,

$$\int_0^\infty f(t)\epsilon^{-st}\,dt = F(s)$$

Integrating both sides of the equality,

$$\int_s^\infty \left[\int_0^\infty f(t)\epsilon^{-st}\,dt\right] ds = \int_s^\infty F(s)\,ds$$

Interchanging the order of integration

$$\int_0^\infty \left[\frac{-f(t)}{t}\,\epsilon^{-st}\right]_s^\infty dt = \int_s^\infty F(s)\,ds$$

Hence

$$\int_0^\infty \frac{f(t)}{t}\,\epsilon^{-st}\,dt = \int_s^\infty F(s)\,ds$$

or

$$\mathcal{L}\left[\frac{f(t)}{t}\right] = \int_s^\infty F(s)\,ds$$

EXAMPLE: Knowing $\mathcal{L}[t] = 1/s^2$, find $\mathcal{L}[u_{-1}(t)]$.

*Procedure*

$$u_{-1}(t) = t \times \frac{1}{t}$$

Hence $\qquad \mathcal{L}[u_{-1}(t)] = \int_s^\infty \frac{ds}{s^2} = \frac{1}{s}$

7. *First Shifting Theorem*

THEOREM

$$\mathcal{L}[\epsilon^{-at}f(t)] = F(s + a)$$

*Proof:* By definition,

$$\mathcal{L}[\epsilon^{-at}f(t)] = \int_0^\infty \epsilon^{-at}f(t)\epsilon^{-st}\, dt$$

Rearranging the exponential coefficients,

$$\mathcal{L}[\epsilon^{-at}f(t)] = \int_0^\infty \epsilon^{-t(s+a)}f(t)\, dt$$

Let $\lambda = s + a$, then $\mathcal{L}[\epsilon^{-at}f(t)] = F(\lambda)$ and, by definition of $\lambda$,

$$\mathcal{L}[\epsilon^{-at}f(t)] = F(s + a)$$

EXAMPLE: Knowing $\mathcal{L}[u_{-1}(t)] = 1/s$, find $\mathcal{L}[\epsilon^{-at}]$.

*Procedure*

$$\mathcal{L}[\epsilon^{-at}] = \mathcal{L}[\epsilon^{-at}u_{-1}(t)]$$

then $\qquad \mathcal{L}[\epsilon^{-at}] = \dfrac{1}{s + a}$

EXAMPLE: Knowing $\mathcal{L}[t] = 1/s^2$, find $\mathcal{L}[t\epsilon^{-at}]$.

*Procedure:* By the first shifting theorem,

$$\mathcal{L}[t\epsilon^{-at}] = \frac{1}{(s + a)^2}$$

8. *Second Shifting Theorem*

THEOREM

$$\mathcal{L}[f(t - a)u_{-1}(t - a)] = \epsilon^{-as}F(s)$$

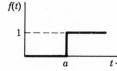

*Proof:* The function $u_{-1}(t - a)$ is the delayed step function shown in the sketch. It is not necessary to have the factor $u_{-1}(t - a)$ if it is kept in mind that the delayed function $f(t - a)$ does not have a value until $t \geq a$. By definition,

$$F(s) = \int_0^\infty f(\lambda)\epsilon^{-\lambda s} \, d\lambda$$

Note that the variable $t$ has been replaced by $\lambda$. This is legitimate, as the Laplace transform is not restricted to a time domain. Let $\lambda = t - a$. The limits of integration are now $a$ and $\infty$. Hence

$$\int_a^\infty f(t - a)\epsilon^{-s(t-a)} \, dt = F(s)$$

$$\epsilon^{as} \int_a^\infty f(t - a)\epsilon^{-st} \, dt = F(s)$$

and
$$\int_a^\infty f(t - a)\epsilon^{-st} \, dt = \epsilon^{-as}F(s)$$

To obtain the proper limits on the integral, the function under the integral sign is multiplied by the delayed step function. Thus

$$\int_0^\infty f(t - a)u_{-1}(t - a)\epsilon^{-st} \, dt = \epsilon^{-as}F(s)$$

Hence,
$$\mathcal{L}[f(t - a)u_{-1}(t - a)] = \epsilon^{-as}F(s)$$

EXAMPLE: Find the Laplace transform of the delayed step function.

*Procedure:* By the second shifting theorem

$$\mathcal{L}[u_{-1}(t-a)] = \frac{\epsilon^{-as}}{s}$$

EXAMPLE: Find the Laplace transform of the time function shown below.

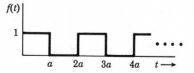

*Procedure:* The time function will be formed as a series of delayed step functions. The first pulse can be formed as $u_{-1}(t) - u_{-1}(t - a)$ and the next pulse as $u_{-1}(t - 2a) - u_{-1}(t - 3a)$. The complete function is now

$$f(t) = u_{-1}(t) - u_{-1}(t - a) + u_{-1}(t - 2a) - u_{-1}(t - 3a) + \cdots$$

Transforming the equation,

$$F(s) = \frac{1}{s} - \frac{\epsilon^{-as}}{s} + \frac{\epsilon^{-2as}}{s} - \frac{\epsilon^{-3as}}{s} + \cdots$$

$$= \frac{1}{s} - \frac{\epsilon^{-as}}{s}[1 - \epsilon^{-as} + \epsilon^{-2as} - \epsilon^{-3as} + \cdots]$$

But      $$\frac{1}{1 + \epsilon^{-as}} = 1 - \epsilon^{-as} + \epsilon^{-2as} - \epsilon^{-3as} + \cdots$$

Hence    $$F(s) = \frac{1}{s} - \frac{\epsilon^{-as}}{s(1 + \epsilon^{-as})} = \frac{1}{s}\left[\frac{1}{1 + \epsilon^{-as}}\right]$$

EXAMPLE: Find the current response of the network below where the system is initially at rest.

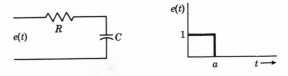

*Procedure:* By Kirchhoff's laws, $e = Ri + \dfrac{1}{C}\displaystyle\int i\, dt$

Transforming,

$$\mathcal{L}[e] = RI(s) + \frac{I(s)}{s} + \left[\frac{\dfrac{1}{C}\displaystyle\int i\, dt}{s}\right]_{t=0^+}$$

But      $$\mathcal{L}[e] = \mathcal{L}[u_{-1}(t) - u_{-1}(t - a)]$$

and      $$\mathcal{L}[e] = \frac{1}{s} - \frac{\epsilon^{-as}}{s}$$

Hence

$$\frac{1}{s} - \frac{\epsilon^{-as}}{s} = \left[R + \frac{1}{Cs}\right]I(s) + \left[\frac{\dfrac{1}{C}\displaystyle\int i\, dt}{s}\right]_{t=0^+}$$

Since     $$\frac{1}{C}\int i\, dt\bigg]_{t=0^+} = 0$$

$$I(s) = \frac{1 - \epsilon^{-as}}{s(R + 1/Cs)}$$

Rearranging the denominator

$$I(s) = \frac{1}{R(s + 1/RC)} - \frac{\epsilon^{-as}}{R(s + 1/RC)}$$

From Eq. (2.10-4),

$$\mathcal{L}[\epsilon^{-t/RC}] = \frac{1}{s + 1/RC}$$

By the second shifting theorem and Eq. (2.10-4),

$$\mathcal{L}[\epsilon^{-(t-a)/RC}u_{-1}(t - a)] = \frac{\epsilon^{-as}}{s + 1/RC}$$

Hence

$$i_{(t)} = \frac{\epsilon^{-t/RC}}{R} - \frac{\epsilon^{-(t-a)/RC}}{R}\,u_{-1}(t - a) \qquad (2.20\text{-}1)$$

This equation is shown in graphical form in Fig. 2.20-1.

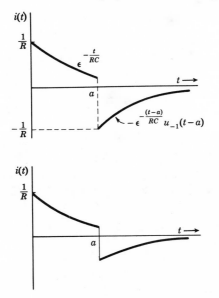

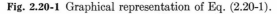

**Fig. 2.20-1** Graphical representation of Eq. (2.20-1).

## 9. *Partial Fractions*

In many cases the function of $s$ can be expressed as a ratio of two polynomials where the denominator is of higher degree than the numerator. The theory of rational fractions states that it is always possible to resolve this ratio into simpler partial fractions. Four cases will now be developed for the function

$$F(s) = \frac{(s + b_1)(s + b_2)\cdots(s + b_m)}{(s + a_1)(s + a_2)\cdots(s + a_n)}$$

where $n > m$.

*Case I.* When the factors of the denominator are all of the first degree and not repeated, the fractions will be of the form

$$F(s) = \frac{A_1}{s + a_1} + \frac{A_2}{s + a_2} + \cdots + \frac{A_n}{s + a_n}$$

where the number of constants to be determined is equal to the degree of the denominator.

EXAMPLE

$$F(s) = \frac{s}{(s + 1)(s + 2)} = \frac{A}{s + 1} + \frac{B}{s + 2}$$

Cross multiplying,

$$s = A(s + 2) + B(s + 1)$$

Since the coefficients of like powers of $s$ on each side of the equality must be identical, $A + B = 1$ and $2A + B = 0$. Hence, since $A = -1$ and $B = 2,$

$$F(s) = -\frac{1}{(s + 1)} + \frac{2}{(s + 2)}$$

Thus          $f(t) = -\epsilon^{-t} + 2\epsilon^{-2t}$

*Case II.* When the factors of the denominator are all of the first degree and some are repeated, there corresponds to every $n$-fold linear factor the sum of $n$ partial fractions as

$$F(s) = \frac{A_n}{(s + a)^n} + \frac{A_{n-1}}{(s + a)^{n-1}} + \cdots + \frac{A}{s + a}$$

$$+ \frac{B_1}{s + a_1} + \frac{B_2}{s + a_2} + \cdots$$

EXAMPLE

$$F(s) = \frac{s}{(s + 2)^2(s + 1)} = \frac{A_2}{(s + 2)^2} + \frac{A_1}{s + 2} + \frac{B}{s + 1}$$

Cross multiplying,

$$s = A_2[s + 1] + A_1[s + 2][s + 1] + B[s + 2]^2$$

Equating coefficients,

$$A_1 + B = 0$$
$$A_2 + 3A_1 + 2B = 1$$
$$A_2 + 2A_1 + 4B = 0$$

Hence $A_1 = 1$, $A_2 = 2$, $B = -1$, and

$$F(s) = \frac{2}{(s+2)^2} + \frac{1}{s+2} - \frac{1}{s+1}$$

Hence

$$f(t) = 2t\epsilon^{-2t} + \epsilon^{-2t} - \epsilon^{-t}$$

*Case III.* When the denominator contains factors of the second degree but none are repeated, to each nonrepeated quadratic factor such as $(s^2 + ps + q)$ there corresponds a partial fraction of the form

$$\frac{As + B}{s^2 + ps + q}$$

EXAMPLE

$$F(s) = \frac{1}{s(s^2 + s + 1)} = \frac{As + B}{s^2 + s + 1} + \frac{C}{s}$$

Cross multiplying,

$$1 = As^2 + Bs + Cs^2 + Cs + C$$

Equating coefficients,

$$A + C = 0, \qquad B + C = 0, \qquad C = 1$$

Hence $C = 1$, $B = -1$, $A = -1$. Thus

$$F(s) = \frac{-s - 1}{s^2 + s + 1} + \frac{1}{s}$$

or $\qquad$ $$F(s) = \frac{-s}{s^2 + s + 1} - \frac{1}{s^2 + s + 1} + \frac{1}{s}$$

Completing the square of the quadratic in the denominator,

$$s^2 + s + \tfrac{1}{4} + 1 - \tfrac{1}{4} = (s + \tfrac{1}{2})^2 + \tfrac{3}{4}$$

Hence,

$$F(s) = \frac{-s}{(s + \tfrac{1}{2})^2 + \tfrac{3}{4}} - \frac{1}{(s + \tfrac{1}{2})^2 + \tfrac{3}{4}} + \frac{1}{s} \qquad (2.20\text{-}2)$$

By the shifting theorem,

$$\mathcal{L}[\epsilon^{-at} \sin \omega t] = \frac{\omega}{(s + a)^2 + \omega^2}$$

and

$$\mathcal{L}[\epsilon^{-at} \cos \omega t] = \frac{(s + a)}{(s + a)^2 + \omega^2}$$

Rearranging Eq. (2.20-2),

$$F(s) = \frac{-(s + \frac{1}{2})}{(s + \frac{1}{2})^2 + \frac{3}{4}} - \frac{(1 - \frac{1}{2})}{(s + \frac{1}{2})^2 + \frac{3}{4}} + \frac{1}{s}$$

and hence,

$$f(t) = -\epsilon^{-t/2} \cos\left(\frac{\sqrt{3}}{2} t\right) - \frac{\sqrt{3}}{3} \epsilon^{-t/2} \sin\left(\frac{\sqrt{3}}{2} t\right) + 1$$

*Case IV.* When the denominator contains factors of the second degree some of which are repeated, to every $n$-fold quadratic factor such as $(s^2 + ps + q)^n$ there corresponds the sum of $n$ partial fractions,

$$\frac{A_n s + B_n}{(s^2 + ps + q)^n} + \frac{A_{n-1}s + B_{n-1}}{(s^2 + ps + q)^{n-1}} + \cdots + \frac{As + B}{(s^2 + ps + q)}$$

10. *Convolution Theorem*

THEOREM

$$\mathcal{L}\left[\int_0^t f_1(\tau)f_2(t - \tau)\, d\tau\right] = F_1(s)F_2(s)$$

where $\mathcal{L}[f_1(t)] = F_1(s)$ and $\mathcal{L}[f_2(t)] = F_2(s)$

The proof of this theorem is omitted, but can be found in C. R. Wylie, *Advanced Engineering Mathematics* (New York: McGraw-Hill Book Company, 1951), p. 188.

EXAMPLE: Given $\mathcal{L}[u_{-1}(t)] = 1/s$, $\mathcal{L}[\epsilon^{-t}] = 1/(s + 1)$, find

$$\mathcal{L}^{-1}\left[\frac{1}{s(s + 1)}\right]$$

*Procedure:* By the theorem,

$$\mathcal{L}^{-1}\left[\frac{1}{s(s + 1)}\right] = \int_0^t u_{-1}(\tau)\epsilon^{-(t-\tau)}\, d\tau$$

and

$$\mathcal{L}^{-1}\left[\frac{1}{s(s + 1)}\right] = \epsilon^{-t}\left[-\epsilon^{-\tau}\right]_0^t = (1 - \epsilon^{-t})$$

This theorem is often written

$$\mathcal{L}^{-1}[F_1(s)F_2(s)] = f_1(t) * f_2(t)$$

which signifies that $f_1(t)$ is convolved with $f_2(t)$ to obtain the desired time response. It is immaterial which portion of the $s$ function is labeled $F_1(s)$ and which $F_2(s)$.

## 2.30 HEAVISIDE'S EXPANSION

The Heaviside's partial fraction expansion theorem presents a simple direct method of finding the coefficients discussed in the preceding section. The theorem may be stated in two parts as follows:

PART A. If a function $F(s)$ can be obtained as a ratio of polynomials

$$F(s) = \frac{(s + a_1)(s + a_2)\cdots(s + a_n)}{(s + b_1)(s + b_2)\cdots(s + b_m)} \tag{2.30-1}$$

where the denominator is of higher order than the numerator and there are no equal roots in the denominator, the function can be expanded as

$$F(s) = \frac{A_1}{s + b_1} + \frac{A_2}{s + b_2} + \cdots + \frac{A_m}{s + b_m} \tag{2.30-2}$$

The coefficients are found by the relationship

$$A_k = \lim_{s \to -b_k} [(s + b_k)F(s)] \tag{2.30-3}$$

Roots of the denominator of Eq. (2.30-1) are termed *poles of* $F(s)$. Roots of the numerator of Eq. (2.30-1) are termed *zeros of* $F(s)$. The values of the coefficients $A_1, \cdots, A_k, \cdots, A_n$ of Eq. (2.30-2) are termed *residues of* $F(s)$. Heaviside's theorem allows one to expand Eq. (2.30-1) about its poles, where the values of the residues are found by Eq. (2.30-3).

*Proof:* To find the $k$th residue of Eq. (2.30-2) multiply through by the $k$th pole; i.e.,

$$(s + b_k)F(s) = \frac{A_1(s + b_k)}{s + b_1} + \cdots + A_k + \cdots + \frac{A_m}{s + b_m}(s + b_k)$$

Taking the limit of both sides of the equality as $s \to -b_k$ (the value of the $k$th pole),

$$\lim_{s \to -b_k} [(s + b_k)F(s)] =$$

$$\lim_{s \to -b_k} \left[ \frac{A_1(s + b_k)}{s + b_1} + \cdots + A_k + \cdots + \frac{A_m}{s + b_m}(s + b_k) \right]$$

Since $\lim_{s \to -b_k} (s + b_k) = 0$,

$$\lim_{s \to -b_k} [(s + b_k)F(s)] = A_k$$

PART B. If $F(s)$ has a multiple pole of order $p$ at $-b_k$, i.e.,

$$F(s) = \frac{(s + a_1)(s + a_2)\cdots(s + a_n)}{(s + b_1)(s + b_2)\cdots(s + b_k)^p\cdots(s + b_m)}$$

then $F(s)$ may be expanded as in PART A for the simple poles and for the multiple poles as

$$\frac{A_{k_0}}{(s + b_k)^p} + \frac{A_{k_1}}{(s + b_k)^{p-1}} + \cdots + \frac{A_{k_{p-1}}}{s + b_k}$$

where
$$A_{k_0} = \lim_{s \to -b_k} [(s + b_k)^p F(s)]$$

$$A_{k_1} = \lim_{s \to -b_k} \left[ \frac{d}{ds} (s + b_k)^p F(s) \right]$$

$$A_{k_2} = \frac{1}{2!} \lim_{s \to -b_k} \left[ \frac{d^2}{ds^2} (s + b_k)^p F(s) \right]$$

.

.

.

$$A_{k_{p-1}} = \frac{1}{(p - 1)!} \lim_{s \to -b_k} \left[ \frac{d^{p-1}}{ds^{p-1}} (s + b_k)^p F(s) \right]$$

*Proof:* The residues of the simple poles may be found in PART A. To find the residues of the multiple-order poles, multiply by the multiple pole; i.e.,

$$(s + b_k)^p F(s) = \frac{A_1}{s + b_1} (s + b_k)^p + \cdots + A_{k_0} + \cdots$$
$$+ A_{k_{p-1}}(s + b_k)^{p-1} + \cdots + \frac{A_m(s + b_k)^p}{s + b_m}$$

Taking the limit of both sides of the equality and knowing $\lim_{s \to -b_k} [s + b_k] = 0$, one obtains

$$\lim_{s \to -b_k} (s + b_k)^p F(s) = A_{k_0}$$

Taking the first derivative of both sides of the equality, one obtains

$$\frac{d}{ds} [(s + b_k)^p F(s)] = A_{k_1} + 2A_{k_2}(s + b_k) + 3A_{k_3}(s + b_k)^3 + \cdots$$

(Only the terms involving the multiple pole are shown.) Hence,

$$\lim_{s \to -b_k} \frac{d}{ds} [(s + b_k)^p F(s)] = A_{k_1}$$

$$\lim_{s \to -b_k} \frac{d^2}{ds^2} [(s + b_k)^p F(s)] = 2A_{k_2}$$

This procedure can now be extended to each residue of the multiple pole. If there are several multiple roots, this procedure holds for each set of residues.

EXAMPLE

$$F(s) = \frac{s}{(s+1)(s+2)}$$

Expanding,

$$F(s) = \frac{A}{s+1} + \frac{B}{s+2}$$

$$A = \lim_{s \to -1} \left( \frac{s}{s+2} \right) = -1$$

$$B = \lim_{s \to -2} \left( \frac{s}{s+1} \right) = 2$$

$$F(s) = \frac{-1}{s+1} + \frac{2}{s+2}$$

EXAMPLE

$$F(s) = \frac{s}{(s+2)^2 (s+1)}$$

Expanding,

$$F(s) = \frac{A_2}{(s+2)^2} + \frac{A_1}{s+2} + \frac{B}{s+1}$$

where

$$A_2 = \lim_{s \to -2} \left[ \frac{s}{s+1} \right] = 2$$

$$A_1 = \lim_{s \to -2} \left[ \frac{d}{ds} \left( \frac{s}{s+1} \right) \right] = 1$$

$$B = \lim_{s \to -1} \left[ \frac{s}{(s+2)^2} \right] = -1$$

An important corollary can be derived from this theorem concerning the existence of a final value of the time function whose Laplace transform is a ratio of polynomials as given by Eq. (2.30-1).

By the expansion theorem,

$$F(s) = \frac{A_1}{s+a_1} + \frac{A_2}{s+a_2} + \cdots + \frac{A_n}{s+a_n}$$

To each pole there corresponds a time function $A_k \epsilon^{-a_k t}$. If the pole is positive, however, the function $A_k \epsilon^{a_k t}$ will appear and this function is not bounded. If the pole is located at a pure imaginary value, there will appear two terms

$$\frac{A_1}{s-j\omega} + \frac{A_2}{s+j\omega}$$

$A_1$ and $A_2$ will be complex conjugates and the time function will be oscillatory. As an example,

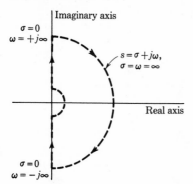

$$\mathcal{L}[\sin \omega t] = \frac{\omega}{s^2 + \omega^2}$$

Now $$\frac{\omega}{s^2 + \omega^2} = \frac{A}{s - j\omega} + \frac{B}{s + j\omega}$$

where

$$A = \lim_{s \to j\omega} \left[ \frac{\omega}{s + j\omega} \right] = \frac{1}{2j}$$

$$B = \lim_{s \to -j\omega} \left[ \frac{\omega}{s - j\omega} \right] = \frac{-1}{2j}$$

**Fig. 2.30-1**   $s$ plane contour for which poles must not occur.

Hence, for a Laplace transform to have a final value the poles must not have a positive real part or be pure imaginary. In Fig. 2.30-1 is shown the contour that is excluded in the Laplace or $s$ domain. Note that in the $s$ plane a simple pole can occur at the origin (this gives rise to a unit step function in the time domain) but not higher orders. The area enclosed by this contour is termed the *right half plane*.

## 2.40 STEADY-STATE SINUSOIDAL RESPONSE

The amplitude and phase of the steady-state response of a linear system to a sinusoidal input can be obtained from the Laplace transform of the system differential equation by replacing $s$ with $j\omega$ with all initial conditions zero. (This holds true only if there are no poles of the transform in the right half $s$ plane.) This can be shown by examining a general linear system with input $x$ and output $y$ which has the differential equation

$$x(t) = \frac{d^m y}{dt^m} + a_1 \frac{d^{m-1}y}{dt^{m-1}} + \cdots + a_m y$$

For $x(t)$ a sinusoid $X_m \sin \omega t$, the Laplace transform of the differential equation may be written

$$Y(s) = G(s) \frac{\omega X_m}{s^2 + \omega^2}$$

In general, $G(s)$ is in the form of a ratio of polynomials $Q(s)/P(s)$ and can be expanded about its poles as

$$Y(s) = \frac{A_1}{s + a_1} + \frac{A_2}{s + a_2} + \cdots + \frac{A_n}{s + a_n} + \frac{B_1}{s + j\omega} + \frac{B_2}{s - j\omega}$$

Since there are no poles in the right half plane (by definition) each term gives rise to a time function $A_k \epsilon^{-a_k t}$. In the limit, these terms approach zero and the remainder is

$$y_{\text{s.s.}} = B_1 \epsilon^{-j\omega t} + B_2 \epsilon^{j\omega t}$$

where $y_{\text{s.s.}}$ is the steady-state value of $y(t)$,

$$B_1 = \lim_{s \to -j\omega} [(s + j\omega) Y(s)] = \frac{X_M}{2j} G(-j\omega)$$

and

$$B_2 = \lim_{s \to j\omega} [(s - j\omega) Y(s)] = \frac{X_M}{2j} G(j\omega)$$

Now

$$|B_1| = |B_2|$$

Since $G(j\omega)$ is a complex number, it has an angle $\psi$ and

$$B_1 = -\psi = G(-j\omega), \qquad B_2 = \psi = G(j\omega)$$

thus

$$y_{\text{s.s.}} = |X_M G(j\omega)| \left[ \frac{\epsilon^{-j\omega t}\epsilon^{-j\psi} + \epsilon^{j\omega t}\epsilon^{j\psi}}{2j} \right]$$

or

$$y_{\text{s.s.}} = |X_M G(j\omega)| \sin (\omega t + \psi)$$

EXAMPLE: Find the steady-state current response of Fig. 2.40-1.

*Procedure:* By Kirchhoff's laws

$$E \sin \omega t = Ri + L \frac{di}{dt}$$

Taking the Laplace transform of both sides,

$$\frac{E\omega}{s^2 + \omega^2} = (R + Ls)I(s)$$

and

$$I(s) = \frac{E\omega}{(R + Ls)(s^2 + \omega^2)}$$

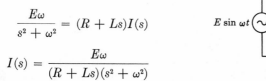

Fig. 2.40-1

Thus

$$G(s) = \frac{1}{R + Ls} \quad \text{and} \quad G(j\omega) = \frac{1}{R + jL\omega}$$

Hence

$$|G(j\omega)| = \frac{1}{\sqrt{R^2 + L^2\omega^2}}$$

$$\psi = -\tan^{-1} \frac{\omega L}{R}$$

$$i_{\text{s.s.}} = \frac{E}{\sqrt{R^2 + \omega^2 L^2}} \sin (\omega t + \psi)$$

## 2.50 LAPLACE TRANSFORM TABLES

In the preceding sections, we have discussed the Laplace transform and have found the transform of several time functions. These transforms

**TABLE 2.50-1** LAPLACE TRANSFORMS DEVELOPED IN THIS CHAPTER

| $f(t)$ | $F(s)$ |
| --- | --- |
| 1. $af(t)$ | $aF(s)$ |
| 2. $f_1(t) + f_2(t)$ | $F_1(s) + F_2(s)$ |
| 3. $\epsilon^{-at}$ | $1/(s + a)$ |
| 4. $\sin \omega t$ | $\omega/(s^2 + \omega^2)$ |
| 5. $\cos \omega t$ | $s/(s^2 + \omega^2)$ |
| 6. $df/dt$ | $sF(s) - f(0^+)$ |
| 7. $d^2f/dt^2$ | $s^2F(s) - sf(0^+) - f'(0^+)$ |
| 8. $u_0(t)$ | $1$ |
| 9. $u_{-1}(t)$ | $1/s$ |
| 10. $u_{-2}(t)$ | $1/s^2$ |

are summarized in Table 2.50-1. To illustrate the use of this table, consider the electrical network as shown in Fig. 2.50-1.

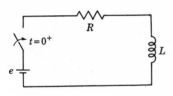

From Kirchhoff's laws, $E = Ri + L(di/dt)$. Transforming the equation,

$$\mathcal{L}[E] = \mathcal{L}[Ri] + \mathcal{L}\left[L\,\frac{di}{dt}\right]$$

From Table 2.50-1,

**Fig. 2.50-1**

$$\frac{E}{s} = RI(s) + LsI(s) - Li(0^+)$$

Since $i(0^+) = 0$,

$$\frac{E}{s} = (R + Ls)I(s) \qquad (2.50\text{-}1)$$

From now on the upper-case letters will stand for the Laplace functions and the lower-case letters for the time functions. Rearranging Eq. (2.50-1),

$$I = \frac{E}{Ls(s + R/L)}$$

This transform is not in Table 2.50-1 but it can be expanded about its poles as follows:

$$I = \frac{A}{s} + \frac{B}{s + R/L}$$

where $A = E/R$, $B = -E/R$. Hence

$$I = \frac{E}{Rs} - \frac{E}{R(s + R/L)}$$

From Table 2.50-1,

$$i = \frac{E}{R}[1 - \epsilon^{-(R/L)t}]$$

This simple example illustrates our procedure for solving the equations of motion of any system and can be summarized in these steps.

1. The characterizing equation of the system is derived from the physical laws of the system.
2. This differential equation is then transformed to the Laplace domain by means of the Laplace integral or from a table of transforms. We now have an algebraic equation in the variable $s$.
3. The unknown quantity is then expressed as a ratio of polynomials in $s$.
4. The time function whose transform is this ratio of polynomials is then obtained from a transform table. If this transform is not available, the theorems developed in this chapter can be used to alter the existing transforms to obtain the desired ratio of polynomials.

This procedure is based on the availability of a complete table of transforms which can readily be identified. We suggest the method used by F. E. Nixon developed in his *Handbook of Laplace Transformation* (Englewood Cliffs, N. J.: Prentice-Hall, Inc., 1960). Each ratio of polynomial in $s$ is assigned a five-digit number. The first two denote the characteristic of the numerator, and the last three, the denominator. The particular significance of each digit is as follows:

First digit indicates the power of $s$ that can be factored out of the numerator.

Second digit indicates the order of $s$ in the numerator after $s$ is factored out.

Third digit indicates the power of $s$ that can be factored out of the denominator.

Fourth digit indicates the number of real roots in the denominator distinct from zero.

Fifth digit indicates the number of pairs of complex roots in the denominator.

As an example, the equation

$$F(s) = \frac{1 + s}{s^2(s + 2)(s^2 + s + 1)}$$

would be given the file number

01.211

Table 2.50-2 lists some transforms taken from Nixon's book.

**TABLE 2.50-2** CODED TRANSFORM PAIRS*

| Eq. no. | $F(s)$ | $f(t) \qquad 0 \leq t$ |
|---|---|---|
| 00.002 | $\dfrac{1}{(1 + s^2/\omega_1^2)^2}$ | $(\omega_1/2)(\sin \omega_1 t - \omega_1 t \cos \omega_1 t)$ |
| 00.011 | $\dfrac{1}{(1 + Ts)(1 + 2\zeta s/\omega_1 + s^2/\omega_1^2)}$ | $\dfrac{T\omega_1^2 \epsilon^{-t/T}}{1 - 2\zeta T\omega_1 + T^2\omega_1^2} + \dfrac{\omega_1 \epsilon^{-\zeta\omega_1 t} \sin(\omega_1 \sqrt{1 - \zeta^2}\, t - \psi)}{[(1 - \zeta^2)(1 - 2\zeta T\omega_1 + T^2\omega_1^2)]^{1/2}}$ <br> where $\psi = \tan^{-1} \dfrac{T\omega_1 \sqrt{1 - \zeta^2}}{1 - T\zeta\omega_1}$ |
| 00.011 | $\dfrac{1}{(1 + Ts)(1 + s^2/\omega_1^2)}$ | $\dfrac{T\omega_1^2}{1 + T^2\omega_1^2} \epsilon^{-t/T} + \dfrac{\omega_1 \sin(\omega_1 t - \psi)}{(1 + T^2\omega_1^2)^{1/2}}$ where $\psi = \tan^{-1} T\omega_1$ |
| 00.020 | $\dfrac{1}{(1 + T_1 s)(1 + T_2 s)}$ | $\dfrac{1}{T_1 - T_2}(\epsilon^{-t/T_1} - \epsilon^{-t/T_2})$ |
| 00.030 | $\dfrac{1}{(1 + T_1 s)(1 + T_2 s)(1 + T_3 s)}$ | $\dfrac{T_1}{(T_1 - T_2)(T_1 - T_3)} \epsilon^{-t/T_1} + \dfrac{T_2}{(T_2 - T_1)(T_2 - T_3)} \epsilon^{-t/T_2} + \dfrac{T_3}{(T_3 - T_1)(T_3 - T_2)} \epsilon^{-t/T_3}$ |
| 00.101 | $\dfrac{1}{s(1 + s^2/\omega_1^2)}$ | $1 - \cos \omega_1 t$ |
| 00.102 | $\dfrac{1}{s(1 + 2\zeta_1 s/\omega_1 + s^2/\omega_1^2)(1 + 2\zeta_2 s/\omega_2 + s^2/\omega_2^2)}$ | $1 + \dfrac{\omega_2^2 \epsilon^{-\zeta_1\omega_1 t} \sin(\omega_1 \sqrt{1 - \zeta_1^2}\, t - \psi_1)}{\sqrt{1 - \zeta_1^2}\,(A^2 + 4AB\zeta_1\omega_1 + 4B^2\omega_1^2)^{1/2}} + \dfrac{\omega_1^2 \epsilon^{-\zeta_2\omega_2 t} \sin(\omega_2 \sqrt{1 - \zeta_2^2}\, t - \psi_2)}{\sqrt{1 - \zeta_2^2}\,(A^2 + 4AB\zeta_2\omega_2 + 4B^2\omega_2^2)^{1/2}}$ <br> where $A = \omega_1^2 - \omega_2^2$, $B = \zeta_2\omega_2 - \zeta_1\omega_1$ <br> $\psi_1 = \tan^{-1} \dfrac{\sqrt{1 - \zeta_1^2}}{-\zeta_1} + \tan^{-1} \dfrac{2B\omega_1 \sqrt{1 - \zeta_1^2}}{-A - 2B\zeta_1\omega_1}$ <br> $\psi_2 = \tan^{-1} \dfrac{\sqrt{1 - \zeta_2^2}}{-\zeta_2} - \tan^{-1} \dfrac{2B\omega_2 \sqrt{1 - \zeta_2^2}}{A + 2B\zeta_2\omega_2}$ |

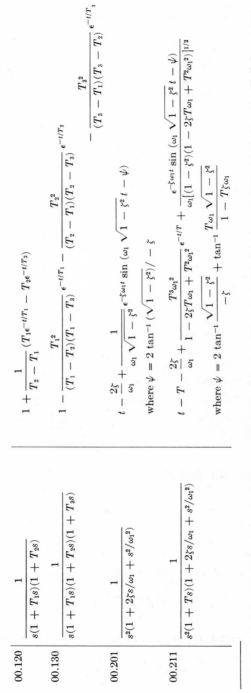

| | | |
|---|---|---|
| 00.120 | $\dfrac{1}{s(1+T_1s)(1+T_2s)}$ | $1 + \dfrac{1}{T_2 - T_1}(T_1\epsilon^{-t/T_1} - T_2\epsilon^{-t/T_2})$ |
| 00.130 | $\dfrac{1}{s(1+T_1s)(1+T_2s)(1+T_3s)}$ | $1 - \dfrac{T_1^2}{(T_1 - T_2)(T_1 - T_3)}\epsilon^{-t/T_1} - \dfrac{T_2^2}{(T_2 - T_1)(T_2 - T_3)}\epsilon^{-t/T_2}$ $- \dfrac{T_3^2}{(T_3 - T_1)(T_3 - T_2)}\epsilon^{-t/T_3}$ |
| 00.201 | $\dfrac{1}{s^2(1 + 2\zeta s/\omega_1 + s^2/\omega_1^2)}$ | $t - \dfrac{2\zeta}{\omega_1} + \dfrac{1}{\omega_1\sqrt{1-\zeta^2}}\epsilon^{-\zeta\omega_1 t}\sin(\omega_1\sqrt{1-\zeta^2}\,t - \psi)$ where $\psi = 2\tan^{-1}(\sqrt{1-\zeta^2})/-\zeta$ |
| 00.211 | $\dfrac{1}{s^2(1 + Ts)(1 + 2\zeta s/\omega_1 + s^2/\omega_1^2)}$ | $t - T - \dfrac{2\zeta}{\omega_1} + \dfrac{T^3\omega_1^2}{1 - 2\zeta T\omega_1 + T^2\omega_1^2}\epsilon^{-t/T} + \dfrac{\epsilon^{-\zeta\omega_1 t}\sin(\omega_1\sqrt{1-\zeta^2}\,t - \psi)}{\omega_1[(1-\zeta^2)(1 - 2\zeta T\omega_1 + T^2\omega_1^2)]^{1/2}}$ where $\psi = 2\tan^{-1}\dfrac{\sqrt{1-\zeta^2}}{-\zeta} + \tan^{-1}\dfrac{T\omega_1\sqrt{1-\zeta^2}}{1 - T\zeta\omega_1}$ |

* Excerpted by permission from F. E. Nixon, *Handbook of Laplace Transformation* (Englewood Cliffs, N. J.: Prentice-Hall, Inc., 1960).

**2.51** THE INVERSION INTEGRAL

The question of inversion has no doubt occurred to the reader before now. Stated another way, given the Laplace transform is there a way to go directly to the time function? The answer is yes, and the inversion process is given by the inversion integral

$$f(t) = \frac{1}{2\pi j} \oint F(s) \epsilon^{st} \, ds$$

where $\oint$ denotes integration about a closed contour. However, the use of this method involves a knowledge of complex variables which is not at every engineer's fingertip. For example, consider

$$F(s) = \frac{1}{s + a}$$

Hence

$$f(t) = \frac{1}{2\pi j} \oint \frac{\epsilon^{st}}{s + a} \, ds$$

The function $1/(s + a)$ has a pole at $s = -a$. Hence, this contour does not enclose any other singularity. Thus the value of this integral is $2\pi j$ times its residue. The value of this residue is

$$\epsilon^{st} \Big]_{s = -a} = \epsilon^{-at} \quad \text{and} \quad f(t) = \epsilon^{-at}$$

This procedure becomes quite complicated as the nature of $F(s)$ varies. In almost every case, the engineer will find that the use of a table of transforms will allow him to handle the problem.

**2.60 SECOND-ORDER EQUATIONS**

Since many physical systems can be adequately represented by a second-order differential equation, it is well worth our time to devote a complete section to a study of the properties of such equations. To offer a motivation, three systems are shown in Fig. 2.60-1. The equation of motion for the $R$-$L$-$C$ circuit may be obtained by Kirchhoff's laws and is

$$e = Ri + L\frac{di}{dt} + \frac{1}{C}\int i \, dt \tag{2.60-1}$$

Transforming the equation and assuming the initial conditions are zero,

$$\frac{E}{s} = \left[R + Ls + \frac{1}{Cs}\right] I$$

and
$$I = \frac{E}{Ls^2 + Rs + 1/C} \tag{2.60-2}$$

Rearranging Eq. (2.60-2) to insure the coefficient of the highest power of $s$ in the denominator is one,

$$I = \frac{E}{L} \frac{1}{s^2 + (R/L)\,s + 1/LC} \tag{2.60-3}$$

A spring and diaphragm valve as shown in Fig. 2.60-1(b) is used quite extensively in the chemical industry to control fluid and gas flows. It is actuated by a pneumatic signal which impinges on the diaphragm and produces a force. This force is opposed by the mass of the stem, the friction of the stem, and the spring force. To determine the differential equation of this system we will define

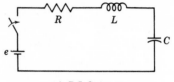

(a) R-L-C circuit

$m$ = mass of stem in lb-sec²/in.

$A$ = area of diaphragm in in.²

$R$ = linear velocity coefficient in lb-sec/in.

$p$ = input pressure in lb/in.²

$x$ = displacement of stem in in.

$v = dx/dt$ = velocity of stem in in./sec.

$k_s$ = spring constant in lb/in

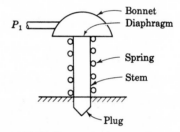

(b) Spring and diaphragm valve

The forces opposing the diaphragm force are

$$f_{\text{mass}} = m\,\frac{dv}{dt} = m\,\frac{d^2x}{dt^2}$$

$$f_{\text{friction}} = Rv = R\,\frac{dx}{dt}$$

$$f_{\text{spring}} = k_s \int v\,dt = k_s x$$

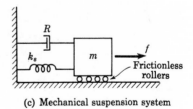

(c) Mechanical suspension system

**Fig. 2.60-1**

The diaphragm force is

$$f = P_1 A_1$$

where $P_1$ is the amplitude of a step function of pressure.

Summing the forces at the diaphragm,

$$P_1 A_1 = m\,\frac{dv}{dt} + Rv + k_s \int v\,dt \tag{2.60-4}$$

Assuming the initial conditions are zero and transforming Eq. (2.60-4),

$$\frac{A_1P_1}{s} = msV + RV + \frac{k_s}{s} V \tag{2.60-5}$$

Solving for $V$,

$$V = \frac{P_1A_1}{s(ms + R + k_s/s)} \tag{2.60-6}$$

Rearranging Eq. (2.60-6),

$$V = \frac{P_1A_1}{m\left(s^2 + \dfrac{R}{m}s + \dfrac{k_s}{m}\right)} \tag{2.60-7}$$

The mechanical suspension system as shown in part (c) of Fig. 2.60-1 is quite similar to the spring and diaphragm valve. The mass $m$ is mounted on frictionless bearings and is restrained by a linear dashpot and a spring. With a step function of force applied to the system, the equations of motion are

$$f_{\text{mass}} = m\frac{dv}{dt} = m\frac{d^2x}{dt^2}$$

$$f_{\text{dashpot}} = Rv = R\frac{dx}{dt}$$

$$f_{\text{spring}} = k_s \int v\, dt = k_s x$$

Summing the forces at the mass,

$$f = m\frac{dv}{dt} + Rv + k_s \int v\, dt \tag{2.60-8}$$

Assuming the initial conditions are zero and transforming Eq. (2.60-8),

$$V = \frac{F}{m\left(s^2 + \dfrac{R}{m}s + \dfrac{k_s}{m}\right)} \tag{2.60-9}$$

These three systems all have second-order characterizing equations but the parameters have different symbols. Hence, to study the general response of such equations, it is necessary to nondimensionalize these equations. Before doing this, let us examine the electrical network. Completing the square of the denominator of Eq. (2.60-3),

$$I = \frac{E/L}{\left(s + \dfrac{R}{2L}\right)^2 + \left(\dfrac{1}{LC} - \dfrac{R^2}{4L^2}\right)} \tag{2.60-10}$$

There are three forms of the time solution of Eq. (2.60-10) depending upon the relationship of $R$, $L$, and $C$. These forms or cases are derived as follows.

*Case a.* $1/LC > R^2/4L^2$ (underdamped case). From Table 2.50-1,

$$\mathfrak{L}[\sin \omega t] = \frac{\omega}{s^2 + \omega^2}$$

By the first shifting theorem,

$$\mathfrak{L}[\epsilon^{-at} \sin \omega t] = \frac{\omega}{(s + a)^2 + \omega^2}$$

Rearranging Eq. (2.60-10),

$$I = \frac{\dfrac{E}{L}}{\sqrt{\dfrac{1}{LC} - \dfrac{R^2}{4L^2}}} \times \frac{\sqrt{\dfrac{1}{LC} - \dfrac{R^2}{4L^2}}}{\left(s + \dfrac{R}{2L}\right)^2 + \left(\dfrac{1}{LC} - \dfrac{R^2}{4L^2}\right)}$$

The time response is now

$$i = \frac{E}{L\sqrt{\dfrac{1}{LC} - \dfrac{R^2}{4L^2}}} \epsilon^{-(R/2L)t} \sin \left(\sqrt{\dfrac{1}{LC} - \dfrac{R^2}{4L^2}} \, t\right) \qquad (2.60\text{-}11)$$

If the exponential were not present, the response would be a pure sine wave. The exponential, however, causes the amplitude of the sine wave to approach zero. For this reason, the term $R/2L$ is referred to as the "damping" of the system. The term $\sqrt{1/LC - R^2/4L^2}$ is the frequency of damped oscillations in radians per second.

*Case b.* $1/LC = R^2/4L^2$ (critically damped case). Equation (2.60-10) now becomes

$$I = \frac{E}{L(s + R/2L)^2} \qquad (2.60\text{-}12)$$

From Table 2.50-1, $\mathfrak{L}[t] = 1/s^2$. By the second shifting theorem,

$$\mathfrak{L}[t\epsilon^{-at}] = \frac{1}{(s + a)^2}$$

The time response of Eq. (2.60-12) is now

$$i = \frac{E}{L} t\epsilon^{-(R/2L)t} \qquad (2.60\text{-}13)$$

*Case c.* $1/LC < R^2/4L^2$ (overdamped case).  Equation (2.60-10) becomes

$$I = \frac{E}{L} \frac{1}{\left(s + \dfrac{R}{2L}\right)^2 + \left(j\sqrt{\dfrac{R^2}{4L^2} - \dfrac{1}{LC}}\right)^2}$$

Utilizing Eq. (2.60-11),

$$i = \frac{E}{L\sqrt{\dfrac{R^2}{4L^2} - \dfrac{1}{LC}}} \epsilon^{-(R/2L)t} \frac{\sin\left(j\sqrt{\dfrac{R^2}{4L^2} - \dfrac{1}{LC}}\, t\right)}{j} \qquad (2.60\text{-}14)$$

From Euler's formula,

$$\sin \omega t = \frac{\epsilon^{j\omega t} - \epsilon^{-j\omega t}}{2j}$$

Hence

$$\sin j\omega t = \frac{\epsilon^{j \cdot j\omega t} - \epsilon^{-j \cdot j\omega t}}{2j} \quad \text{or } \sin j\omega t = -\left[\frac{\epsilon^{\omega t} - \epsilon^{-\omega t}}{2j}\right]$$

But $1/j = -j$, and thus

$$\sin j\omega t = j\left[\frac{\epsilon^{\omega t} - \epsilon^{-\omega t}}{2}\right] \quad \text{or} \quad \frac{\sin j\omega t}{j} = \sinh \omega t$$

Equation (2.60-14) becomes

$$i = \frac{E}{L\sqrt{\dfrac{R^2}{4L^2} - \dfrac{1}{LC}}} \epsilon^{-(R/2L)t} \sinh\left(\sqrt{\dfrac{R^2}{4L^2} - \dfrac{1}{LC}}\, t\right) \qquad (2.60\text{-}15)$$

These three cases are shown in graphical form in Fig. 2.60-2.

We can now proceed to nondimensionalize the general second-order equations. First a nondimensional damping ratio $\zeta$ is defined as

$$\zeta = \frac{\text{actual damping}}{\text{critical damping}}$$

Another parameter $\omega_n$, which is the undamped angular frequency, is defined as the frequency at which the system would oscillate were there no damping.

Equation (2.60-3) can be nondimensionalized by first noting that critical damping occurs at

$$\frac{1}{LC} = \frac{R^2}{4L^2} \qquad (2.60\text{-}16)$$

or where
$$\frac{R}{2L} = \frac{1}{\sqrt{LC}} \qquad (2.60\text{-}17)$$

The frequency at which the system will oscillate with no damping is

$$\omega_n = \frac{1}{\sqrt{LC}} \qquad (2.60\text{-}18)$$

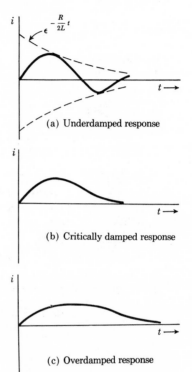

To show this, consider Eq. (2.60-3) for $R = 0$. The equation becomes

$$I = \frac{E}{L(s^2 + 1/LC)} \qquad (2.60\text{-}19)$$

(a) Underdamped response

From Table 2.50-1, $\mathcal{L}[\sin \omega t] = \omega/(s^2 + \omega^2)$. Hence, the time response of Eq. (2.60-19) is

$$i = E\sqrt{\frac{C}{L}} \sin\left(\sqrt{\frac{1}{LC}}\, t\right)$$

(b) Critically damped response

From Eqs. (2.60-16) and (2.60-17) critical damping occurs at $R/2L = \omega_n$ and the actual damping is $R/2L$. Thus $\zeta = R/2L\omega_n$ and

$$2\zeta\omega_n = \frac{R}{L} \qquad (2.60\text{-}20)$$

(c) Overdamped response

**Fig. 2.60-2** Possible responses for Eq. (2.60-2).

Substituting Eqs. (2.60-20) and (2.60-18) into Eq. (2.60-3) the nondimensional response becomes

$$I = \frac{E/L}{s^2 + 2\zeta\omega_n s + \omega_n^2} \qquad (2.60\text{-}21)$$

For Eq. (2.60-7), the nondimensional parameters are

$$2\zeta\omega_n = R/m \quad \text{and} \quad \omega_n^2 = k_s/m$$

For Eq. (2.60-9), the nondimensional parameters are

$$2\zeta\omega_n = R/m \quad \text{and} \quad \omega_n^2 = k_s/m$$

Equation (2.60-21) can now be written as

$$I = \frac{E/L}{(s + \zeta\omega_n)^2 + (\omega_n\sqrt{1 - \zeta^2})^2} \qquad (2.60\text{-}22)$$

Thus for $\zeta < 1$, the system is underdamped, for $\zeta = 1$ the system is critically damped, and for $\zeta > 1$, the system is overdamped. The three time responses are:

Case a. $\zeta < 1$;

$$i = \frac{E/L}{\omega_n \sqrt{1 - \zeta^2}} \epsilon^{-\zeta \omega_n t} \sin (\omega_n \sqrt{1 - \zeta^2}\, t) \qquad (2.60\text{-}23)$$

Case b. $\zeta = 1$;

$$i = \frac{E}{L} t\epsilon^{-\omega_n t} \qquad (2.60\text{-}24)$$

Case c. $\zeta > 1$;

$$i = \frac{E/L}{\omega_n \sqrt{\zeta^2 - 1}} \epsilon^{-\zeta \omega_n t} \sinh (\omega_n \sqrt{\zeta^2 - 1}\, t) \qquad (2.60\text{-}25)$$

Some properties of a second-order characterizing equation can now be developed. One important property is the maximum value of the time response. The maximum of a function is found by differentiating the function and equating the result to zero. Following this procedure in Eq. (2.60-22) we note that

$$\lim_{s \to \infty} sI(s) = 0$$

Hence the differentiation theorem may be used.

$$\mathcal{L}\left[\frac{di_1}{dt}\right] = \frac{s}{(s + \zeta \omega_n)^2 + (\omega_n \sqrt{1 - \zeta^2})^2} \qquad (2.60\text{-}26)$$

(the constant $L/E$ has been incorporated into $i_1$). Rearranging Eq. (2.60-26),

$$\mathcal{L}\left[\frac{di_1}{dt}\right] = \frac{(s + \zeta \omega_n)}{(s + \zeta \omega_n)^2 + (\omega_n \sqrt{1 - \zeta^2})^2}$$
$$- \frac{\zeta \omega_n}{(s + \zeta \omega_n)^2 + (\omega_n \sqrt{1 - \zeta^2})^2} \qquad (2.60\text{-}27)$$

From Table 2.50-1, $\mathcal{L}[\cos \omega t] = \dfrac{s}{(s^2 + \omega^2)}$. By the first shifting theorem

$$\mathcal{L}[\epsilon^{-at} \cos \omega t] = \frac{s + a}{(s + a)^2 + \omega^2}$$

Hence, the time response of Eq. (2.60-26) is

$$i_1' = \epsilon^{-\zeta \omega_n t} \cos (\omega_n \sqrt{1 - \zeta^2}\, t) - \frac{\zeta \omega_n}{\omega_n \sqrt{1 - \zeta^2}} \sin (\omega_n \sqrt{1 - \zeta^2}\, t)$$

Equating to zero and canceling the exponential term,

$$\cos (\omega_n \sqrt{1 - \zeta^2}\, t) = \frac{\zeta}{\sqrt{1 - \zeta^2}} \sin (\omega_n \sqrt{1 - \zeta^2}\, t)$$

or

$$\tan (\omega_n \sqrt{1 - \zeta^2}\, t) = \frac{\sqrt{1 - \zeta^2}}{\zeta} \qquad (2.60\text{-}28)$$

The function $\tan X$ is a multiple-valued function, each value being repeated at $X + 2\pi k$ where $k = 1, 2, \cdots, n$. However, we will only calculate the first and largest maximum.

From Eq. (2.60-28),

$$\omega_n \sqrt{1 - \zeta^2}\, t = \tan^{-1} \frac{\sqrt{1 - \zeta^2}}{\zeta}$$

or

$$\omega_n t_{\max} = \frac{1}{\sqrt{1 - \zeta^2}} \tan^{-1} \frac{\sqrt{1 - \zeta^2}}{\zeta} \qquad (2.60\text{-}29)$$

Substituting this value of time into Eq. (2.60-23),

$$i_{\max} = \frac{E/L}{\omega_n \sqrt{1 - \zeta^2}} \epsilon^{-\zeta \omega_n t_{\max}} \sin \left[ \tan^{-1} \frac{\sqrt{1 - \zeta^2}}{\zeta} \right] \qquad (2.60\text{-}30)$$

Let us define $\theta = \tan^{-1} \sqrt{1 - \zeta^2}/\zeta$. By sketching a triangle to illustrate this as shown in Fig. 2.60-3 it is seen that $\sin \theta = \sqrt{1 - \zeta^2}$. Equation (2.60-30) now becomes

$$i_{\max} = \frac{E}{L\omega_n} \epsilon^{-\zeta \omega_n t_{\max}}$$

A second maximum will occur at

$$i_{\max} = \frac{E}{L\omega_n} \epsilon^{-\zeta [\omega_n t_{\max} + 2\pi]}$$

and the $k$th maximum at

$$i_{\max} = \frac{E}{L\omega_n} \epsilon^{-\zeta [\omega_n t_{\max} + 2(k-1)\pi]}$$

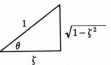

Fig. 2.60-3

Note that the ratio of any two consecutive maximum is a constant, i.e.,

$$\frac{i_{\max_k}}{i_{\max_{k+1}}} = \epsilon^{2\pi \zeta}$$

The same procedure can be applied to the critically damped case since $\lim_{s \to \infty} sI(s) = 0$. Hence

$$\frac{di_1}{dt} = \epsilon^{-\omega_n t} - \omega_n t \epsilon^{-\omega_n t} = 0$$

and $\omega_n t = 1$ or $t_{max} = 1/\omega_n$. Substituting into Eq. (2.60-24),

$$i_{max} = \frac{E}{L\omega_n} \epsilon^{-1}$$

The overdamped case is solved in the same way and is left as a problem for this chapter.

Suppose now the variable of interest in Fig. 2.60-1(a) were the charge in the circuit, i.e. $q = \int i \, dt$, or in the case of (b) and (c) the displacement, i.e. $x = \int v \, dt$. If the initial conditions are zero, $Q = I/s$. Eq. (2.60-3) becomes

$$Q = \frac{E/L}{s\left(s^2 + \frac{R}{L}s + \frac{1}{LC}\right)} \tag{2.60-31}$$

In nondimensional form, this can be written

$$Q = \frac{E/L}{s(s^2 + 2\zeta\omega_n s + \omega_n^2)} \tag{2.60-32}$$

From theorem 5, we know that

$$\mathcal{L}^{-1}\left[\frac{F(s)}{s}\right] = \int_0^t f(t) \, dt$$

Hence

$$q = \frac{E}{L}\int_0^t \left[\frac{\epsilon^{-\zeta\omega_n t}}{\omega_n \sqrt{1 - \zeta^2}} \sin\left(\omega_n \sqrt{1 - \zeta^2}\, t\right)\right] dt, \qquad \zeta < 1 \tag{2.60-33}$$

$$q = \frac{E}{L}\int_0^t t\epsilon^{-\omega_n t} \, dt, \qquad \zeta = 1 \tag{2.60-34}$$

and

$$q = \frac{E}{L}\int_0^t \left[\frac{\epsilon^{-\zeta\omega_n t}}{\omega_n \sqrt{\zeta^2 - 1}} \sinh\left(\omega_n \sqrt{\zeta^2 - 1}\, t\right)\right] dt; \qquad \zeta > 1 \tag{2.60-35}$$

The solutions to these equations are straightforward and are shown below; the file numbers given refer to Table 2.50-2.

*Case a.* $\zeta < 1$. File No. 00.101.

$$q = \frac{E}{L}\left[\frac{1}{\omega_n^2} + \frac{1}{\omega_n^2 \sqrt{1 - \zeta^2}} \epsilon^{-\zeta\omega_n t} \sin\left(\omega_n \sqrt{1 - \zeta^2}\, t + \psi\right)\right] \tag{2.60-36}$$

where
$$\psi = \tan^{-1} - \frac{\sqrt{1 - \zeta^2}}{\zeta^2}$$

*Case b.* $\zeta = 1$. File No. 00.120.

$$q = \frac{E}{L\omega_n^2} [1 - (1 + \omega_n t)\epsilon^{-\omega_n t}] \tag{2.60-37}$$

*Case c.* $\zeta > 1$. File No. 00.120.

$$q = \frac{E}{L\omega_n^2} \left[ 1 + \frac{1}{\sqrt{\zeta^2 - 1}} \epsilon^{-\zeta\omega_n t} \sinh (\omega_n \sqrt{\zeta^2 - 1}\, t - \psi) \right] \tag{2.60-38}$$

where
$$\psi = \tanh^{-1} - \frac{\sqrt{\zeta^2 - 1}}{\zeta^2}$$

The maximum values of these cases are obtained from Eqs. (2.60-33) to (2.60-35) as follows:

*Case a.*

$$\frac{L}{E} q' = \epsilon^{-\zeta\omega_n t} \sin (\omega_n \sqrt{1 - \zeta^2}\, t) = 0$$

Hence

$$\sin (\omega_n \sqrt{1 - \zeta^2}\, t) = 0, \qquad \omega_n t_{max} = \frac{2\pi}{\sqrt{1 - \zeta^2}}$$

Substituting into equation 2.60-36

$$q_{max} = \frac{E}{L\omega_n^2} \left[ 1 + \frac{\epsilon^{-\zeta\omega_n t}}{\sqrt{1 - \zeta^2}} \sin (-\psi) \right]$$

But $\sin (-\psi) = \sqrt{1 - \zeta^2}$ and hence,

$$q_{max} = \frac{E}{L\omega_n^2} [1 + \epsilon^{-2\pi\zeta/\sqrt{1-\zeta^2}}] \tag{2.60-39}$$

*Case b.*

$$q' = t\epsilon^{-\omega_n t} = 0$$

hence $t_{max} = 0$ or $t_{max} = \infty$. But the maximum cannot occur at zero as the system is at rest there. Hence $t_{max} = \infty$

or

$$q_{max} = \frac{E}{L\omega_n^2}$$

This of course means that the maximum value is reached after the transient has disappeared. The same statement will apply to case $c$.

Nondimensional time curves are shown in Fig. 2.60-4 and 2.60-5 of the two second order equations.

$$\Theta(s) = \frac{1}{\left(\dfrac{s}{\omega_n}\right)^2 + \dfrac{2\zeta s}{\omega_n} + 1} \tag{2.60-40}$$

and

$$\Theta(s) = \frac{1}{s\left(\left[\dfrac{s}{\omega_n}\right]^2 + \dfrac{2\zeta s}{\omega_n} + 1\right)} \tag{2.60-41}$$

which are plotted against the nondimensional time $\omega_n t$.

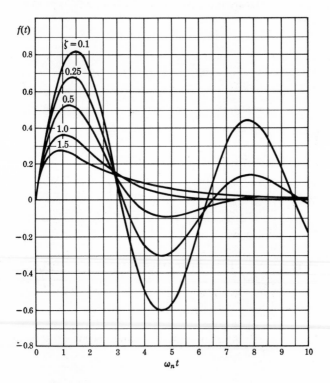

**Fig. 2.60-4** Time response of

$$\Theta(s) = \frac{1}{\left(\dfrac{s}{\omega_n}\right)^2 + 2\zeta\,\dfrac{s}{\omega_n} + 1}$$

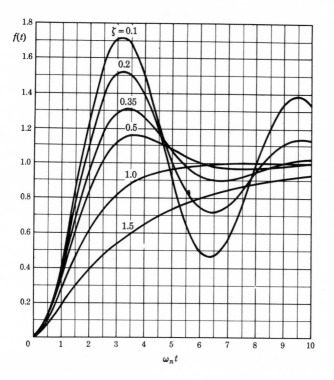

**Fig. 2.60-5** Time response of

$$\Theta(s) = \frac{1}{s\left[\left(\dfrac{s}{\omega_n}\right)^2 + 2\zeta\,\dfrac{s}{\omega_n} + 1\right]}$$

## 2.70 POLE-ZERO LOCATION

Considerable information is available from the pole-zero location of a ratio of polynomials in $s$, even though the time response is unknown. From the partial fraction expansion theorem, it was seen that the location of the poles determined the exponential coefficients and the zeros and poles determined the magnitude of the time response. To illustrate this, let us consider the system shown in Fig. 2.60-1. The Laplace response is

$$I = \frac{E/L}{s^2 + 2\zeta\omega_n s + 1}$$

This system has two poles and no zeros. The poles are located at

$$s_1,\, s_2 = -\zeta\omega_n \pm \sqrt{\zeta_2 - 1}$$

For $\zeta > 1$ two real poles are obtained, for $\zeta = 1$ two equal poles are obtained, and for $\zeta < 1$ two complex poles are obtained. The pole location is shown in Fig. 2.70-1. The Laplace function of Fig. 2.60-1(a) considering charge $q$ as the variable has three poles, one located at the origin and the other two as shown in Fig. 2.70-1.

Suppose a system is considered with one zero and two poles as

$$\Theta(s) = \frac{s + a}{s^2 + 2\zeta\omega_n s + 1} \tag{2.70-1}$$

The pole-zero locations are shown in Fig. 2.70-2 for $\zeta < 1$. The time response of this equation can be found from Table 2.50-2, File No. 01.001, and is

$$\theta(t) = \frac{\sqrt{(a - \zeta\omega_n)^2 + \omega_n^2(1 - \zeta^2)}}{\omega_n\sqrt{1 - \zeta^2}}\, \epsilon^{-\zeta\omega_n t} \sin(\omega_n\sqrt{1 - \zeta^2}\, t + \psi)$$

where

$$\psi = \tan^{-1}\frac{\omega_n\sqrt{1 - \zeta^2}}{a - \zeta\omega_n}$$

The effect of the pole-zero locations on the transient response of a system can be summarized as follows:

1. To every real pole at $-a$, there corresponds a time function $\epsilon^{-at}$.
2. To every pair of complex poles there corresponds a time function

$$\epsilon^{-\zeta\omega_n t} \sin[\omega_n\sqrt{1 - \zeta^2}\, t + \psi].$$

3. To every real pole of order two at $-a$ there correspond terms $t\epsilon^{-at}$ and $\epsilon^{-at}$.
4. The zero locations affect the magnitude of the time function, but not the form.

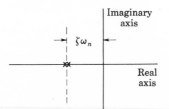

(a) Pole locations for $\zeta > 1$

(b) Pole locations for $\zeta = 1$

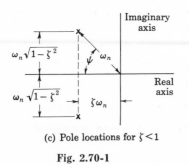

(c) Pole locations for $\zeta < 1$

Fig. 2.70-1

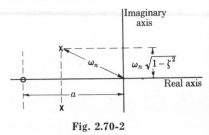

Fig. 2.70-2

It is helpful to show that the locus of poles with constant $\omega_n$ are circles and the locus of poles with constant $\zeta$ are radial lines. This can be shown from Fig. 2.70-1(c). The constant $\omega_n$ circles are evident. To find the locus of constant $\zeta$ consider the angle $\psi$ as shown in Fig. 2.70-1.(c). Hence $\cos\psi = \zeta\omega_n/\omega_n = \zeta$ and $\psi = \cos^{-1}\zeta$. These facts are illustrated in·Fig. 2.70-3.

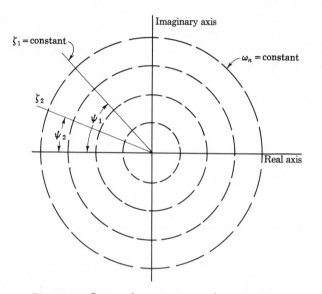

**Fig. 2.70-3** Locus of constant $\omega_n$ and constant $\zeta$.

One other concept remains to be correlated with the pole-zero locations of the $F(s)$ function. This is the concept of a time constant. To motivate this, consider the $F(s)$ function

$$\Theta(s) = \frac{1}{s(s + a)} \qquad \text{(File No. 00.110)}$$

The time response is

$$\theta(t) = \frac{1}{a}(1 - \epsilon^{-at}) \qquad\qquad (2.70\text{-}2)$$

Since in many systems it is desired to have the transient response approach zero as rapidly as possible, some figure of merit is necessary to measure this transient response so that different systems can be compared. The time to reach the final value cannot be used as this time is infinite. The obvious procedure is to choose a particular value of $f(t)$ as a reference.

Consider Eq. (2.70-2) for $t = 1/a$. Hence Eq. (2.70-2) becomes

$$\theta\left(\frac{1}{a}\right) = \frac{1}{a}[1 - 0.368] = \frac{0.632}{a}$$

The time constant of a system is thus defined as the time necessary to reach 63.2% of final value. It follows that the smaller the time constant, the faster the transient response of a system approaches zero. The time constant of a system with only one pole distinct from zero is the reciprocal of that pole. If a system has more than one real pole distinct from zero, one usually refers to the time constant of each pole. These facts are illustrated in Fig. 2.70-4.

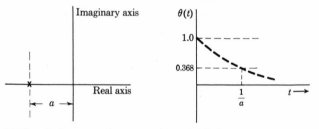

(a) Transient response of a system with one real pole

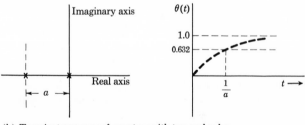

(b) Transient response of a system with two real poles
    one of which is at the origin

**Fig. 2.70-4** Correlation of transient response, pole-zero locations, and time constant.

## 2.80 FREQUENCY RESPONSE AND POLE-ZERO LOCATIONS

In Sec. 2.40 it was shown that the steady-state response of a system could be found from the Laplace transform of the characterizing differential equation. This was done by replacing the Laplace variable $s$ with $j\omega$. The resulting equation was then a vector (phasor). The magnitude of this vector is the amplitude ratio of the input and output, and the angle of this vector determines the phase difference between the input sine wave and the output sine wave. For instance, a system with the characterizing equation

$$y = \frac{dx}{dt} + ax$$

has the Laplace transform

$$Y = (s + a)X \qquad (2.80\text{-}1)$$

if the initial conditions are zero.

To obtain the steady-state response to a sine wave, i.e.,

$$y = E \sin \omega t$$

we now let $s = j\omega$ (Eq. 2.80-1) and obtain

$$\frac{X}{Y}(j\omega) = \frac{1}{a + j\omega}$$

Dividing the denominator by the real part of the vector,

$$\frac{X}{Y}(j\omega) = \frac{1/a}{1 + j\omega/a}$$

The magnitude of this vector is

$$\left| \frac{X}{Y}(j\omega) \right| = \frac{1/a}{\sqrt{1 + \omega^2/a^2}}$$

and the phase is

$$\psi j\omega = - \tan^{-1} \omega/a$$

The output sine wave is now

$$x(t) = \frac{E}{a\sqrt{1 + \omega^2/a^2}} \sin (\omega t - \psi)$$

Since in many cases one wants the output to follow the input, some figure of merit is desirable to measure how closely the output wave follows the input. At zero frequency (d-c) the output amplitude and phase are

$$\left. \left| \frac{X}{Y}(j\omega) \right| \right|_{\omega=0} = \frac{1}{a} \quad \text{and} \quad \psi = 0$$

At a frequency $\omega = a$,

$$\left| \frac{X}{Y}(ja) \right| = \frac{0.707}{a} \quad \text{and} \quad \psi(ja) = -45°$$

This frequency is called the *break frequency*. The amplitude has decreased by 0.707 of the zero-frequency value and the phase shift is 45°.

It is now evident that the time constant of a system and its break frequency are simply related if the characterizing equation is of the first order. Defining the time constant as $\tau$,

$$\tau = \frac{1}{\omega_{\text{break}}}$$

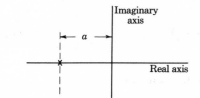

(a) Pole-zero location of a first order system

where $\omega_{\text{break}}$ is in radians and $\tau$ is in sec. This is illustrated in Fig. 2.80-1.

The relationship between the pole-zero locations, transient response, and frequency response is not as simple for a system characterized by a second-order equation. As an example, consider the system whose characterizing equation is

$$y = \frac{d^2x}{dt^2} + 2\zeta\omega_n \frac{dx}{dt} + \omega_n^2 x$$

With the initial conditions zero, the Laplace transform is

$$\frac{X}{Y}(s) = \frac{1}{s^2 + 2\zeta\omega_n s + \omega_n^2}$$

If $\zeta \geq 1$, this equation has two real roots and can be expanded about its poles. Then one can speak of the break frequency associated with each pole. For example, if $\zeta = 1$,

$$\frac{X}{Y}(s) = \frac{1}{(s + \omega_n)^2}$$

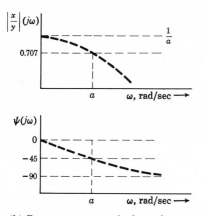

(b) Frequency response of a first order system

Fig. 2.80-1 Correlation of pole location and frequency response of first order system.

The break frequency is $\omega_n$ but the amplitude ratio is 0.5 and the phase shift at $\omega_n$ is 90°. For $\zeta > 1$, the equation becomes

$$\frac{X}{Y}(s) = \frac{\sqrt{\zeta^2 - 1}}{\omega_n[s + \omega_n(\zeta - \sqrt{\zeta^2 - 1})]} - \frac{\sqrt{\zeta^2 - 1}}{\omega_n[s + \omega_n(\zeta + \sqrt{\zeta^2 - 1})]}$$

The two break frequencies are

$$\omega_1, \omega_2 = \omega_n(\zeta \pm \sqrt{\zeta^2 - 1})$$

For the underdamped case ($\zeta < 1$), let us first substitute $s = j\omega$

$$\frac{X}{Y}(j\omega) = \frac{1}{(\omega_n^2 - \omega^2) + j2\zeta\omega_n\omega}$$

Dividing the numerator and denominator by $\omega_n^2$,

$$\frac{X}{Y}(j\omega) = \frac{1/\omega_n^2}{1 - \left(\frac{\omega}{\omega_n}\right)^2 + j\frac{2\zeta\omega}{\omega_n}}$$

Define a new nondimensional frequency ratio $u = \omega/\omega_n$. Hence, the equation becomes

$$\omega_n^2 \frac{X}{Y}(ju) = \frac{1}{(1 - u^2) + j2\zeta u} \tag{2.80-2}$$

Nondimensional curves of Eq. (2.80-2) are shown in Fig. 2.80-2. Let us now define $M$ as

$$M = \left| \omega_n^2 \frac{X}{Y}(ju) \right| = \frac{1}{\sqrt{(1 - u^2)^2 + 4\zeta^2 u^2}} \tag{2.80-3}$$

To find the maximum value of $M$ as a function of $u$, the first derivative of $M$ with respect to $u$ must be obtained and equated to zero.

The value of $u$ is then substituted into Eq. (2.80-3) and this is the maximum magnitude or $M_p$. This can be done as follows:

$$M^2 = \frac{1}{(1 - u^2)^2 + 4\zeta^2 u^2}$$

$$2M \frac{dM}{du} = \frac{-[-4u(1 - u^2) + 8\zeta^2 u]}{[(1 - u^2)^2 + 4\zeta^2 u^2]^2}$$

and

$$-[1 - u^2] + 2\zeta^2 = 0 \tag{2.80-4}$$

Solving (2.80-4),

$$u_{\max} = \sqrt{1 - 2\zeta^2}$$

and

$$\omega_{\max} = \omega_n \sqrt{1 - 2\zeta^2} \tag{2.80-5}$$

Hence

$$\left| \frac{X}{Y}(j\omega) \right| = \frac{1/\omega_n^2}{2\zeta \sqrt{1 - \zeta^2}} \tag{2.80-6}$$

Equation (2.80-5) states that a value of $\omega_n^2 M > 1$ will not occur for $\zeta \geq 0.707$.

In Fig. 2.80-2 (see page 52) is shown a plot of Eq. (2.80-2) for several values of $\zeta$.

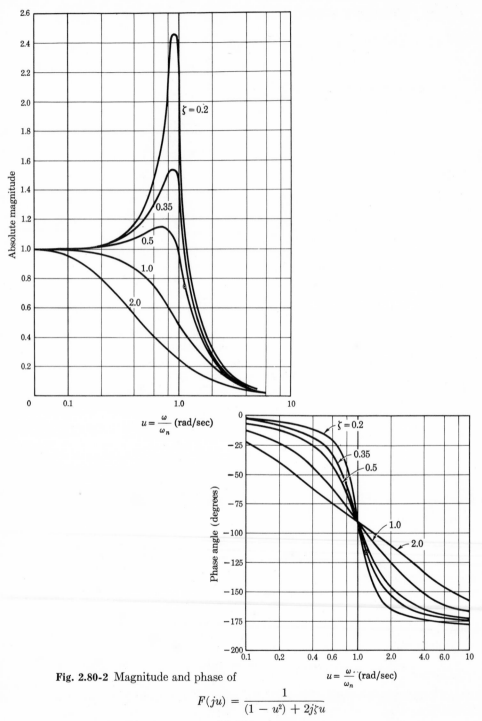

**Fig. 2.80-2** Magnitude and phase of

$$F(ju) = \frac{1}{(1 - u^2) + 2j\zeta u}$$

(a) Magnitude response; (b) Phase response.

## 2.90 PROBLEMS

1. By use of the definition, determine the Laplace transforms of the following functions:

   (a)  $\cos \omega t$
   (b)  $\cosh \omega t$
   (c)  $t \epsilon^{at}$
   (d)  $\cos^2 \omega t$
   (e)  $\dfrac{d^3 f(t)}{dt^3}$

2. Determine the current flowing in resistor $R_2$ in the following circuit:

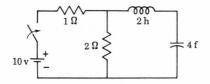

3. Determine whether the following differential equations have a final value:

   (a)  $\dfrac{d^3 x}{dt^3} + 2 \dfrac{d^2 x}{dt^2} + 4x = 5$

   (b)  $\dfrac{d^4 x}{dt^4} + \dfrac{d^3 x}{dt^3} + \dfrac{d^2 x}{dt^2} + \dfrac{dx}{dt} + x = 1$

   (c)  $\dfrac{d^3 x}{dt^3} + 2 \dfrac{d^2 x}{dt^2} + \dfrac{dx}{dt} + x = 2$

4. Sketch the time function whose Laplace transform is

$$F(s) = \frac{\epsilon^{-as}}{1 - \epsilon^{-as}}$$

5. Using only the theorems developed in this chapter and knowing $\mathcal{L}[u_{-1}(t)] = 1/s$, find the following transforms:

   (a)  $f(t) = t$
   (b)  $f(t) = \epsilon^{-at}$
   (c)  $f(t) = \sin \omega t$
   (d)  $f(t) = \epsilon^{-at} \cos \omega t$

6. Using the results of Prob. 5 and the theorems developed in this chapter find the following inverse transforms:

   (a)  $F(s) = 1/s^2$
   (b)  $F(s) = \epsilon^{-as}/(s^2 + 2s + 1)$
   (c)  $F(s) = s/(s + 1)$

(d) $F(s) = 1/(s + a)$

(e) $F(s) = \tanh as$

7. Solve the differential equation

$$\frac{dy}{dt} + t\frac{dy}{dt} = 4; \qquad y(o^+) = 0$$

8. Find the Laplace transform of the following functions:

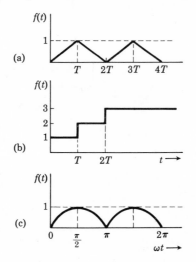

9. By means of the derivative theorem and knowing the Laplace transform of $\sin \omega t$, find $\mathcal{L} (\cos \omega t)$.

10. By means of the Heaviside's expansion theorem find the time functions associated with

(a) $s/[(s + 4)(s + 5)]$        (b) $1/(s^2 + 4s + 3)$

(c) $(1 - \epsilon^{-as})/[s(s + 4)]$       (d) $s(s + 4)/[(s + 5)(s^2 + s + 1)]$

11. Sketch the time function whose Laplace transforms are

(a) $(1 - \epsilon^{-as})/s$     (b) $\coth (as)$       (c) $s/(1 - \epsilon^{-as})$

12. A system is characterized by the set of differential equations

$$\frac{dx^2}{dt^2} + 2\frac{dx}{dt} + 4y = 5$$

$$2\frac{dy}{dt} - 4\frac{dx}{dt} = 8$$

The initial conditions are

$$t = 0, \quad x = 0, \quad y = 0, \quad x' = -8$$

Solve for the $x$ and $y$ response of the system. Is this system stable?

13. By means of partial fractions solve for the time functions whose Laplace transforms are

(a) $\dfrac{s + 1}{(s^2 + 4s + 3)(s + 2)}$

(b) $\dfrac{(s^2 + s + 1)}{(s + 3)^2(s + 4)(s + 5)}$

(c) $\dfrac{(s + 1)^2}{(s^2 + 8s + 2)(s + 3)}$

(d) $\dfrac{(s + 2)^2}{(s^2 + s + 1)^2(s + 4)(s + 5)}$

14. Nondimensionalize the following equations and determine the damping ratio and natural frequency of each.

(a) $\dfrac{1}{4s^2 + 5s + 4}$

(b) $\dfrac{1}{10s^2 + 8s + 1}$

(c) $\dfrac{4}{6s^2 + 5s + 4}$

(d) $\dfrac{10}{3s^2 + s + 10}$

15. By means of Fig. 2.80-2 determine the frequency response of a system whose response has the Laplace transform

(a) $\dfrac{1}{s^2 + 4s + 4}$

(b) $\dfrac{1}{s^2 + 0.5s + 0.25}$

(c) $\dfrac{4}{s^2 + 4s + 100}$

(d) $\dfrac{10}{s^2 + 4s + 1}$

16. By means of Fig. 2.60-4 graph the time response of the function whose Laplace transform is

$$\frac{X_0}{X_i}(s) = \frac{4}{s^2 + 4s + 100}; \; x_i(t) = u_0(t)$$

17. Solve the following differential equations

(a) $2\dfrac{dv}{dt} + v = 6 \sin t$:   $v(0^+) = 0$

(b) $6\dfrac{d^2x}{dt^2} + 24\dfrac{dx}{dt} + 18x = t$:   $x(0^+) = 1$;   $x'(0^+) = -2$

(c) $\dfrac{d^2x}{dt^2} + 2\dfrac{dx}{dt} + x = 5$:   $x(0^+) = 0$;   $x'(0^+) = 0$

(d) $\dfrac{di}{dt} + 4i + 5 \int i \, dt = \sin 2t$:   $i(0^+) = 0$;   $i'(0^+) = 0$

18. Determine the code number of the Laplace transforms in Problem 13.

19. By means of the convolution theorem find the Laplace transforms of

(a) $\dfrac{s}{(s + 4)(s + 5)}$

(b) $\dfrac{1}{(s^2 + 4s + 16)(s + 1)}$

(c) $\dfrac{1}{(s + 2)(s^2 + 9)}$

(d) $\dfrac{1}{(s + 2)^2}$

20. Determine the initial and final values of the functions whose Laplace transforms are

(a) $\dfrac{(s + 1)}{s^4 + 5s^3 + 6s^2 + 8s + 1}$

(b) $\dfrac{1}{(s + 1)(s + 2)(s^2 + 4s + 1)}$

(c) $\dfrac{8s + 5}{(s^3 + 2s + 1)(s + 4)}$

(d) $\dfrac{s^4 + 5s^3 + 3s^2 + 8s + 1}{s(s^2 + 4)(s^2 + 9)(s^2 + s + 1)}$

(e) $\dfrac{5s + 4}{(s + 2)(s + 3)(s + 4)}$

(f) $\dfrac{(s^2 + 4)}{s^2(s + 4)(s^2 + s + 1)}$

# CHAPTER THREE

# DYNAMIC ANALOGIES

## 3.00 INTRODUCTION

In Chap. 1 it was explained that the mathematical forms describing the behavior of different physical systems are often the same. This behavior for many systems can be approximated by linear differential equations with constant coefficients. The forms of the solutions to this class of equations will not vary with the meaning of the parameters or coefficients in the real world. Therefore, if we learn the form of a solution *and* the analogies between parameters and coefficients in various engineering fields, we will significantly reduce the amount of learning required to understand a variety of dynamic problems. The analogies among electrical, mechanical rectilineal, mechanical rotational, hydraulic, pneumatic, and thermodynamic systems will be discussed. In most cases the various laws that lead to the same form of equation will be given. The transform techniques of Chap. 2 will be used to obtain solutions to the differential equations.

## 3.10 LAWS OF PHYSICAL BEHAVIOR

The rules governing the behavior of various physical systems have their origins in laws, derivations, and empirical observations. Most of the relations involving energy dissipating elements, for example, have been generated on the basis of experimental evidence. When the evidence becomes overwhelming, we sometimes acknowledge this fact by elevating the rule to the status of a law. Ohm's law is an example of an experimental observation that has been stated formally as a law.

Three types of elements will be encountered in examining the behavior of systems. Two of these are energy storage devices; the third is an energy dissipating device. Since the law of conservation of energy is a universal fact, the meaning of dissipation is usually that the energy is transformed and lost by the system under consideration. The energy dissipated in an electric resistance is lost as heat or visible light. Thermodynamic systems, unlike the others, contain only one type of energy storage element.

**3.11** ELECTRIC SYSTEMS

Almost the first fact we learn in electrical engineering is Ohm's law, which states that the voltage drop across a resistance is equal to the product of the current times the resistance and is in the direction of the current flow. Stated mathematically in terms of the current, the law is

$$e = iR \qquad\qquad (3.11\text{-}1)$$

The same law can be stated in terms of charge, since current is the time rate of change of charge:

$$e = R\frac{dq}{dt} \qquad\qquad (3.11\text{-}2)$$

The power dissipated in a resistance is

$$\text{power} = i^2R \qquad\qquad (3.11\text{-}3)$$

The energy dissipated is

$$W = \int \text{power } dt = \int i^2R\, dt \qquad\qquad (3.11\text{-}4)$$

To arrive at the relation for the voltage across an inductance, we must consider two laws. Faraday's law says that the voltage induced by changing the magnetic flux through a fixed circuit is equal to the time rate of change of flux, or

$$e = \frac{d\phi}{dt} \qquad\qquad (3.11\text{-}5)$$

where $\phi$ is the flux. Ampere's law states that the flux in a paramagnetic or diamagnetic medium is proportional to the current, or

$$\phi = Li \qquad\qquad (3.11\text{-}6)$$

where $\phi$ is the flux and $L$ is the constant of proportionality called *inductance*. If we differentiate both sides of Eq. (3.11-6) and substitute the expression for $(d\phi/dt)$ in Eq. (3.11-5), the result is

$$e = L\frac{di}{dt} \qquad\qquad (3.11\text{-}7)$$

This equation states that the voltage across an inductance is the product of the inductance and the time rate of change of current. Again this equation can be stated in terms of charge rather than current:

$$e = L\frac{d^2q}{dt^2} \qquad\qquad (3.11\text{-}8)$$

We are going to examine the analogies among various physical systems, but we can also obtain analogies within a given physical system. In

electric-circuit analysis the concept of duality, in which the roles of current
and voltage are reversed, is simply recognition of analogous equations. To
demonstrate this analog, other relations involving the parameters and
elements must be developed. If we multiply both sides of Eq. (3.11-7) by
$dt/L$ and integrate, the result is

$$i = \frac{1}{L} \int e \, dt \tag{3.11-9}$$

which states that the current through an inductance is equal to $(1/L)$
times the integral of the voltage across the inductance.

The inductance $L$ represents an energy storage device; the energy is
stored in the magnetic field. We see this energy used by conversion to
mechanical energy when a relay is closed. The energy stored in an inductance is the time integral of the instantaneous power, the product of $e$ and $i$:

$$W = \int ei \, dt = \int L \frac{di}{dt} i \, dt = L \int i \, di \tag{3.11-10}$$

$$W = \tfrac{1}{2} Li^2 \tag{3.11-11}$$

The voltage across a capacitance $C$ is

$$e = \frac{1}{C} \int i \, dt \tag{3.11-12}$$

Since the time integral of current is the charge, the voltage across a
capacitance can be expressed also as

$$e = \frac{q}{C} \tag{3.11-13}$$

If we differentiate both sides of Eq. (3.11-12) with respect to $t$ and multiply
both sides by $C$, we obtain

$$i = C \frac{de}{dt} \tag{3.11-14}$$

which states that the current through a capacitance is proportional to the
time rate of change of voltage.

Capacitance $C$, like inductance, represents an energy storage device;
in the case of capacitance, the energy is stored in the electric field. Again
the energy stored is the time integral of the instantaneous power.

$$W = \int ei \, dt = \int eC \frac{de}{dt} \, dt = C \int e \, de \tag{3.11-15}$$

or

$$W = \tfrac{1}{2} Ce^2 \tag{3.11-16}$$

Expressions have now been presented that relate voltage and current for the three basic passive elements of electric systems—resistance, inductance, and capacitance. We will now look at the equivalents in mechanical rectilineal systems.

## 3.12 MECHANICAL RECTILINEAL SYSTEMS

There is no mechanics law equivalent to Ohm's law. However, it has been observed that some bodies in motion require a force proportional to velocity to maintain a constant velocity. This observation leads to the mathematical statement

$$f = Rv \tag{3.12-1}$$

where $f$ is the force, $R$ is the friction coefficient, called viscous friction in this case, and $v$ is the velocity. A more general case for the force necessary to maintain a body in motion at constant velocity is

$$f = Rv^\gamma \tag{3.12-2}$$

where $\gamma$ is an exponent which may vary from values less than one to values greater than one. We will restrict our discussion to those cases in which $\gamma$ is equal to one. Since velocity is the time rate of change of displacement, Eq. (3.12-1) can be restated as

$$f = R\frac{dx}{dt} \tag{3.12-3}$$

The friction represents a dissipative element. The energy loss appears as heat or turbulence.

The power dissipated due to friction is

$$\text{power} = v^2R \tag{3.12-4}$$

and the energy lost is

$$W = \int \text{power } dt = \int v^2R \, dt \tag{3.12-5}$$

From Hooke's law we derive the fact that within the elastic limits of a spring, the elongation or compression of a spring is proportional to the force causing the elongation or compression. The constant of proportionality $k$ is a measure of the spring stiffness. The stiffer the spring, the smaller will be the displacement for a given force:

$$f = kx \tag{3.12-6}$$

If Hooke's law is stated in terms of velocity it becomes

$$f = k \int v \, dt \tag{3.12-7}$$

Energy is stored in a spring when it is distorted from its neutral position. The energy is

$$W = \int f \, dx \tag{3.12-8}$$

From Eq. (3.12-6) we can write $dx$ as

$$dx = \frac{1}{k} \, df \tag{3.12-9}$$

If this is now substituted in Eq. (3.12-8) and the integration performed, the result is

$$W = \frac{1}{2k} f^2 \tag{3.12-10}$$

Newton's second law says that a body's time rate of change of momentum is proportional to the force applied. In equation form, the law is

$$f = \frac{d}{dt} (mv) \tag{3.12-11}$$

where $m$ is the mass and $v$ the velocity. If we perform the indicated derivative operation, the result is

$$f = m \frac{dv}{dt} + v \frac{dm}{dt} \tag{3.12-12}$$

We are more used to seeing the special case in which the mass is constant and $dm/dt$ therefore zero. In this special case we usually write $dv/dt$ as $a$ for acceleration and we have the familiar

$$f = ma \tag{3.12-13}$$

which can be expressed as

$$f = m \frac{dv}{dt} \tag{3.12-14}$$

or

$$f = m \frac{d^2x}{dt^2} \tag{3.12-15}$$

Mass as demonstrated in the daily descriptions of automobile accidents is an energy storage element. The general expression for mechanical energy is given by Eq. (3.12-8). If we recognize that

$$dx = v \, dt \tag{3.12-16}$$

and we use the expression for $f$ in Eq. (3.12-14), we find that

$$W = \int f \, dx = \int m \frac{dv}{dt} v \, dt \tag{3.12-17}$$

or

$$W = \tfrac{1}{2}mv^2 \tag{3.12-18}$$

### 3.13 MECHANICAL ROTATIONAL SYSTEMS

The basic parameters of mechanical rotational systems are *torque* and *angular displacement*. We may choose to treat angular velocity as one of the basic parameters just as we may choose current rather than charge in an electrical system. The status of law has not yet been attached to the effect of rotational resistance, so we accept the empirical observation that in some cases the torque required to maintain a given angular velocity is proportional to angular velocity. Stated mathematically,

$$T = B\omega \tag{3.13-1}$$

where $T$ is the torque, $B$ is the rotational resistance (sometimes called the damping coefficient or viscous damping), and $\omega$ is the angular velocity.

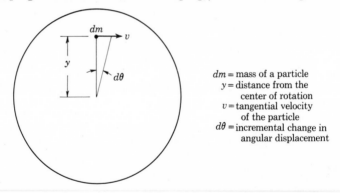

$dm$ = mass of a particle
$y$ = distance from the center of rotation
$v$ = tangential velocity of the particle
$d\theta$ = incremental change in angular displacement

**Fig. 3.13-1** Diagram for application of Newton's second law to a rotating mass.

Since $\omega$ is the time rate of change of angular displacement, Eq. (3.13-1) can be expressed as

$$T = B\dot{\theta} \tag{3.13-2}$$

The power dissipated in a rotational resistance is

$$\text{power} = B\omega^2 \tag{3.13-3}$$

and the energy lost is

$$W = \int \text{power} \, dt = \int B\omega^2 \, dt \tag{3.13-4}$$

We can derive the relationship between torque, angular acceleration, and moment of inertia by considering the special case of Newton's second law and the diagram of Fig. 3.13-1.

Newton's law for an incremental force acting on an incremental mass is

$$df = a\,dm \tag{3.13-5}$$

where $df$ represents the incremental force, $dm$ the incremental or particle mass, and $a$ the linear acceleration. Torque is defined as the product of a force and its lever arm. For an incremental force, the incremental torque, $dT$, is

$$dT = y\,df \tag{3.13-6}$$

or

$$df = \frac{dT}{y} \tag{3.13-7}$$

The tangential velocity is equal to the angular velocity times the radius, or

$$v = y\dot{\theta} \tag{3.13-8}$$

Since acceleration is the time rate of change of velocity,

$$a = \frac{dv}{dt} = y\ddot{\theta} \tag{3.13-9}$$

when $y$ is independent of time as in the case of a rigid body.   If we substitute the expression given for $df$ in Eq. (3.13-7) and that for $a$ in Eq. (3.13-9) into Eq. (3.13-5), we have

$$\frac{dT}{y} = y\ddot{\theta}\,dm \tag{3.13-10}$$

If both sides of Eq. (3.13-10) are multiplied by $y$ and the right side is rearranged, the result is

$$dT = \ddot{\theta}y^2\,dm \tag{3.13-11}$$

Since $\ddot{\theta}$ is not a function of the geometry, both sides of Eq. (3.13-11) can be integrated to get

$$T = \ddot{\theta} \int y^2\,dm \tag{3.13-12}$$

The integral in the right-hand side of Eq. (3.14-12) is by definition the polar moment of inertia $J$, so it can be rewritten as

$$T = J\ddot{\theta} \tag{3.13-13}$$

or

$$T = J\dot{\omega} \tag{3.13-14}$$

The energy stored due to the angular velocity is

$$W = \tfrac{1}{2}J\omega^2 \tag{3.13-15}$$

This storage of energy in a rotating body is commonly called the *flywheel effect*.

Our remaining task in rotational systems is to explain the behavior of rotational springs, also called *rotational compliances*. We can do this by converting Hooke's law to a rotational system. The incremental tangential displacement $dx$ in a rotating system is

$$dx = y\, d\theta \tag{3.13-16}$$

where $y$ is the radial distance to the point at which the force is applied and $d\theta$ is the incremental angular displacement. If Hooke's law is written for an incremental force, it becomes

$$df = k\, dx \tag{3.13-17}$$

If we now substitute the expression for $df$ in Eq. (3.13-7) and that for $dx$ in Eq. (3.13-16) into Eq. (3.13-17), we get an equation relating torque and angular displacement.

$$\frac{dT}{y} = ky\, d\theta \tag{3.13-18}$$

Multiplying both sides by $y$ and integrating, we obtain

$$T = ky^2\theta \tag{3.13-19}$$

$ky^2$ is defined as the rotational spring constant $c$ and Eq. (3.13-19) becomes

$$T = c\theta \tag{3.13-20}$$

Other forms of rotational springs such as torsion bars can also be represented by $c$. In terms of angular velocity,

$$T = c \int \omega\, dt \tag{3.13-21}$$

A rotational spring, like its rectilineal counterpart, can store energy. The energy stored is

$$W = \frac{1}{2}\frac{T^2}{c} \tag{3.13-22}$$

## 3.14 HYDRAULIC SYSTEMS

In hydraulic systems the fundamental parameters are pressure $p$ and volumetric flow rate $q$. The first equation of behavior is an empirical one showing the effect of hydraulic resistance. Most of us have had the exas-

perating experience of witnessing this phenomenon when someone starts
watering the garden while we are using the water somewhere else in the
house. The increase of water flow through the line from the city supply
causes the pressure to decrease at the exit, and lower flows result wherever
the water is turned on. The problem is similar to that of an unregulated
power supply. Its voltage decreases when the current is increased. The
equation is

$$p = qR \qquad (3.14\text{-}1)$$

where $p$ is the pressure, $R$ the hydraulic resistance, and $q$ the volumetric
flow rate.

The power dissipated appears as heat and is

$$\text{power} = q^2R \qquad (3.14\text{-}2)$$

and the energy lost is

$$W = \int \text{power } dt = \int q^2R \, dt \qquad (3.14\text{-}3)$$

The concept of inertance, one of the energy storage elements of hydraulic systems, can be derived from the special case of Newton's
second law,

$$f = m \frac{dv}{dt} \qquad (3.14\text{-}4)$$

Let us examine a fluid conductor of uniform cross section $A$ with pressures
$p_2$ and $p_1$, separated by a distance $l$, and volumetric flow $q$. A diagram is
shown in Fig. 3.14-1. We will assume that the conductor offers no resistance
to flow. The fluid has density $\rho$. The force acting on the volume of liquid
contained in the length $l$ is

$$f = p_2A - p_1A \qquad (3.14\text{-}5)$$

since force is equal to pressure times the area
over which it acts. The volume of the fluid
contained in the length $l$ is

$$V = lA \qquad (3.14\text{-}6)$$

and its mass is

$$m = \frac{\rho V}{g} = \frac{\rho lA}{g} \qquad (3.14\text{-}7)$$

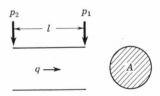

Fig. 3.14-1 A hydraulic
conductor.

where $\rho$ is the density and $g$ the acceleration of gravity.

Let us next consider an interface in the fluid conductor. If the interface
moves a distance $\Delta x$, then the volume displaced is $A \, \Delta x$. If this displacement occurs in time $\Delta t$, then the volumetric flow rate is

$$q = A \frac{\Delta x}{\Delta t} \qquad (3.14\text{-}8)$$

In the limit as $\Delta t$ approaches zero, Eq. (3.14-8) becomes

$$q = A\frac{dx}{dt} = Av \qquad (3.14\text{-}9)$$

where $v$ is the lineal velocity. If we solve Eq. (3.14-9) for $v$ and differentiate with respect to $t$, we get

$$\frac{dv}{dt} = \frac{1}{A}\frac{dq}{dt} \qquad (3.14\text{-}10)$$

We now have in Eqs. (3.14-5), (3.14-7), and (3.14-10) expressions for force, mass, and acceleration. Substituting these equivalents into Eq. (3.14-4), we have

$$p_2 A - p_1 A = \left[\frac{\rho l A}{g}\right]\left[\frac{1}{A}\frac{dq}{dt}\right] \qquad (3.14\text{-}11)$$

If $A$ is canceled on both sides of Eq. (3.14-11), the result is

$$p_2 - p_1 = \frac{\rho l}{gA}\frac{dq}{dt} \qquad (3.14\text{-}12)$$

We can now define the inertance $M$ as

$$M = \frac{\rho l}{gA} \qquad (3.14\text{-}13)$$

and state that the pressure drop through a fluid conductor due to the rate of change of flow is proportional to the inertance.

$$p = M\frac{dq}{dt} \qquad (3.14\text{-}14)$$

In hydraulic systems a second type of energy storage exists. It is related to the compressibility of the fluid or the elasticity of the container. We see both effects when we fill a balloon with a compressible fluid. Energy is stored because the fluid is compressed and because the balloon has stretched. The stored energy can be changed to kinetic energy by letting the fluid escape, and the energy is distributed between the balloon and the fluid. The bulk modulus of elasticity for a liquid is

$$B = \frac{dp}{dV/V} \qquad (3.14\text{-}15)$$

where $B$ is the bulk modulus of elasticity and $dp$ is the increment of pressure applied to the volume of liquid $V$ to cause a decrease in volume $dV$. We have previously defined $q$ as the volume rate of flow, so

$$dV = q\,dt \qquad (3.14\text{-}16)$$

If we substitute this expression for $dV$ in Eq. (3.14-15) and solve for $dp$, we get

$$dp = \frac{B}{V} q \, dt \qquad (3.14\text{-}17)$$

and by integrating we have

$$p = \frac{B}{V} \int q \, dt \qquad (3.14\text{-}18)$$

Equation (3.14-18) describes the build-up of pressure as a compressible liquid flows into an inelastic container. If the liquid is incompressible but the vessel elastic, then

$$dp = K \, dV \qquad (3.14\text{-}19)$$

where $dp$ is the change in pressure for the change in volume $dV$ in an elastic vessel whose geometry and modulus of elasticity are included in the particular value of $K$. We can again apply Eq. (3.14-16) and integrate to obtain

$$p = K \int q \, dt \qquad (3.14\text{-}20)$$

This equation describes the build-up of pressure in an elastic vessel as an incompressible liquid flows into it. If the liquid is compressible *and* the vessel elastic, the pressure is

$$p = \left( \frac{B}{V} + K \right) \int q \, dt \qquad (3.14\text{-}21)$$

We now define the hydraulic capacitance $C$ as

$$C = \frac{1}{(B/V + K)} \qquad (3.14\text{-}22)$$

The energy stored in the hydraulic capacitance is

$$W = \tfrac{1}{2} C p^2 \qquad (3.14\text{-}23)$$

## 3.15 PNEUMATIC SYSTEMS

Pneumatic systems, like hydraulic systems, are concerned with pressure and flow relationships. The same dynamic equations apply in both systems, although the equations for the elements vary in some cases because of the differences between liquids and gases.

Although pneumatic resistances are often nonlinear, they can often be handled as linear elements by the approximation techniques given in Chap. 7. The basic equation is

$$p = Rq \qquad (3.15\text{-}1)$$

in which $p$ is the pressure, $R$ is the pneumatic resistance, and $q$ is the volumetric flow. The power dissipated is

$$\text{power} = q^2 R \tag{3.15-2}$$

and the energy lost is

$$W = \int \text{power } dt = \int q^2 R \, dt \tag{3.15-3}$$

The derivation for pneumatic inertance will not be repeated since it is exactly the same as that for hydraulic inertance, namely

$$p = M \frac{dq}{dt} \tag{3.15-4}$$

where $p$ is the pressure drop, $M$ is the inertance, and $q$ is the volumetric flow. The inertance $M$ is

$$M = \frac{\rho l}{gA} \tag{3.15-5}$$

where $\rho$ is the gas density, $l$ the length of the pneumatic conductor, $g$ the acceleration of gravity, and $A$ the cross-sectional area of the conductor. The energy stored is

$$W = \tfrac{1}{2} M q^2 \tag{3.15-6}$$

The concept of pneumatic capacitance is fundamentally nonlinear. We must consider two cases—isothermal and isentropic or adiabatic. The law for a perfect gas can be stated as

$$p = \rho R T \tag{3.15-7}$$

where $p$ is the pressure, $\rho$ is the density, $R$ is the gas constant, and $T$ is the absolute temperature. In an isothermal process $T$ is constant. If the derivative of both sides of Eq. (3.15-7) is taken under this condition, the result is

$$\frac{dp}{dt} = \frac{d\rho}{dt} R T \tag{3.15-8}$$

An inelastic pneumatic vessel has a constant volume $V_0$. Then

$$\frac{dp}{dt} = \frac{1}{V_0} \frac{dw}{dt} \tag{3.15-9}$$

where $w$ is the weight of the gas. The rate of change of weight ($dw/dt$) in the volume $V_0$ is the volumetric flow rate into $V_0$ times the density, or

$$\frac{dw}{dt} = q\rho \tag{3.15-10}$$

Equation (3.15-8) can now be rewritten as

$$\frac{dp}{dt} = \frac{1}{V_0} q\rho RT \tag{3.15-11}$$

Since $\rho RT$ is equal to $p$ by Eq. (3.15-7),

$$\frac{dp}{dt} = \frac{p}{V_0} q \tag{3.15-12}$$

If we assume only small variations in pressure, then we can assume that the ratio $p/V_0$ is constant and write

$$\frac{dp}{dt} = \frac{p_0}{V_0} q \tag{3.15-13}$$

or

$$p = \frac{p_0}{V_0} \int q \, dt \tag{3.15-14}$$

The pneumatic capacitance $C$ for an isothermal process is now defined as

$$C = \frac{V_0}{p_0} \tag{3.15-15}$$

and Eq. (3.15-14) becomes

$$p = \frac{1}{C} \int q \, dt \tag{3.15-16}$$

where $p$ is the pressure, $C$ is the pneumatic capacitance, and $q$ is the volumetric flow.

For an isentropic process with constant $\gamma$, the ratio of the specific heat at constant pressure to the specific heat at constant volume, the gas law is

$$p = k\rho^\gamma \tag{3.15-17}$$

where $p$ is the pressure, $k$ is a constant, $\rho$ is the gas density and $\gamma$ is the ratio of specific heats. Starting with Eq. (3.15-17) and going through a derivation similar to that for the isothermal case, we obtain

$$p = \frac{\gamma p_0}{V_0} \int q \, dt \tag{3.15-18}$$

We now define the pneumatic capacitance $C$ for an isentropic process as

$$C = \frac{V_0}{\gamma p_0} \tag{3.15-19}$$

and

$$p = \frac{1}{C} \int q \, dt \tag{3.15-20}$$

The difference between the capacitance for isothermal and isentropic processes is the factor $\gamma$. The energy stored in a pneumatic capacitance $C$ is

$$W = \tfrac{1}{2}Cp^2 \tag{3.15-21}$$

where $W$ is the energy and $p$ is the pressure.

### 3.16 THERMODYNAMIC SYSTEMS

Thermodynamic systems differ from the other physical systems previously discussed in three ways: (1) one of the principal parameters, heat flow, is dimensionally the same as power, (2) all matter is striving to reach the same temperature, and (3) there is only one kind of energy storage element in thermodynamic systems. The last condition is important because it means that no passive thermodynamic system can have an oscillatory response to other than an oscillatory forcing function. Despite these differences, temperature differential, heat flow, thermal resistance, and thermal capacitance obey the same dynamic equations that the parameters and elements of the other systems do.

We will first look at thermal resistance. It can be of three kinds— thermal conductivity resistance, film resistance at the interface between a solid and a liquid or gas, and finally radiation resistance when a surface is radiating heat. The methods for calculating the values of these three types of thermal resistance will be given in Sec. 3.30. The equation relating thermal resistance, heat flow, and temperature difference is

$$\theta = Rq \tag{3.16-1}$$

where $\theta$ is the temperature difference (just as we use $e$ as the potential difference in electrical systems), $R$ is the thermal resistance, and $q$ is the heat flow. Since $q$ is the time rate of change of heat, an alternate form is

$$\theta = R\frac{dH}{dt} \tag{3.16-2}$$

where $H$ represents the heat energy.

The second thermal element is thermal capacitance. We have all seen that a certain amount of heat is required to increase the temperature of a given object as when we heat a pot on the stove. We see that the energy is stored because the pot does not immediately return to room temperature when we remove it from the stove. The thermal capacitance of a body depends on its specific heat $sh$ which is the heat required to increase the temperature of a unit weight of the material one degree. For a given body, the total heat capacity is the specific heat times the total weight, or

$$C = shV\rho \tag{3.16-3}$$

where $C$ is the thermal capacitance, $sh$ is the specific heat, $V$ is the volume, and $\rho$ is the density. We can now write

$$\theta = \frac{1}{C} \int q \, dt \tag{3.16-4}$$

in which $\theta$ is the temperature difference, $C$ is the thermal capacitance of the body, and $q$ is the heat flow into or out of the body. By differentiating both sides of Eq. (3.16-4), we can solve for the flow as

$$q = C \frac{d\theta}{dt} \tag{3.16-5}$$

which tells us that the heat flow into or out of a body is proportional to the thermal capacitance and the time rate of change of temperature.

Energy relationships for thermal systems will not be stated explicitly because the entire subject is dealing with energy states. There is, however, a requirement for an additional thermodynamic relation in our studies of hydraulic systems. When liquids at different temperatures are mixed, the temperature of the mixture ends up somewhere in between. The exception to this rule may be the case in which there is a heat of mixing for the liquids involved; that is, the mixing of the two liquids actually generates heat. In the case with no heat of mixing, we simply sum the changes in heat in the individual liquids and equate it to zero. The equation for the change in heat in a single liquid is

$$\Delta H = \rho V sh(\theta_f - \theta) \tag{3.16-6}$$

where $\Delta H$ is the change in heat content, $\rho$ is the density, $V$ is the volume, $sh$ is the specific heat, $\theta_f$ is the final temperature, and $\theta$ is the initial temperature. If we mix several liquids with different starting temperatures, they all reach the same final temperature. Using subscripts to represent the different liquids, we can write

$$\rho_1 V_1 sh_1(\theta_f - \theta_1) + \rho_2 V_2 sh_2(\theta_f - \theta_2)$$
$$+ \rho_3 V_3 sh_3(\theta_f - \theta_2) + \cdots = 0 \tag{3.16-7}$$

If we solve Eq. (3.16-7) for $\theta_f$, the result is

$$\theta_f = \frac{\rho_1 V_1 sh_1 \theta_1 + \rho_2 V_2 sh_2 \theta_2 + \rho_3 V_3 sh_3 \theta_3 + \cdots}{\rho_1 V_1 sh_1 + \rho_2 V_2 sh_2 + \rho_3 V_3 sh_3 + \cdots} \tag{3.16-8}$$

If there is heat of mixing, the net change in heat is not zero and Eq. (3.16-7) becomes

$$\rho_1 V_1 sh_1(\theta_f - \theta_1) + \rho_2 V_2 sh_2(\theta_f - \theta_2)$$
$$+ \rho_3 V_3 sh_3(\theta_f - \theta_3) + \cdots = H_m \tag{3.16-9}$$

The heat of mixing can usually be determined on a per-pound basis so that

$$H_m = h_m \times \text{weight} \tag{3.16-10}$$

For example, in a polyethylene process where benzene and ethylene are being mixed, the specific heat of mixing might be 0.6 BTU per pound of organics. If we solve Eq. (3.16-9) for $\theta_f$, the result is

$$\theta_f = \frac{H_m + \rho_1 V_1 sh_1 \theta_1 + \rho_2 V_2 sh_2 \theta_2 + \rho_3 V_3 sh_3 \theta_3 + \cdots}{\rho_1 V_1 sh_1 + \rho_2 V_2 sh_2 + \rho_3 V_3 sh_3 + \cdots} \tag{3.16-11}$$

The only difference between Eq. (3.16-8) and Eq. (3.16-11) is that the additional term $H_m$ appears in the numerator of Eq. (3.16-11)

## 3.20 UNITS AND SYMBOLS

The parameters and elements of the various systems have been discussed without explicit definition of their dimensions or units. In Table 3.20-1 the symbols and units for all parameters and elements are listed. The units listed are the ones that will be used throughout the book with few exceptions. The units within each system are consistent. The basic unit of time is the second for all systems.

**TABLE 3.20-1** SYMBOLS AND UNITS

| System | Parameter or element | Symbol | Unit | Pictorial symbol |
|---|---|---|---|---|
| 1. *Electrical* | Voltage | $e$ | volt | |
| | Current | $i$ | ampere | $R$ |
| | Charge | $q$ | coulomb | |
| | Power | power | watt | |
| | Angular velocity | $\omega$ | radians/second | $L$ |
| | Energy | $W$ | joule | |
| | Resistance | $R$ | ohm | |
| | Conductance | $G$ | mho | $C$ |
| | Inductance | $L$ | henry | |
| | Capacitance | $C$ | farad | |
| 2. *Mechanical rectilineal* | Force | $f$ | pounds | |
| | Velocity | $v$ | feet/second | |
| | Displacement | $x$ | feet | $R$ |
| | Acceleration | $a$ | feet/second$^2$ | |
| | Acceleration of gravity | $g$ | 32.2 feet/second$^2$ | |
| | Power | power | foot-pound/second | $m$ |
| | Energy | $W$ | foot-pound | |
| | Viscous friction | $R$ | pound-second/foot | $k$ |
| | Mass | $m$ | pound-second$^2$/foot | |
| | Spring constant | $k$ | pound/foot | |

**TABLE 3-20.1** SYMBOLS AND UNITS (*Cont.*)

| System | Parameter or element | Symbol | Unit | Pictorial symbol |
|---|---|---|---|---|
| 3. *Mechanical rotational* | Torque | $T$ | pounds-feet | |
| | Angular velocity | $\omega, \dot{\theta}$ | radians/second | $B$ |
| | Angular displacement | $\theta$ | radians | |
| | Power | power | foot-pound/second | $J$ |
| | Energy | $W$ | foot-pound | |
| | Rotational friction | $B$ | pound-foot-second | |
| | Inertia | $J$ | pound-foot-second$^2$ | $c$ |
| | Rotational spring constant | $c$ | pound-foot/radian | |
| 4. *Hydraulic* | Pressure | $p$ | pound/foot$^2$ | |
| | Flow rate | $q$ | foot$^3$/second | |
| | Volume | $V$ | foot$^3$ | $R$   $R$ |
| | Power | power | foot-pound/second | |
| | Energy | $W$ | foot-pound | |
| | Resistance | $R$ | pound-second/foot$^5$ | $M$ |
| | Inertance | $M$ | pound-second$^2$/foot$^5$ | $C$ |
| | Capacitance | $C$ | foot$^5$/pound | |
| | Bulk modulus | $B$ | pound/foot$^2$ | |
| | Density | $\rho$ | pound/foot$^3$ | |
| 5. *Pneumatic* | Pressure | $p$ | pound/foot$^2$ | |
| | Flow rate | $q$ | foot$^3$/second | $R$   $R$ |
| | Volume | $V$ | foot$^3$ | |
| | Power | power | foot-pound/second | $M$ |
| | Energy | $W$ | foot-pound | |
| | Resistance | $R$ | pound-second/foot$^5$ | $C$ |
| | Inertance | $M$ | pound-second$^2$/foot$^5$ | |
| | Capacitance | $C$ | foot$^5$/pound | |
| 6. *Thermodynamic* | Temperature | $\theta$ | °F | $R$ |
| | Heat flow | $q$ | BTU/second | |
| | Heat | $H$ | BTU | |
| | Resistance | $R$ | degree-second/BTU | $C$ |
| | Capacitance | $C$ | BTU/degree | |

## 3.30 DETERMINATION OF VALUES

The relationships among parameters and elements in the various systems have been described, and consistent sets of units have been given for them. The next requirement is rules, empirical or derived, for determining the values of the elements. Although there are numerous formulas for calculating resistance, inductance, and capacitance in electrical systems, the usual case is to buy elements of a specified value off the shelf. In other systems, design is often not dependent *per se* on the equivalents of resistance, inductance, and capacitance; so one does not, for example, walk into a plumbing shop and ask for a pipe with such and such an inertance.

### 3.31 MECHANICAL RECTILINEAL SYSTEMS

Mechanical rectilineal systems depend almost entirely on actual measurements to determine values. Viscous friction resistance depends on the surface conditions of the moving object and the object over which it is moving. To develop a formula for calculating the value of viscous friction is difficult, so an actual measurement is the most reliable method.

To determine the mass of a body, we simply weigh it and divide by the acceleration of gravity, 32.2 feet per second squared at the surface of the earth.

The spring constant, like viscous friction, is usually measured. A known weight is attached to the spring so that it is free to hang vertically. The displacement is measured; the spring constant $k$ is equal to the weight divided by the displacement. The procedure should be repeated several times to get an average value.

### 3.32 MECHANICAL ROTATIONAL SYSTEMS

We are constrained to measure both rotational resistance and the rotational spring constant, but we can calculate the moment of inertia $J$. The formula is

$$J = \int y^2 \, dm \qquad (3.32\text{-}1)$$

Although the formulas for moment of inertia of regular bodies are available in standard handbooks, it is worthwhile to illustrate with one example.

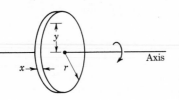

Let us calculate the moment of inertia of a disk about a line through its center as shown in Fig. 3.32-1. The disk is characterized by a uniform density of $\rho$, a radius $r$, and a thickness $x$. To make the calculation, the elemental mass $dm$ is needed. The elemental mass $dm$ is

**Fig. 3.32-1** Moment of inertia axis for disk example.

$$dm = \frac{\rho}{g} \, dV \qquad (3.32\text{-}2)$$

where $\rho$ is the density, $g$ is the acceleration of gravity, and $dV$ is the incremental volume. The incremental volume at a distance $y$ from the axis of rotation is the difference in volume of a disk of radius $y + dy$ and one with radius $y$, or

$$dV = \pi(y + dy)^2 \, x - \pi y^2 \, x = 2\pi \, x \, y \, dy \qquad (3.32\text{-}3)$$

if second-order differentials are neglected. $x$ is the disk thickness. Applying Eqs. (3.32-2) and (3.32-3) to Eq. (3.32-1) we have

$$J = \int_0^r y^2 \frac{\rho}{g} 2\pi \times y \, dy \qquad (3.32\text{-}4)$$

or

$$J = \frac{2\pi x\rho}{g} \int_0^r y^3 \, dy = \frac{2\pi x\rho}{g} \left[\frac{y^4}{4}\right]_0^r = \frac{\pi r^4 x\rho}{2g} \qquad (3.32\text{-}5)$$

where $r$ is the disk radius, $x$ the disk thickness, $\rho$ the density, and $g$ the
acceleration of gravity. If we recognize that the mass $m$ of the disk is
$(\pi r^2 x\rho/g)$, we can rewrite Eq. (3.32-5) as

$$J = \frac{mr^2}{2} \qquad (3.32\text{-}6)$$

## 3.33  HYDRAULIC SYSTEMS

Resistance in hydraulic systems may stem from several kinds of
hardware—straight circular tubes, bends, valves, or orifices. It is likely
to be extremely nonlinear; in particular, different formulas may apply
depending on whether the flow is laminar or turbulent. By *laminar* is
meant the type of flow in which the fluid moves in layers with interchange
between layers at a minimum. The primary forces acting are due to viscous
shear in the fluid. On the other hand *turbulent* flow is characterized by
more or less violent mixing normal to the direction of flow so that there
are no identifiable layers. A convenient, if not always clear-cut, measure
of whether the flow is laminar or turbulent is the dimensionless quantity
$\mathcal{R}$ called Reynolds' number. It is defined as follows:

$$\mathcal{R} = \frac{\rho v D}{\mu} \qquad (3.33\text{-}1)$$

in which $\rho$ is the density, $v$ is the velocity, $D$ is the diameter, and $\mu$ is
the viscosity. Very low values of $\mathcal{R}$ correspond to laminar flow, high
values to turbulent flow. The dividing line for steady flow through circular
tubes is about 2000—below, laminar; above, turbulent. The formula for
calculating the resistance of a circular tube with laminar flow is

$$R = \frac{0.78\mu l}{A^2} \qquad (3.33\text{-}2)$$

where $R$ is the hydraulic resistance in lb-sec/ft$^5$, $\mu$ is the viscosity in
lb-sec/ft$^2$, $l$ is the tube length in feet, and $A$ is the tube cross-sectional
area in ft$^2$.

The resistance of a circular tube to turbulent flow is

$$R = \frac{4fl\rho q}{gDA^2} \qquad (3.33\text{-}3)$$

where $R$ is the hydraulic resistance in lb-sec/ft$^5$, $f$ is the Fanning factor (dimensionless), $l$ is the tube length in ft, $\rho$ is the density in lb/ft$^3$, $q$ is the average flow in ft$^3$/sec, $g$ is the acceleration of gravity equal to 32.2 ft/sec$^2$, $D$ is the tube diameter in ft, and $A$ is the cross-sectional area in ft$^2$. The Fanning factor is a dimensionless quantity related to the surface roughness of the pipe as well as the geometry of the pipe. A typical Fanning factor value is 0.042 for straight, smooth pipe of 0.5 in. diameter when the average velocity is 0.5 ft/sec. Additional values of the Fanning factor can be found in H. W. King, C. O. Wisler, and J. G. Woodburn, *Hydraulics* (New York: John Wiley & Sons, Inc., 1958).

The resistance of valves is

$$R = \frac{2Gq}{C_v^2} \qquad (3.33\text{-}4)$$

where $R$ is the hydraulic resistance in lb-sec/ft$^5$, $G$ is the specific gravity of the liquid, $q$ is the flow in ft$^3$/sec, and $C_v$ is the constant that is the flow of water in ft$^3$/sec necessary to cause a pressure drop of 1 lb/ft$^2$.

We have previously found that the inertance $M$ of a hydraulic conductor can be calculated from the geometry and the particular liquid involved. Equation (3.14-13) is repeated here with a description of the units:

$$M = \frac{\rho l}{gA} \qquad (3.33\text{-}5)$$

where $M$ is the inertance in lb-sec$^2$/ft$^5$, $\rho$ is the liquid density in lb/ft$^3$, $l$ is the length in ft, $g$ is the acceleration of gravity equal to 32.2 ft/sec$^2$, and $A$ is the cross-sectional area in ft$^2$.

The formula for calculating hydraulic capacitance $C$ was given in Eq. (3.14-22) and is

$$C = \frac{1}{[(B/V) + K]} \qquad (3.33\text{-}6)$$

in which $C$ is the hydraulic capacitance in ft$^5$/lb, $B$ is the bulk modulus of the liquid in lb/ft$^2$ or [(lb/ft$^2$)(ft$^3$/ft$^3$)], $V$ is the volume in ft$^3$, and $K$ is the constant related to the effect of an elastic vessel in lb/ft$^5$. If the vessel is inelastic, $K$ is zero. If the liquid is incompressible, the hydraulic capacitance is simply $1/K$.

## 3.34 PNEUMATIC SYSTEMS

Pneumatic resistance can exist in the form of tubes, orifices, nozzles, or valves. For a capillary tube the resistance to laminar flow is the same as for hydraulic tubes:

$$R = \frac{0.78\mu l}{A^2} \qquad (3.34\text{-}1)$$

where $R$ is the pneumatic resistance in lb-sec/ft$^5$, $\mu$ is the viscosity in lb-sec/ft$^2$, $l$ is the length in ft, and $A$ is the cross-sectional area in ft$^2$.

Resistance calculations for restrictions such as valves and orifices in gas systems must be divided into two categories. As an approximation we will make the division on the basis of whether the pressure downstream of the restriction is less than or greater than one-half the upstream pressure. For the downstream pressure $p_2$ greater than one-half the upstream pressure $p_1$,

$$R = 5.5 \times 10^3 \, \frac{q_r g p_1}{C_v^2 \theta p_2} \qquad (3.34\text{-}2)$$

where $R$ is the pneumatic resistance in lb-sec/ft$^5$, $q_r$ is the measured flow in ft$^3$/*hour* at standard atmospheric pressure and 60°F temperature, $g$ is the acceleration of gravity equal to 32.2 ft/sec$^2$, $p_1$ is the upstream pressure in lb/ft$^2$ absolute, $C_v$ is a measured constant equal to the flow of water in gallons per minute required to produce a pressure drop of 1 lb/in.$^2$ across the restriction, $\theta$ is the temperature at $p_1$ in °K, and $p_2$ is the downstream pressure in lb/ft$^2$ absolute. The quantities in Eq. (3.34-2) do require measurements, but once these have been made the calculated resistance can be used for dynamic problems. If the downstream pressure $p_2$ is less than one-half the upstream pressure $p_1$,

$$R = 1.16 \times 10^3 \, \frac{p_1 \sqrt{g}}{C_v} \qquad (3.34\text{-}3)$$

where all quantities are the same as defined for Eq. (3.34-2). Inertance for pneumatic systems is calculated by the same formula as for hydraulic systems. Repeating Eq. (3.15-5),

$$M = \frac{\rho l}{gA} \qquad (3.34\text{-}4)$$

where $M$ is the inertance in lb-sec$^2$/ft$^5$, $\rho$ is the gas density in lb/ft$^3$, $l$ is the pneumatic conductor length in ft, $g$ is the acceleration of gravity equal to 32.2 ft/sec$^2$, and $A$ is the cross-sectional area of the conductor in ft$^2$.

For an isothermal process, the pneumatic capacitance from Eq. (3.15-15) is

$$C = \frac{V_0}{p_0} \tag{3.34-5}$$

where $C$ is the capacitance in ft$^5$/lb, $V_0$ is the initial volume in ft$^3$, and $p_0$ is the initial pressure in lb/ft$^2$. For an adiabatic process, the pneumatic capacitance is, from Eq. (3.15-19),

$$C = \frac{V_0}{\gamma p_0} \tag{3.34-6}$$

where $C$ is the capacitance in ft$^5$/lb, $V_0$ is the initial volume in ft$^3$, $\gamma$ is the ratio of the specific heat at constant pressure to the specific heat at constant volume, and $p_0$ is the initial pressure in lb/ft$^2$.

### 3.35 THERMODYNAMIC SYSTEMS

Thermal resistance occurs under several conditions of heat transfer—transfer by thermal conduction, transfer across the boundary between a solid and a liquid or gas, and transfer from a surface by radiation. For thermal conduction the thermal resistance is

$$R = \frac{l}{kA} \tag{3.35-1}$$

where $R$ is the resistance in °F/(BTU/sec), $l$ is the length of the conduction path in ft, $k$ is the thermal conductivity in (BTU/sec-ft$^2$)/(°F/ft), and $A$ is the cross-sectional area of the conduction path in ft$^2$. When heat is transferred across the boundary between a solid and a liquid or gas, the thermal resistance due to film coefficient is

$$R = \frac{1}{hA} \tag{3.35-2}$$

where $R$ is the resistance in °F/(BTU/sec), $h$ is the film coefficient in BTU/(sec-°F-ft$^2$), and $A$ is the cross-sectional area of the boundary in ft$^2$. When heat is radiated, the thermal resistance is

$$R = \frac{5.22 \times 10^5}{\epsilon A} \left[ \frac{0.173\epsilon}{(q_r/3600A) + (\theta_e/100)^4} \right]^{3/4} \tag{3.35-3}$$

where $R$ is the resistance in °F/(BTU/sec), $\epsilon$ is the emissivity, $A$ is the cross-sectional area of the radiating surface in ft$^2$, $q_r$ is the radiant heat flow in BTU/sec, and $\theta_e$ is the temperature of the receiving surface in °R.

Equation (3.16-3) states that

$$C = shV\rho \qquad\qquad (3.35\text{-}4)$$

where $C$ is the thermal capacitance in BTU/°F, $sh$ is the specific heat in BTU/(lb-°F), $V$ is the volume in ft³, and $\rho$ is the density in lb/ft³.

## 3.40  RULES GOVERNING SUMMATION OF PARAMETERS

The basic equations relating the parameters and elements of the various systems have been given, consistent sets of units have been given and some methods for calculating values of the elements have been given. Since more than one kind of element can appear in a given physical problem as well as different configurations of the elements, we must examine the rules for summing the parameters in the different systems.

### 3.41  ELECTRICAL SYSTEMS

Kirchhoff's laws of voltage and current are the fundamental rules governing the summation of parameters in electrical systems. These are:

VOLTAGE LAW: The sum of the voltages around any closed circuit is zero.

CURRENT LAW: The sum of the currents flowing into a point is equal to the sum of the currents flowing away from the point.

To apply these laws we must know several ancillary rules:

1. Source voltages are positive when summing around the circuit in a direction from negative to positive through the source; they are negative when summing around the circuit in a direction from positive to negative through a source.
2. Voltages across elements are negative when summing around the circuit in the direction of current flow; they are positive when summing around the circuit in the direction opposite to that of current flow.
3. Directions of current flow can be assigned arbitrarily; if the wrong direction is assumed for cases of unidirectional flow, the solution will be negative indicating that the current actually flows in the opposite direction. For oscillating currents, the phase relation to the reference will still work out.
4. An arbitrary reference phase, that is, positive and negative terminals, can be assigned when there is only one voltage source in a circuit. If there is more than one voltage source, the relative phases must be included.

In Fig. 3.41-1 is shown an electric circuit that can be used to illustrate some of the above rules. It is a series-parallel circuit containing all three elements—resistance, inductance, and capacitance. The differential equations describing the behavior are three in number: two are based on the voltage law obtained by applying rules 1 and 2 to the closed paths numbered 1 and 2; the third is based on applying the current law at point $a$. We see that there are three independent equations and three unknowns—$i_1$, $i_2$, and $i_3$. Other equations can sometimes be written, but there cannot be more independent equations than there are unknowns. In this case we could have chosen a path to include the voltage source $e$, $R_1$, $L_1$, and $C$ but it would not have been independent of the three equations in Eq. (3.41-1). To insure that all the necessary independent equations are used, it is necessary and sufficient to choose the voltage law paths such that all sources and elements are included in at least one path and that the current law applications include branch points such that all currents are included at least once.

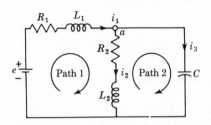

**Fig. 3.41-1** Series-parallel electric circuit.

$$e - R_1 i_1 - L_1 \frac{di_1}{dt} - R_2 i_2 - L_2 \frac{di_2}{dt} = 0$$

$$-\frac{1}{C} \int i_3 \, dt + L_2 \frac{di_2}{dt} + R_2 i_2 = 0 \qquad (3.41\text{-}1)$$

$$i_1 = i_2 + i_3$$

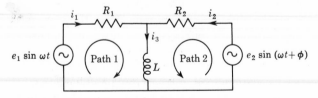

**Fig. 3.41-2** Electric circuit with two a-c voltage sources.

The circuit of Fig. 3.41-2 is shown to illustrate rule 4. Since the circuit contains two a-c voltage sources, the relative phase ($\phi$) of $e_2$ to $e_1$ must be specified. The equations describing the behavior are

$$e_1 \sin \omega t - i_1 R_1 - L \frac{di_3}{dt} = 0$$

$$e_2 \sin (\omega t + \phi) - i_2 R_2 - L \frac{di_3}{dt} = 0 \qquad (3.41\text{-}2)$$

$$i_1 + i_2 = i_3$$

Solutions to these types of equations will be given in Secs. 3.60 and 3.70. The best circuits, however, for direct illustration of analogies are the series $R$-$L$-$C$ with a voltage source and the parallel $R$-$L$-$C$ with a current

Fig. 3.41-3 Series $R$-$L$-$C$ circuit.          Fig. 3.41-4 Parallel $R$-$L$-$C$ circuit.

source. The series circuit is shown in Fig. 3.41-3 and the parallel circuit in Fig. 3.41-4. The equation for the circuit of Fig. 3.41-3 is

$$e - iR - L \frac{di}{dt} - \frac{1}{C} \int i \, dt = 0 \qquad (3.41\text{-}3)$$

and the equation for the circuit of Fig. 3.41-4 is

$$i = \frac{e}{R} + \frac{1}{L} \int e \, dt + C \frac{de}{dt} \qquad (3.41\text{-}4)$$

If we transpose the left-hand side of Eq. (3.41-4) and rearrange the order of the terms, the result is

$$i - \frac{e}{R} - C \frac{de}{dt} - \frac{1}{L} \int e \, dt = 0 \qquad (3.41\text{-}5)$$

Equations (3.41-3) and (3.41-5) are exactly the same form with $e$ and $i$ interchanged, $C$ and $L$ interchanged, and $R$ and $1/R$ interchanged. The two circuits described by these analogous equations are called the *duals* of each other. Duals exist in the other systems and are sometimes used, for example, in analyzing mechanical systems.

## 3.42 MECHANICAL RECTILINEAL SYSTEMS

Although there are exact analogies relating the parameters and elements of electrical and mechanical systems, the analytical methods differ.

The difference occurs because there is no continuity law in mechanical systems analogous to Kirchhoff's current law. The basic rule by which mechanical systems are governed is D'Alembert's principle which states: the summation of forces at a point is zero.

To apply this rule, we must recognize that there will be two kinds of forces acting at a point—action forces and reaction forces. This statement is in effect Newton's third law—that for every action there exists an equal and opposite reaction. In applying D'Alembert's principle it is necessary to designate each force acting at a point as either an action or a reaction force. The force of the point element being examined is always a reaction force; that is, if the summation of forces acting on a mass is being considered then the force equal to $ma$ is a reaction force, if the summation of forces acting on a mechanical resistance such as a dashpot is being considered then the force equal to $R\dot{x}$ is a reaction force, and if the summation of forces acting on a spring is being considered then the force equal to $kx$ is a reaction force. These same forces, however, become action forces when their effects on other members are considered. For example, the spring force $kx$ represents an action force when its effect on the summation of forces on a mass to which it is attached is considered. Conversely, the mass force $ma$ represents an action force when its effect on the summation of forces on a spring to which it is attached is considered. The concept of action and reaction forces is best demonstrated by examples, but let us first establish the other procedures for writing the equations for mechanical rectilineal systems.

1. An origin and positive direction for $x$ must be assigned. Once the geometrical coordinate system is defined, external forces acting in the positive $x$ direction are positive and vice versa.

2. A separate $x$ variable—$x_1$, $x_2$, $x_3$, and so on—must be assigned for each point in a sytem where different velocities can exist. A mass, unless otherwise noted, is a rigid body, so both sides of it must be at the same velocity relative to a fixed reference in the line of action. A spring is not a rigid body and therefore must have two variables, $x_1$ and $x_2$, assigned to its ends unless one end is fixed. The assignment of variables to a viscous friction component depends on the particular configuration used to represent viscous friction. Perhaps the most widely used is that shown in Fig. 3.42-1(a). It is a floating dashpot composed of a hydraulic cylinder with a plunger free to move back and forth in the cylinder. The force is transmitted through the fluid to the end of the cylinder. The plunger and cylinder can move at different velocities and require the assignment of two variables unless one end is fixed. The force required to actuate the system is proportional to the relative velocity between the plunger and the cylinder. A second kind of resistance is shown in Fig. 3.42-1(b). It represents the sliding friction associated with a mass and its force is

characterized by a single velocity. When the resistance is directly associated with a mass, the combination must be treated as a single point in
summing forces with its reaction force equal to $R\dot{x} + m\ddot{x}$. An exception
would be the case in which the mass was sliding on a moving medium
such as a conveyor belt.

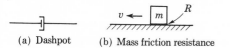

(a) Dashpot          (b) Mass friction resistance

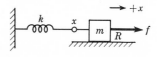
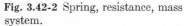

**Fig. 3.42-1** Two kinds of rectilineal
resistance.

**Fig. 3.42-2** Spring, resistance, mass
system.

The corollary procedures for writing the equations of mechanical systems have been established, so we will now demonstrate the application
of D'Alembert's principle. The diagram of Fig. 3.42-2 shows a spring,
resistance, mass system. The spring is attached to the ground at one end
and a force $f$ acts on the mass $m$ in the positive $x$ direction. Since the
system is rigidly connected from the point marked $x$ to the point of applying the force $f$, the system is characterized by one velocity, and only one
variable has to be assigned. Remembering that the mass and resistance
must be treated as a single point, we can write the
summation of forces on the mass-resistance as

$$f - kx - (R\ddot{x} + m\dot{x}) = 0 \qquad (3.42\text{-}1)$$

The force $f$ is written positive because it is in the $+x$
direction, the spring force $kx$ negative because as the
spring is stretched in the $+x$ direction it exerts a backward pull on the resistance-mass combination and
finally the resistance-mass force $(R\dot{x} + m\ddot{x})$ negative because it is a reaction force. We can rewrite Eq. (3.42-1) as

$$m\ddot{x} + R\dot{x} + kx = f \qquad (3.42\text{-}2)$$

If we choose to write Eq. (3.42-2) in terms of velocity,
it becomes

$$m\frac{dv}{dt} + Rv + k \int v \, dt = f \qquad (3.42\text{-}3)$$

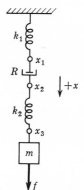

Two-spring,
floating-dashpot,
mass system.

Figure 3.42-3 shows a more complicated mechanical system. It consists
of two springs, a floating dashpot, and a mass. The points marked $x_1$, $x_2$,
and $x_3$ can have different velocities with respect to a given reference, so
they must be assigned independent variables. The origin is at the point
where the spring $k_1$ is fixed. We treat mass as existing at a point just as we

treat electrical elements as existing at a point in lumped circuit theory. In Chap. 10 nonlumped or distributed constants will be discussed.

We have now assigned the necessary independent variables and established the coordinates, so we can proceed to apply D'Alembert's principle. The action forces on the mass $m$ are a positive force $f$ and a negative force due to the pull of the spring $k_2$ equal to $k_2(x_3 - x_2)$. The reaction force of the mass $m$ is $m\ddot{x}_3$. Summing these forces, we get

$$f - k_2(x_3 - x_2) - m\ddot{x}_3 = 0 \qquad (3.42\text{-}4)$$

The forces acting between the spring $k_2$ and the resistance $R$ are $k_2(x_3 - x_2)$ and $R(\dot{x}_2 - \dot{x}_1)$. Therefore,

$$k_2(x_3 - x_2) = R(\dot{x}_2 - \dot{x}_1) \qquad (3.42\text{-}5)$$

The forces acting between the resistance $R$ and the spring $k_1$ are $R(\dot{x}_2 - \dot{x}_1)$ and $k_1x_1$. Therefore,

$$k_1x_1 = R(\dot{x}_2 - \dot{x}_1) \qquad (3.42\text{-}6)$$

Equations (3.42-4) through (3.42-6) are simultaneous differential equations in three unknowns. In every case of rectilineal systems, application of D'Alembert's principle at enough points to include the effect of each element at least once either as an action or as a reaction force will result in the required number of independent equations to solve for the independent variables.

The application of D'Alembert's principle is the classic approach to solving mechanical rectilineal problems. An alternate approach is given in Sec. 4.25. It is a more convenient way to derive electrical equivalents of mechanical systems.

### 3.43 MECHANICAL ROTATIONAL SYSTEMS

Rotational systems, like their lineal counterparts, do not obey a rule of continuity analogous to Kirchhoff's current law. The basic behavior is governed by D'Alembert's principle of moments, which states that the summation of moments or torques at a point is zero. There will be both action and reaction torques, and the rules for handling them are exactly equivalent to those for handling action and reaction forces in rectilineal systems. The same approach is also used in setting up the equations by assignment of independent variables where different angular velocities can exist.

The opposite ends of a rotational spring can be at different velocities, so two variables must be assigned unless one end is fixed. Rotational dashpots also can have different angular velocities at opposite ends. These dashpots can be magnetic devices that produce a reaction torque proportional to angular velocity or they can be hydraulic devices that produce a reaction torque proportional to angular velocity. The symbol we will use for a rotational dashpot that can have different velocities is shown in Fig. 3.43-1. It is in effect a paddle wheel inside a cylinder containing fluid. The torque is transmitted by the fluid to the cylinder, which can then rotate also. If the viscous friction is associated with the rotating mass characterized by moment of inertia $J$, then the two are inextricably tied together and the same angular velocity applies to both. The same exception would apply as in the rectilineal case.

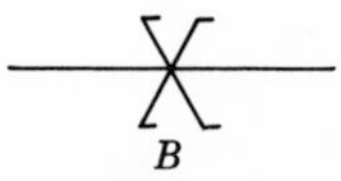

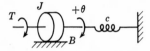

**Fig. 3.43-1** Symbol for rotational dashpot.

**Fig. 3.43-2** Mechanical rotational system.

The diagram of Fig. 3.43-2 shows a rotational system characterized by a single angular velocity. A disk with moment of inertia $J$ has a torque $T$ applied to its shaft. It is in contact with a surface such that part of the applied torque is taken up by the resistance $B$. It is also coupled to a rotational spring that has a constant $c$ and is fixed at one end. If we apply D'Alembert's principle to the disk assuming the clockwise direction as positive, looking at the free or left end, then the applied torque $T$ is a positive action torque. On the other side of the shaft the rotational spring contributes a negative action torque. These must then be summed with the negative reaction torque of the inertia-resistance combination, or

$$T - c\theta - (B\theta + J\ddot{\theta}) = 0 \tag{3.43-1}$$

which can be rewritten as

$$J\ddot{\theta} + B\dot{\theta} + c\theta = T \tag{3.43-2}$$

or, since $\omega$ is equal to $\dot{\theta}$,

$$J\dot{\omega} + B\omega + c \int \omega \, dt = T \tag{3.43-3}$$

A more complicated rotational system analogous to the lineal system of Fig. 3.42-3 is shown in Fig. 3.43-3. It consists of two rotational springs, a floating rotational dashpot, and an inertia $J$ with a torque $T$ applied. As before we must assign independ-

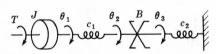

**Fig. 3.43-3** Two-spring, floating-dashpot, inertia rotational system.

ent variables $\theta_1$, $\theta_2$, and $\theta_3$ to points where different angular velocities can exist and then proceed to apply D'Alembert's principle. On the inertia $J$

there is a positive action torque $T$ and a negative one due to the spring $c_1$ equal to $c_1(\theta_2 - \theta_1)$. Summing these with the reaction torque of the inertia, we have

$$T - c_1(\theta_2 - \theta_1) - J\ddot{\theta}_1 = 0 \qquad (3.43\text{-}4)$$

Between the spring $c_1$ and the resistance $B$, the torques are $c_1(\theta_2 - \theta_1)$ and $B(\dot{\theta}_3 - \dot{\theta}_2)$. Therefore,

$$B(\dot{\theta}_3 - \dot{\theta}_2) = c_1(\theta_2 - \theta_1) \qquad (3.43\text{-}5)$$

Between the resistance $B$ and the spring $c_2$, the torques are $B(\dot{\theta}_2 - \dot{\theta}_3)$ and $c_2\theta_3$. Therefore,

$$c_2\theta_3 = B(\dot{\theta}_2 - \dot{\theta}_3) \qquad (3.43\text{-}6)$$

Equations (3.43-4) through (3.43-6) constitute a series of simultaneous differential equations describing the behavior of the system of Fig. 3.43-3.

## 3.44 HYDRAULIC SYSTEMS

The rules for handling hydraulic systems are almost the exact analogies of the voltage and current laws of Kirchhoff. These are (1) the sum of the pressure drops around any closed path is zero and (2) the sum of the flows into any point is equal to the sum of the flows away from that point. The analogy breaks down on rule 2 because the flows referred to in this case are weights per unit time rather than volumes per unit time. The balance of weights in a hydraulic (or chemical) process is known as *stoichiometric* balance. It is a direct result of the law of conservation of matter and can be stated in a verbal equation as

$$\text{weight in} = \text{weight out} + \text{weight held up} \qquad (3.44\text{-}1)$$

If the changes in density due to changes in pressure (and/or temperature) are small, then the stoichiometric balance can be equated to a volume balance since

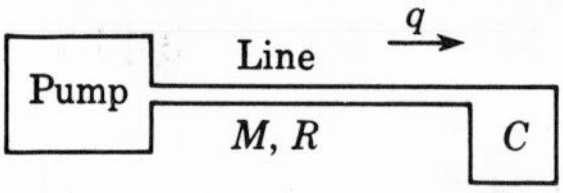

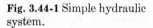

$$V = W/\rho \qquad (3.44\text{-}2)$$

**Fig. 3.44-1** Simple hydraulic system.

where $V$ is the volume of the liquid, $W$ is the weight of the liquid, and $\rho$ is the density of the liquid. In other words, if the density $\rho$ is constant for all practical purposes, then the volume is constant. To examine the application of hydraulic rules let us consider the system of Fig. 3.44-1. It consists of a pump which raises the pressure of a liquid above that of the atmosphere by an amount $p$; a pipe line which is characterized by a resistance $R$, an inertance $M$, and a negligible capacitance; and a tank characterized by a hydraulic capacitance $C$. The equation describing the system is

$$p - Rq - M\frac{dq}{dt} - \frac{1}{C}\int q\,dt = 0 \qquad (3.44\text{-}3)$$

which we get by application of the first rule for hydraulic systems. In this example the closed path was represented by atmosphere pressure through the pump, through the pipe, and through the tank wall back to atmospheric pressure. In effect, atmospheric pressure was the same as ground potential in an electrical system. In electrical systems, any two points at the same potential (or voltage) can be connected without disturbing the system and with no current flow between the two points. The analogous situation is true in hydraulic systems—that any two points with the same pressure can be connected and there will be no flow between the two points.

### 3.45  PNEUMATIC SYSTEMS

Pneumatic systems behave exactly like hydraulic systems insofar as the rules for setting up the equations are concerned. The equivalents to both of Kirchhoff's laws exist, with the exception previously noted that the exact analogy to the current law is a weight flow rather than a volumetric flow. In fact we can use the diagram of Fig. 3.44-1 to illustrate a simple pneumatic system. The values of $R$, $M$, and $C$ would of course have to be recalculated for the characteristics of the gas used in place of the liquid. The equation describing the system would be

$$p - Rq - M\frac{dq}{dt} - \frac{1}{C}\int q\,dt = 0 \qquad (3.45\text{-}1)$$

where $p$ is the pump pressure above atmosphere, $R$ is the resistance of the pneumatic line, $M$ is the pneumatic inertance of the line, and $C$ is the pneumatic capacitance of the tank.

### 3.46  THERMODYNAMIC SYSTEMS

Thermodynamic systems are constrained by a law of continuity which is really the law of conservation of energy. So there are exact analogies for both Kirchhoff's laws. These are

1. the sum of the temperature drops around any closed path is zero, and
2. the sum of the heat flows into a point is equal to the sum of the heat flows away from a point.

As mentioned before, thermodynamic systems are always trying to reach an equilibrium. In setting up many problems we must assume infinite sinks. For example, if heat is being lost from a process to the atmosphere we assume that the atmosphere is an infinite sink and consequently the temperature of the atmosphere is not elevated by the heat lost from the process.

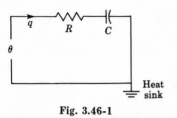

Fig. 3.46-1

Figure 3.46-1 represents a simple thermodynamic system consisting of a heat source at temperature $\theta$ with respect to a reference which is the infinite sink. The heat is flowing through a thermal conductance and thermal capacitance to the sink. The diagram is shown exactly like an electric circuit. One difference is that it is easier to obtain electrical elements that can be represented as a single type in many practical applications; that is, a pure resistance, inductance, or capacitance. In thermodynamic systems, thermal resistance and capacitance are always tied together in the same elements. However, a good metallic conductor with a large cross-sectional area and large volume can represent a good approximation to a pure thermal capacitance, and thermal resistance due to film coefficient can represent a good approximation to a pure thermal resistance. The equation describing the thermal circuit of Fig. 3.46-1 is

$$\theta - qR - \frac{1}{C} \int q \, dt = 0 \qquad (3.46\text{-}1)$$

or

$$qR + \frac{1}{C} \int q \, dt = \theta \qquad (3.46\text{-}2)$$

where $q$ is the heat flow, $R$ is the thermal resistance, $C$ is the thermal capacitance, and $\theta$ is the driving temperature.

For a more complex thermal system let us consider the diagram of Fig. 3.46-2. It consists of a heat source connected to two thermal resistances which are connected at their other ends to a common heat capacitance tied to an infinite sink whose temperature is the reference. Applying the thermal equivalents of Kirchhoff's laws, we obtain the following set of simultaneous equations:

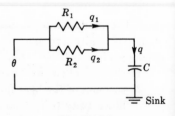

Fig. 3.46-2

$$q = q_1 + q_2$$

$$\theta - R_1 q_1 - \frac{1}{C} \int q \, dt = 0 \qquad (3.46\text{-}3)$$

$$\theta - R_2 q_2 - \frac{1}{C} \int q \, dt = 0$$

| e-degree-contain-lements | Reference equation number | Power dissipation | Energy Storage | | System |
|---|---|---|---|---|---|
| | | | 1 | 2 | |
| $\int i\,dt = e$ | (3.41-3) | power $= i^2 R$ | $W = \frac{1}{2}Li^2$ | $W = \frac{1}{2}Ce^2$ | Electrical |
| $\int e\,dt = i$ | (3.41-4) | power $= e^2 G$ | $W = \frac{1}{2}Ce^2$ | $W = \frac{1}{2}Li^2$ | |
| $\int v\,dt = f$ | (3.42-3) | power $= v^2 R$ | $W = \frac{1}{2}mv^2$ | $W = \frac{1}{2}\frac{1}{k}f^2$ | Mechanical Rectilineal |
| $\int f\,dt = v$ | | power $= \dfrac{f^2}{R}$ | $W = \frac{1}{2}\frac{1}{k}f^2$ | $W = \frac{1}{2}mv^2$ | |
| $\int \omega\,dt = T$ | (3.43-3) | power $= \omega^2 B$ | $W = \frac{1}{2}J\omega^2$ | $W = \frac{1}{2}\frac{1}{c}T^2$ | Mechanical Rotational |
| $\int T\,dt = \omega$ | | power $= \dfrac{T^2}{R}$ | $W = \frac{1}{2}\frac{1}{c}T^2$ | $W = \frac{1}{2}J\omega^2$ | |
| $\int q\,dt = p$ | (3.44-3) | power $= q^2 R$ | $W = \frac{1}{2}Mq^2$ | $W = \frac{1}{2}Cp^2$ | Hydraulic |
| $\int p\,dt = q$ | | power $= \dfrac{p^2}{R}$ | $W = \frac{1}{2}Cp^2$ | $W = \frac{1}{2}Mq^2$ | |
| $\int q\,dt = p$ | (3.45-1) | power $= q^2 R$ | $W = \frac{1}{2}Mq^2$ | $W = \frac{1}{2}Cp^2$ | Pneumatic |
| $\int p\,dt = q$ | | power $= \dfrac{p^2}{R}$ | $W = \frac{1}{2}Cp^2$ | $W = \frac{1}{2}Mq^2$ | |
| $\int q\,dt = \theta$ | (3.46-2) | | | | Thermodynamic |
| $+ G\theta = q$ | | | | | |

| System | Parameters | | | Elements | | |
|---|---|---|---|---|---|---|
| | Forcing function | Response function | Alternate response | Dissipative | Energy Storage | |
| | | | | | 1 | 2 |
| Electrical | voltage $e$ | current $i$ | charge $q$ | resistance $R$ | inductance $L$ | capacitance $C$ |
| | current $i$ | voltage $e$ | | conductance $G$ | capacitance $C$ | inductance $L$ |
| Mechanical Rectilineal | force $f$ | velocity $v$ | displacement $x$ | rectilineal resistance $R$ | mass $m$ | reciprocal of spring constant $1/k$ |
| | velocity $v$ | force $f$ | | reciprocal of rectilineal resistance $1/R$ | reciprocal of spring constant $1/k$ | mass $m$ |
| Mechanical Rotational | torque $T$ | angular velocity $\omega$ | angular displacement $\theta$ | rotational resistance $B$ | moment of inertia $J$ | reciprocal of rotational spring constant $1/c$ |
| | angular velocity $\omega$ | torque $T$ | | reciprocal of rotational resistance $1/B$ | reciprocal of rotational spring constant $1/c$ | moment of inertia $J$ |
| Hydraulic | pressure $p$ | volumetric flow $q$ | volume $V$ | hydraulic resistance $R$ | inertance $M$ | hydraulic capacitance $C$ |
| | volumetric flow $q$ | pressure $p$ | | reciprocal of hydraulic resistance $1/R$ | hydraulic capacitance $C$ | inertance $M$ |
| Pneumatic | pressure $p$ | volumetric flow $q$ | volume $V$ | pneumatic resistance $R$ | inertance $M$ | pneumatic capacitance $C$ |
| | volumetric flow $q$ | pressure $p$ | | reciprocal of pneumatic resistance $1/R$ | pneumatic capacitance $C$ | inertance $M$ |
| Thermodynamic | temperature $\theta$ | heat flow $q$ | heat $H$ | thermal resistance $R$ | | thermal capacitance $C$ |
| | heat flow $q$ | temperature $\theta$ | | thermal conductance $G$ | thermal capacitance $C$ | |

**TABLE 3.50-1** SUMMARY OF ANALOGIES

| Relations between Parameters and Elements | | | | | | Equation of s... of-freedom sy... ing all types |
|---|---|---|---|---|---|---|
| Response Function | | | Alternate Response | | | |
| | Energy Storage | | | Energy Storage | | |
| Dissipative | 1 | 2 | Dissipative | 1 | 2 | |
| $e = Ri$ | $e = L\dfrac{di}{dt}$ | $e = \dfrac{1}{C}\displaystyle\int i\,dt$ | $e = R\dfrac{dq}{dt}$ | $e = L\dfrac{d^2q}{dt^2}$ | $e = \dfrac{q}{C}$ | $L\dfrac{di}{dt} + Ri +$ |
| $i = Ge$ | $i = C\dfrac{de}{dt}$ | $i = \dfrac{1}{L}\displaystyle\int e\,dt$ | | | | $C\dfrac{de}{dt} + Ge +$ |
| $f = Rv$ | $f = m\dfrac{dv}{dt}$ | $f = k\displaystyle\int v\,dt$ | $f = R\dfrac{dx}{dt}$ | $f = m\dfrac{d^2x}{dt^2}$ | $f = kx$ | $m\dfrac{dv}{dt} + Rv +$ |
| $v = \dfrac{f}{R}$ | $v = \dfrac{1}{k}\dfrac{df}{dt}$ | $v = \dfrac{1}{m}\displaystyle\int f\,dt$ | | | | $\dfrac{1}{k}\dfrac{df}{dt} + \dfrac{f}{R} +$ |
| $T = B\omega$ | $T = J\dfrac{d\omega}{dt}$ | $T = c\displaystyle\int \omega\,dt$ | $T = B\dfrac{d\theta}{dt}$ | $T = J\dfrac{d^2\theta}{dt^2}$ | $T = c\theta$ | $J\dfrac{d\omega}{dt} + B\omega +$ |
| $\omega = \dfrac{T}{B}$ | $\omega = \dfrac{1}{c}\dfrac{dT}{dt}$ | $\omega = \dfrac{1}{J}\displaystyle\int T\,dt$ | | | | $\dfrac{1}{c}\dfrac{dT}{dt} + \dfrac{T}{B} +$ |
| $p = Rq$ | $p = M\dfrac{dq}{dt}$ | $p = \dfrac{1}{C}\displaystyle\int q\,dt$ | $p = R\dfrac{dV}{dt}$ | $p = M\dfrac{d^2V}{dt^2}$ | $p = \dfrac{V}{C}$ | $M\dfrac{dq}{dt} + Rq +$ |
| $q = \dfrac{p}{R}$ | $q = C\dfrac{dp}{dt}$ | $q = \dfrac{1}{M}\displaystyle\int p\,dt$ | | | | $C\dfrac{dp}{dt} + \dfrac{p}{R} +$ |
| $p = Rq$ | $p = M\dfrac{dq}{dt}$ | $p = \dfrac{1}{C}\displaystyle\int q\,dt$ | $p = R\dfrac{dV}{dt}$ | $p = M\dfrac{d^2V}{dt^2}$ | $p = \dfrac{V}{C}$ | $M\dfrac{dq}{dt} + Rq +$ |
| $q = \dfrac{p}{R}$ | $q = C\dfrac{dp}{dt}$ | $q = \dfrac{1}{M}\displaystyle\int p\,dt$ | | | | $C\dfrac{dp}{dt} + \dfrac{p}{R} +$ |
| $\theta = Rq$ | | $\theta = \dfrac{1}{C}\displaystyle\int q\,dt$ | $\theta = R\dfrac{dH}{dt}$ | | $\theta = \dfrac{H}{C}$ | $Rq +$ |
| $q = G\theta$ | $q = C\dfrac{d\theta}{dt}$ | | | | | |

Thermal elements can be put together in ways to get systems of high complexity that are described by higher-order differential equations. In most cases higher-order equations indicate the possibility of one or more modes of natural oscillation. As previously indicated, this is not so for passive thermal systems because they contain only one kind of energy storage element, and the basic reason for oscillatory responses of physical systems is exchange of energy between two kinds of energy storage devices.

## 3.50  SUMMARY OF EQUIVALENTS

The equations relating parameters and elements of six kinds of systems have been stated, and the rules for setting up the equations describing specific arrangements of the elements have been demonstrated. To emphasize the sameness of the forms the equations for the systems are summarized in Table 3.50-1. For each of the six systems, the two principal parameters are given in both roles as forcing functions and as response functions. The two representations of the same system are called *duals*. The missing energy storage element in thermodynamic systems prevents the two versions from being duals.

This table appears inside the front and back covers.

## 3.60  DYNAMIC EXAMPLES AND SOLUTIONS

In this section illustrative problems in the six systems will be solved to show the forms of solutions to be encountered. The first examples will be general in nature and will be used to develop the concepts of time constants, damping and resonant frequencies. The second series of examples will illustrate dynamic analyses of simple but actually useful systems.

## 3.61  FIRST-ORDER SYSTEMS

First-order systems are characterized by the fact that they contain only one energy storage element. A trivial exception is the case where more than one are so connected that they can be treated as one element. Two masses rigidly connected, for example, can be treated as a single mass. Since there are two kinds of energy storage elements in all systems except thermodynamic, there can be two basic first-order equations containing an energy storage element and a dissipative element. The two kinds are shown in Figs. 3.61-1 and 3.61-2.

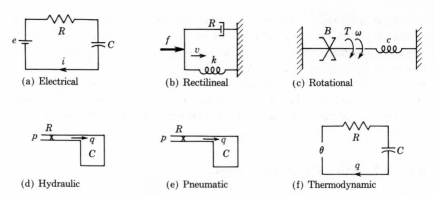

(a) Electrical            (b) Rectilineal            (c) Rotational

(d) Hydraulic            (e) Pneumatic            (f) Thermodynamic

**Fig. 3.61-1** First order capacitance systems.

The equations describing the systems of Fig. 3.61-1 are

electrical: $$Ri + \frac{1}{C} \int i \, dt = e \qquad\qquad (3.61\text{-}1)$$

rectilineal: $$R + k \int v \, dt = f \qquad\qquad (3.61\text{-}2)$$

rotational: $$B\omega + c \int \omega \, dt = T \qquad\qquad (3.61\text{-}3)$$

hydraulic: $$Rq + \frac{1}{C} \int q \, dt = p \qquad\qquad (3.61\text{-}4)$$

pneumatic: $$Rq + \frac{1}{C} \int q \, dt = p \qquad\qquad (3.61\text{-}5)$$

thermodynamic: $$Rq + \frac{1}{C} \int q \, dt = \theta \qquad\qquad (3.61\text{-}6)$$

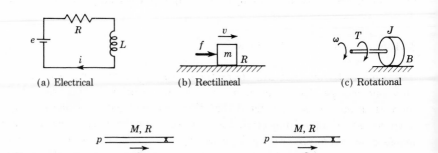

(a) Electrical            (b) Rectilineal            (c) Rotational

(d) Hydraulic            (e) Pneumatic

**Fig. 3.61-2** First order inductive system and equivalents.

If we assume that in each case the forcing function is a constant applied at time equal to zero, then the solutions for the dependent variables in the Laplace domain are

electrical: $\qquad I(s) = \dfrac{e - e_c(0^+)}{R} \dfrac{1}{s + 1/RC}$ $\qquad\qquad$ (3.61-7)

rectilineal: $\qquad V(s) = \dfrac{f - f_k(0^+)}{R} \dfrac{1}{s + k/R}$ $\qquad\qquad$ (3.61-8)

rotational: $\qquad \Omega(s) = \dfrac{T - T_c(0^+)}{B} \dfrac{1}{s + c/B}$ $\qquad\qquad$ (3.61-9)

hydraulic: $\qquad Q(s) = \dfrac{p - p_c(0^+)}{R} \dfrac{1}{s + 1/RC}$ $\qquad\qquad$ (3.61-10)

pneumatic: $\qquad Q(s) = \dfrac{p - p_c(0^+)}{R} \dfrac{1}{s + 1/RC}$ $\qquad\qquad$ (3.61-11)

thermodynamic: $\; Q(s) = \dfrac{\theta - \theta_c(0^+)}{R} \dfrac{1}{s + 1/RC}$ $\qquad\qquad$ (3.61-12)

where $e_c(0^+)$ is the initial voltage across the capacitance and is equal to initial charge divided by capacitance; $f_k(0^+)$ is the initial force on the spring and is equal to initial displacement times the spring constant; $T_c(0^+)$ is the initial torque on the rotational spring and is equal to initial angular displacement times the rotational spring constant; $p_c(0^+)$ for both hydraulic and pneumatic systems is the initial pressure in the capacitance; and $\theta(0^+)$ is the initial temperature of the thermal capacitance with respect to the same temperature as $\theta$ is referred to.

We shall now generalize Eqs. (3.61-7) through (3.61-12) by letting the dependent variable be $Z(s)$, the constant multiplier be $A$, and the constant added to $s$ be $1/\tau$. So

$$Z(s) = A \frac{1}{s + 1/\tau} \qquad\qquad (3.61\text{-}13)$$

The solution to Eq. (3.61-13) in the time domain is

$$z(t) = A\epsilon^{-t/\tau} \qquad\qquad (3.61\text{-}14)$$

In each case the response of the system is described by a decaying exponential. In Table 3.61-1 are tabulated the time constants or $\tau$'s of the various systems. Equation (3.61-14) is doubly significant: (1) it has been generalized to describe the behavior of six different kinds of systems and (2) it has been normalized for all possible combinations of values of dissipative and capacitive elements. In other words the plot of Fig. 3.61-3 can be used as the solution for all equations of this type. To get magnitudes versus time for a given value in Eq. (3.61-14), it is only necessary to multiply the ordinate by the particular value of $A$ and the abscissa by the particular value of $\tau$.

**TABLE 3.61-1** DISSIPATIVE-CAPACITIVE TIME CONSTANTS

| System | $\tau$ | Dissipative unit | Capacitive unit | $\tau$ unit |
|---|---|---|---|---|
| Electrical | $RC$ | ohm | farad | sec |
| Rectilineal | $R/k$ | lb-sec/ft | lb/ft | sec |
| Rotational | $B/c$ | lb-ft/sec | lb-ft/rad | sec |
| Hydraulic | $RC$ | lb-sec/ft$^5$ | ft$^5$/lb | sec |
| Pneumatic | $RC$ | lb-sec/ft$^5$ | ft$^5$/lb | sec |
| Thermodynamic | $RC$ | °F-sec/BTU | BTU/°F | sec |

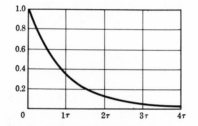

**Fig. 3.61-3** Exponential decay by time constant.

The equations describing the systems of Fig. 3.61-2 are

electrical:
$$L\frac{di}{dt} + Ri = e \qquad (3.61\text{-}15)$$

rectilineal:
$$m\frac{dv}{dt} + Rv = f \qquad (3.61\text{-}16)$$

rotational:
$$J\frac{d\omega}{dt} + B\omega = T \qquad (3.61\text{-}17)$$

hydraulic:
$$M\frac{dq}{dt} + Rq = p \qquad (3.61\text{-}18)$$

pneumatic:
$$M\frac{dq}{dt} + Rq = p \qquad (3.61\text{-}19)$$

The equation for a thermodynamic system is missing because there is no equivalent to inductance. If we again assume that the forcing functions in Eqs. (3.61-15) through (3.61-19) are constants applied at time equal to zero, the solutions for the dependent variables in the Laplace domain are

$$\text{electrical:} \qquad I(s) = \frac{\dfrac{e}{R} + i(0^+)\dfrac{L}{R}s}{s\left(\dfrac{L}{R}s + 1\right)} \qquad\qquad (3.61\text{-}20)$$

$$\text{rectilineal:} \qquad V(s) = \frac{\dfrac{f}{R} + v(0^+)\dfrac{m}{R}s}{s\left(\dfrac{m}{R}s + 1\right)} \qquad\qquad (3.61\text{-}21)$$

$$\text{rotational:} \qquad \Omega(s) = \frac{\dfrac{T}{B} + \omega(0^+)\dfrac{J}{B}s}{s\left(\dfrac{J}{B}s + 1\right)} \qquad\qquad (3.61\text{-}22)$$

$$\text{hydraulic:} \qquad Q(s) = \frac{\dfrac{p}{R} + q(0^+)\dfrac{M}{R}s}{s\left(\dfrac{M}{R}s + 1\right)} \qquad\qquad (3.61\text{-}23)$$

$$\text{pneumatic} \qquad Q(s) = \frac{\dfrac{p}{R} + q(0^+)\dfrac{M}{R}s}{s\left(\dfrac{M}{R}s + 1\right)} \qquad\qquad (3.61\text{-}24)$$

By application of the final value theorem given in Chap. 2, it can be shown that the first term of the numerator of each equation is the final value. By writing the coefficients of $s$ in the above equations as $\tau$ and writing the final values as $z_f$ and the initial conditions as $z_i$, Eqs. (3.61-20) through (3.61-24) can be generalized as

$$Z(s) = \frac{z_f + z_i\tau s}{s(\tau s + 1)} \qquad (3.61\text{-}25)$$

The time solution of Eq. (3.61-25) is

$$z(t) = z_f[1 - \epsilon^{-t/\tau}] + z_i\epsilon^{-t/\tau} \qquad (3.61\text{-}26)$$

If the initial condition is zero, $z(t)$ reduces to

$$z(t) = z_f[1 - \epsilon^{-t/\tau}] \qquad (3.61\text{-}27)$$

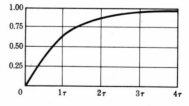

Fig. 3.61-4 Response of dissipative-inductive first order system.

As before, a single curve plotted in terms of time constants or $\tau$'s can be used to find the response to all equations of the form of Eq. (3.61-27).

To get the magnitude the ordinate is multiplied by $z_f$ and the abscissa is
multiplied by the value of the constant. The expression for the time
constants of the systems in Fig. 3.61-2 are shown in Table 3.61-2.

**TABLE 3.61-2** DISSIPATIVE-INDUCTIVE TIME CONSTANTS

| System | $\tau$ | Dissipative unit | Inductive unit | $\tau$ unit |
|---|---|---|---|---|
| Electrical | $L/R$ | ohm | henry | sec |
| Rectilineal | $m/R$ | lb-sec/ft | lb-sec$^2$/ft | sec |
| Rotational | $J/B$ | lb-ft-sec | lb-ft-sec$^2$ | sec |
| Hydraulic | $M/R$ | lb-sec/ft$^5$ | lb-sec$^2$/ft$^5$ | sec |
| Pneumatic | $M/R$ | lb-sec/ft$^5$ | lb-sec$^2$/ft$^5$ | sec |

### 3.62 SECOND-ORDER SYSTEMS

Figure 3.62-1 shows second-order systems with a single degree of
freedom; that is, they are characterized by only one dependent variable.
No thermodynamic system is shown because it is impossible to have a

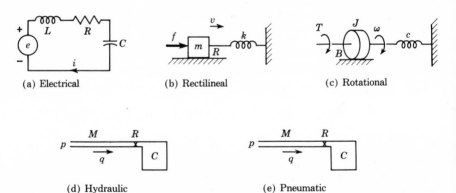

(a) Electrical          (b) Rectilineal                    (c) Rotational

(d) Hydraulic                    (e) Pneumatic

**Fig. 3.62-1** Second-order, single-degree-of-freedom systems.

second-order, single-degree-of-freedom system with only one kind of energy
storage device. A second-order, two-degree-of-freedom thermodynamic
system is shown in Fig. 3.62-2 and will be discussed separately.

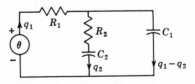

**Fig. 3.62-2** Second-order, two-degree-of-freedom thermodynamic system.

The equations that describe the systems of Fig. 3.62-1 are

electrical:
$$L\frac{di}{dt} + Ri + \frac{1}{C}\int i\,dt = e \qquad (3.62\text{-}1)$$

rectilineal:
$$m\frac{dv}{dt} + Rv + k\int v\,dt = f \qquad (3.62\text{-}2)$$

rotational:
$$J\frac{d\omega}{dt} + B\omega + c\int \omega\,dt = T \qquad (3.62\text{-}3)$$

hydraulic:
$$M\frac{dq}{dt} + Rq + \frac{1}{C}\int q\,dt = p \qquad (3.62\text{-}4)$$

pneumatic:
$$M\frac{dq}{dt} + Rq + \frac{1}{C}\int q\,dt = p \qquad (3.62\text{-}5)$$

If the forcing functions are all constants, the solutions for the dependent variables in the Laplace domain are

electrical:
$$I = \frac{1}{L}\frac{e - e_{c_0} + sLi(0^+)}{\left(s^2 + \dfrac{R}{L}s + \dfrac{1}{LC}\right)} \qquad (3.62\text{-}6)$$

rectilineal:
$$V = \frac{1}{m}\frac{f - f_{k_0} + smv(0^+)}{\left(s^2 + \dfrac{R}{m}s + \dfrac{k}{m}\right)} \qquad (3.62\text{-}7)$$

rotational:
$$\Omega = \frac{1}{J}\frac{T - T_{c_0} + sJ\omega(0^+)}{\left(s^2 + \dfrac{B}{J}s + \dfrac{c}{J}\right)} \qquad (3.62\text{-}8)$$

hydraulic:
$$Q = \frac{1}{M}\frac{p - p_{c_0} + sMq(0^+)}{\left(s^2 + \dfrac{R}{M}s + \dfrac{1}{MC}\right)} \qquad (3.62\text{-}9)$$

pneumatic:
$$Q = \frac{1}{M}\frac{p - p_{c_0} + sMq(0^+)}{\left(s^2 + \dfrac{R}{M}s + \dfrac{1}{MC}\right)} \qquad (3.62\text{-}10)$$

In Chap. 2 a special form of the denominators of Eqs. (3.62-6) through (3.62-10) was given as $s^2 + 2\zeta\omega_n s + \omega_n^2$, where $\zeta$ is the ratio of actual damping to critical damping and $\omega_n$ is the undamped natural frequency. We shall now generalize these equations by letting the response function equal $z$, by letting the inductive type element equal $D$, by letting the difference between the forcing function magnitude and the initial value on the capacitive type element equal $K_1$, and by using the special form $s^2 + \zeta\omega_n s + \omega_n^2$. They become

$$Z(s) = \frac{1}{D} \frac{K_1 + Dz(0^+)s}{(s^2 + 2\zeta\omega_n s + \omega_n^2)} \tag{3.62-11}$$

The time response $z(t)$ depends on the value of $\zeta$ as follows:

For $\zeta < 1$,

$$z(t) = \frac{K_1}{D\omega_n} \left[ \frac{1 - \dfrac{2Dz(0^+)}{K_1}\zeta\omega_n + \dfrac{D^2z^2(0^+)\omega_n^2}{K_1^2}}{1 - \zeta^2} \right]^{1/2}$$
$$\epsilon^{-\zeta\omega_n t} \sin(\omega_n \sqrt{1 - \zeta^2}\, t + \psi) \tag{3.62-12}$$

where

$$\psi = \tan^{-1} \left[ \frac{\dfrac{Dz(0^+)}{K_1}\omega_n \sqrt{1 - \zeta^2}}{1 - \dfrac{Dz(0^+)}{K_1}\zeta\omega_n} \right] \tag{3.62-13}$$

For $\zeta = 1$,

$$z(t) = \left[ \frac{K_1 - \omega_n Dz(0^+)}{D} t + z(0^+) \right] \epsilon^{-\omega_n t} \tag{3.62-14}$$

For $\zeta > 1$,

$$z(t) = \frac{K_1 - r_1 Dz(0^+)}{2\omega_n D \sqrt{\zeta^2 - 1}} \epsilon^{-r_1 t} + \frac{K_1 - r_2 Dz(0^+)}{2\omega_n D \sqrt{\zeta^2 - 1}} \epsilon^{-r_2 t} \tag{3.62-15}$$

where

$$r_1 = \zeta\omega_n - \omega_n \sqrt{\zeta^2 - 1} \tag{3.62-16}$$

and

$$r_2 = \zeta\omega_n + \omega_n \sqrt{\zeta^2 - 1} \tag{3.62-17}$$

Equations (3.62-12) through (3.62-17) represent the three forms the responses the systems of Fig. 3.62-1 can have to a constant forcing function. In Table 3.62-1 are shown the expressions for $\omega_n$, $\zeta$, $K_1$, $D$, and $z(0^+)$.

**TABLE 3.62-1** SYSTEM CONSTANTS

| System | $\omega_n$ | $\zeta$ | $K_1$ | $D$ | $z(0^+)$ |
|---|---|---|---|---|---|
| Electrical | $1/\sqrt{LC}$ | $R/(2\sqrt{L/C})$ | $e - e_{c_0}$ | $L$ | $i(0^+)$ |
| Rectilineal | $\sqrt{k/m}$ | $R/(2\sqrt{mk})$ | $f - f_{k_0}$ | $m$ | $v(0^+)$ |
| Rotational | $\sqrt{c/J}$ | $B/(2\sqrt{Jc})$ | $T - T_{c_0}$ | $J$ | $\omega(0^+)$ |
| Hydraulic | $1/\sqrt{MC}$ | $R/(2\sqrt{M/C})$ | $p - p_{c_0}$ | $M$ | $q(0^+)$ |
| Pneumatic | $1/\sqrt{MC}$ | $R/(2\sqrt{M/C})$ | $p - p_{c_0}$ | $M$ | $q(0^+)$ |

The thermodynamic system of Fig. 3.62-2 is a second-order system characterized by two independent flows; therefore it has two degrees of freedom. It has only two *independent* flows because the third flow can be expressed in terms of the other two. The equations describing the system are

$$\theta - q_1 R_1 - q_2 R_2 - \frac{1}{C_2} \int q_2 \, dt = 0 \tag{3.62-18}$$

$$\theta - q_1 R_1 - \frac{1}{C_1} \int (q_1 - q_2) \, dt = 0 \tag{3.62-19}$$

If Eqs. (3.62-18) and (3.62-19) are transformed and rearranged, they become

$$R_1 Q_1 + \left(R_2 + \frac{1}{C_2 s}\right) Q_2 = \Theta - \frac{\theta_{C_{2_0}}}{s} \tag{3.62-20}$$

$$\left(R_1 + \frac{1}{C_1 s}\right) Q_1 - \frac{1}{C_1 s} Q_2 = \Theta - \frac{\theta_{C_{1_0}}}{s} \tag{3.62-21}$$

where $\theta_{C_{2_0}}$ is the initial temperature of $C_2$ (above the reference) and $\theta_{c_{1_0}}$ is the initial temperature of $C_1$ (above the reference). If Eqs. (3.62-20) and (3.62-21) are solved for $Q_1$, the result is

$$Q_1 = \frac{1}{R_1} \frac{\Theta s(\tau_1 \tau_2 s + \tau_1 + \tau_2) - \tau_3 \theta_{C_{2_0}} - (\tau_1 \tau_2 s + \tau_1)\theta_{C_{1_0}}}{\tau_1 \tau_2 s^2 + (\tau_1 + \tau_2 + \tau_3)s + 1} \tag{3.62-22}$$

where $\tau_1$ is $R_1 C_1$, $\tau_2$ is $R_2 C_2$ and $\tau_3$ is $R_1 C_2$.

If $\theta(t)$ is a step function of magnitude $K$, then $\Theta$ is $K/s$ and Eq. (3.62-22) becomes

$$Q_1 = \frac{1}{R_1} \frac{K(\tau_1 \tau_2 s + \tau_1 \tau_2) - \tau_3 \theta_{C_{2_0}} - (\tau_1 \tau_2 s + \tau_1)\theta_{C_{1_0}}}{\tau_1 \tau_2 s^2 + (\tau_1 + \tau_2 + \tau_3)s + 1} \tag{3.62-23}$$

The time response of Eq. (3.62-23) will be of the form

$$q_1(t) = A_1 \epsilon^{-t/B_1} + A_2 \epsilon^{-t/B_2} \tag{3.62-24}$$

because the system must be overdamped. This can be demonstrated by examining the discriminant of the denominator, which is

$$(\tau_1 + \tau_2 + \tau_3)^2 - 4\tau_1 \tau_2$$

or $\qquad \tau_1^2 + \tau_2^2 + \tau_3^2 + 2\tau_1 \tau_3 + 2\tau_2 \tau_3 - 2\tau_1 \tau_2$

or $\qquad (\tau_1 - \tau_2)^2 + \tau_3^2 + 2\tau_1 \tau_3 + 2\tau_2 \tau_3$

This last expression is obviously positive, so the roots will both be real and the system is overdamped. All second-order thermodynamic systems will be overdamped because there is only one type of energy storage element.

## 3.63  HIGHER-ORDER SYSTEMS

The order of a linear system is determined by the number of *independent* energy storage elements. Elements are independent in this sense if they cannot be combined with other elements of the same kind. An inductance and capacitance in series constitute a second-order system whereas two inductances in series do not. Since there are two types of energy storage elements in all but heat systems, and only one in them, higher than second-order equations can stem only from systems with more than one degree of freedom. Electrical systems higher than second order must be series-parallel combinations and the other systems must be the equivalents. The *minimum* number of degrees of freedom to yield any order above first will always be higher for thermodynamic systems. Dissipative elements can increase the number of degrees of freedom but can never increase the order of the system. A complicated pure resistance network can be characterized by many degrees of freedom but still must remain a zero-order system with respect to current and voltage.

Since systems of higher order than second must have more than one degree of freedom, sets of simultaneous equations are required to describe

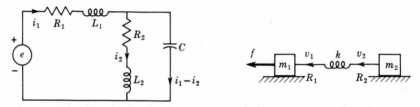

**Fig. 3.63-1** Electrical and mechanical third-order, two-degree-of-freedom systems.

them. Figure 3.63-1 shows two third-order, two-degree-of-freedom systems—one electrical and one mechanical rectilinear. The equations describing them are Eqs. (3.63-1) and (3.63-2).

$$R_1 i_1 + L_1 \frac{di_1}{dt} + \frac{1}{C} \int (i_1 - i_2)\, dt = e$$

$$R_2 i_2 + L_2 \frac{di_2}{dt} - \frac{1}{C} \int (i_1 - i_2)\, dt = 0$$

(3.63-1)

$$R_1 v_1 + m_1 \frac{dv_1}{dt} + k \int (v_1 - v_2)\, dt = f$$

$$R_2 v_2 + m_2 \frac{dv_2}{dt} - k \int (v_1 - v_2)\, dt = 0$$

(3.63-2)

The solutions in the Laplace domain to Eqs. (3.63-1) and (3.63-2) are given in Eqs. (3.63-3) through (3.63-6). The numerators of these equations are divided into two distinct parts—one containing the transform of the forcing function and the other containing the initial conditions.

$$I_1 = \frac{1}{L_1L_2C}\, \frac{\{E[L_2Cs^2 + R_2Cs + 1]\} + \{\dot{i}_1(0)[L_1L_2Cs^2 + R_2L_1Cs + L_1] - e_{C_0}[L_2Cs + R_2C] + \dot{i}_2(0)[L_2]\}}{\left[s^3 + \left(\frac{R_1}{L_1} + \frac{R_2}{L_2}\right)s^2 + \left(\frac{1}{L_1C} + \frac{R_1R_2}{L_1L_2} + \frac{1}{L_2C}\right)s + \left(\frac{R_1}{L_1L_2C} + \frac{R_2}{L_1L_2C}\right)\right]}$$

(3.63-3)

$$I_2 = \frac{1}{L_1L_2C}\, \frac{\{E\} + \{\dot{i}_2(0)[L_1L_2Cs^2 + R_1L_2Cs + L_2] + e_{C_0}[L_1Cs + R_1C] + \dot{i}_1(0)[L_1]\}}{\left[s^3 + \left(\frac{R_1}{L_1} + \frac{R_2}{L_2}\right)s^2 + \left(\frac{1}{L_1C} + \frac{R_1R_2}{L_1L_2} + \frac{1}{L_2C}\right)s + \left(\frac{R_1}{L_1L_2C} + \frac{R_2}{L_1L_2C}\right)\right]}$$

(3.63-4)

$$V_1 = \frac{k}{m_1m_2}\, \frac{\left\{F\left[\frac{m_2}{k}s^2 + \frac{R_2}{k}s + 1\right]\right\} + \left\{v_1(0)\left[\frac{m_1m_2}{k}s^2 + \frac{R_2m_1}{k}s + m_1\right] - f_{k_0}\left[\frac{m_2}{k}s + \frac{R_2}{k}\right] + v_2(0)[m_2]\right\}}{\left[s^3 + \left(\frac{R_1}{m_1} + \frac{R_2}{m_2}\right)s^2 + \left(\frac{k}{m_1} + \frac{R_1R_2}{m_1m_2} + \frac{k}{m_2}\right)s + \left(\frac{R_1k}{m_1m_2} + \frac{R_2k}{m_1m_2}\right)\right]}$$

(3.63-5)

$$V = \frac{k}{m_1m_2}\, \frac{\{F\} + \left\{v_2(0)\left[\frac{m_1m_2}{k}s^2 + \frac{R_1m_2}{k}s + m_2\right] + f_{k_0}\left[\frac{m_1}{k}s + \frac{R_1}{k}\right] + v_1(0)[m_1]\right\}}{\left[s^3 + \left(\frac{R_1}{m_1} + \frac{R_2}{m_2}\right)s^2 + \left(\frac{k}{m_1} + \frac{R_1R_2}{m_1m_2} + \frac{k}{m_2}\right)s + \left(\frac{R_1k}{m_1m_2} + \frac{R_2k}{m_1m_2}\right)\right]}$$

(3.63-6)

where $i_1(0)$ and $i_2(0)$ are the initial currents, $e_{C_0}$ is the initial voltage on the capacitance, $v_1(0)$ and $v_2(0)$ are the initial velocities, $f_{k_0}$ is the initial force on the spring, and all other symbols except the Laplace operator $s$ are the same as indicated in Fig. 3.63-1.

We will not give the time-domain solutions of Eqs. (3.63-3) through (3.63-6) because it becomes too laborious to solve cubics without numerical values. The solutions will, however, consist of three parts: (1) a response due to the forcing function of the same form as the forcing function or its derivatives or combinations of the forcing function and its derivatives, (2) a transient due to application of the forcing function, and (3) a transient due to the initial energy storage in the system. The transient solutions from both the forcing function and initial energy storage will be of exactly the same form, although the coefficients of one part may be zero in a given case. For example, if the general form of the transient solution to a second-order system were

$$z(t) = A\epsilon^{-at} \cos \omega t + B\epsilon^{-at} \sin \omega t \qquad (3.63\text{-}7)$$

$A$ might be zero for the transient response due to the forcing function while neither $A$ nor $B$ was zero for the transient response due to initial energy storage. If any roots of the denominator are repeated (multiple poles) or if a root of the denominator is the same as a root of the forcing function, a special case exists. This case will be covered in Sec. 3.64, and the following discussion is limited to the case of nonrepeated roots (first-order poles).

As previously mentioned, the solutions to Eqs. (3.63-3) through (3.63-6) will be of the form

$$z(t) = \phi_1(t) + \phi_2(t) + \phi_3(t) \qquad (3.63\text{-}8)$$

where $\phi_1(t)$ is the response of the same form as the forcing function and its derivatives and depends on the magnitude and form of the forcing function as well as the values of the elements; $\phi_2(t)$ is the transient due to the forcing function and depends on the same things as $\phi_1(t)$; and $\phi_3(t)$ is the transient due to initial energy storage, of the same form as $\phi_2(t)$, but depends on the initial conditions and the values of the elements. In Table 3.63-1 are shown the various possibilities for third- and fourth-order systems with *no repeated roots*. An additional restriction is that these responses apply only to passive, linear systems with constant coefficients. All other possible cases must contain repeated roots.

Specific cases will not be given for systems of higher order than the fourth. However, all higher-order, passive, linear systems with constant coefficients have transient responses which are linear combinations of the forms

$$A\epsilon^{-at} \quad \text{and} \quad B_1\epsilon^{-bt}\sin\omega t + B_2\epsilon^{-bt}\cos\omega t$$

when none of the roots of the system are repeated and when none correspond to roots of the forcing function. If any are repeated, we encounter different responses.

**TABLE 3.63-1** TRANSIENT RESPONSES OF THIRD- AND FOURTH-ORDER
SYSTEMS WITH NONREPEATED ROOTS

| Order | Case | Form of $\phi_2(t)$ and $\phi_3(t)$ |
|---|---|---|
| Third | 1. Three distinct real roots | 1. $A_1\epsilon^{-a_1t} + A_2\epsilon^{-a_2t} + A_3\epsilon^{-a_3t}$ |
| | 2. One real root, two complex roots (conjugates) | 2. $A_1\epsilon^{-a_1t} + B_1\epsilon^{-bt}\sin\omega t + B_2\epsilon^{-bt}\cos\omega t$ |
| Fourth | 1. Four distinct real roots | 1. $A_1\epsilon^{-a_1t} + A_2\epsilon^{-a_2t} + A_3\epsilon^{-a_3t} + A_4\epsilon^{-a_4t}$ |
| | 2. Two distinct real roots, two complex roots (conjugates) | 2. $A_1\epsilon^{-a_1t} + A_2\epsilon^{-a_2t} + B_1\epsilon^{-bt}\sin\omega t + B_2^{-bt}\cos\omega t$ |
| | 3. Two distinct sets of complex conjugate roots | 3. $A_1\epsilon^{-at}\sin\omega_1 t + A_2\epsilon^{-at}\cos\omega_1 t + B_1\epsilon^{-bt}\sin\omega_2 t$ $+ B_2\epsilon^{-bt}\cos\omega_2 t$ |

## 3.64 REPEATED ROOTS IN HIGHER SYSTEMS

The first case to consider is repeated real roots in the system with no correspondence to roots of the forcing function. The form of $\phi_1(t)$, previously defined as the nontransient response to the forcing function, will not be affected by the existence of repeated roots. The transient responses due to both the forcing function and initial conditions, $\phi_2(t)$ and $\phi_3(t)$, will be changed in form. Consider the transform

$$Z(s) = \frac{Y(s)}{(s+a)^n} + H(s) \tag{3.64-1}$$

where $Y(s)$ is a polynomial in $s$ of less degree than $n$, and $H(s)$ contains all other roots including those of the forcing function. The time function is

$$z(t) = (A_1 + A_2t + A_3t^2 + \cdots + A_nt^{n-1})\epsilon^{-at} + \mathcal{L}^{-1}[H(s)] \tag{3.64-2}$$

Some of the $A$ coefficients may be zero, depending on the particular expression for $Y(s)$. If $H(s)$ contains no repeated roots, its inverse transform will consist of the nontransient response to the forcing function plus decreasing exponentials and damped sine and cosine functions corresponding to the nonrepeated roots. $H(s)$ might still contain repeated roots which would again constitute a special case.

The second case is that of repeated complex roots in the system with no correspondence to roots of the forcing function. Consider the function

$$Z(s) = \frac{Y(s)}{(s_2 + 2\zeta\omega_0 s + \omega_0^2)^n} + H(s) \tag{3.64-3}$$

where $Y(s)$ is a polynomial in $s$ of degree less than $2n$, $\zeta$ is the damping coefficient which must be less than one for complex roots, and $H(s)$ contains all other roots including those of the forcing function. The time function corresponding to Eq. (3.64-3) will be of the form

$$z(t) = (A_1 + A_2 t + A_3 t^2 + \cdots + A_n t^{n-1})\epsilon^{-bt} \sin \omega t$$
$$+ (B_1 + B_2 t + B_3 t^2 + \cdots + B_n t^{n-1})\epsilon^{-bt} \cos \omega t$$
$$+ \mathcal{L}^{-1}[H(s)] \tag{3.64-4}$$

The last case we will examine is that in which one or more roots of the forcing function are the same as the roots of the physical system. This case is somewhat trivial because it means that the forcing function contains components of the forms

$$A\epsilon^{-at} \quad \text{or} \quad B_1\epsilon^{-bt}\sin \omega t + B_2\epsilon^{-bt}\cos \omega t$$

In practice we seldom encounter forcing functions of these forms. When they do occur, the responses resulting are the same as previously discussed for a given order of repetition. The only difference is that $\phi_1$, the response to the forcing function, and $\phi_2$, the transient response due to the forcing function, become inextricably tied together.

## 3.70 APPLICATIONS

The examples used to explain the responses of the various systems have not been concerned with actual uses. The purpose of the following examples is to show practical applications.

## 3.71 ELECTRICAL SYSTEM APPLICATION

A two-stage rocket motor powers a surface-to-surface missile. The first stage boosts the missile into the air and subsequently burns out. After burnout it is dropped off or separated from the second stage. If the second stage fires before the first stage has dropped away an appreciable distance, an excessive pressure develops in the chamber of the second stage because its exhaust cannot escape fast enough. To prevent excessive pressure build-up and possible structural failure, a time delay is introduced between separation and second-stage ignition. The required time delay is 40 milliseconds of which 35 milliseconds occur due to normal electrical and mechanical delays after the ignition signal is applied.

The circuit for obtaining the additional 5 milliseconds time delay is shown in Fig. 3.71-1. The switch marked SW is closed by a mechancial connection activated by first-stage separation. When the switch is closed, the current begins to build up and when it reaches a specified value, the relay closes and activates the second-stage ignition circuit. The delay must be $5 \pm 0.5$ milliseconds. The solution for the current $i$ is

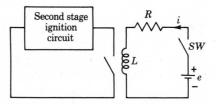

**Fig. 3.71-1** Electrical circuit for time delay.

$$i = \frac{e}{R}(1 - \epsilon^{-Rt/L}) \qquad (3.71\text{-}1)$$

Since there will be some "slop" in the value of $i$ necessary to close the relay, we want to choose the value $L/R$ so that $i$ is still changing fairly fast when it goes through the nominal closing current value. The current will then cover the "slop" zone in a short time so that the tolerance or "slop" in the time delay will be kept within the prescribed limits of $\pm 0.5$ milliseconds. At the end of a single time constant this condition is met, so we choose $L/R$ as 5 milliseconds. The closing current must then be $0.632(e/R)$. Since 8 volts d-c is available in the missile, that will be used as the supply voltage $e$. A 100-ohm resistance will give a maximum current of 80 milliamps. The value specified for the closing current is 0.632 times 80 or 50.6 milliamps. The value of $L$ is found by multiplying the required time constant by $R$ since $L/R$ is the time constant.

$$L = 100 \times 0.005 = 0.5 \text{ henries}$$

To determine the allowable tolerance in closing currents, a safety factor of 0.1 milliseconds is imposed. The relay can then close at $5 \pm 0.4$ milliseconds. The current at 4.6 milliseconds is

$$i = \tfrac{8}{100}[1 - \epsilon^{-(0.0046/0.005)}]$$
$$= 0.08(1 - \epsilon^{-0.92}) = 48.1 \text{ milliamps}$$

At 5.4 milliseconds

$$i = \tfrac{8}{100}[1 - \epsilon^{-(0.0054/0.005)}]$$
$$= 0.08(1 - \epsilon^{-1.08}) = 52.8 \text{ milliamps}$$

The relay is then specified to the manufacturer as a single-pole, normally open relay with inductance of 0.5 henries and closing current between 48.1 and 52.8 milliamps. The relay contacts must withstand 50 milliamps, based on the second-stage ignition requirements.

There are other factors that enter into the design such as the tolerance of the resistance, the vibration to which the relay will be subjected, and the temperature it must withstand; but the problem illustrates a first cut at a practical application of electrical transients.

### 3.72 MECHANICAL RECTILINEAL APPLICATION

A missile fire-control computer weighing 200 pounds is mounted on a vehicle. To protect the computer from shocks due to rough terrain, it is mounted on shock absorbers. The system can be represented by the diagram in Figure 3.72-1. The computer is represented by mass $m$, the spring by spring constant $k$, and the dashpot by resistance $R$. $k$ is 400 lb/ft and $R$, 100 lb-sec/ft.

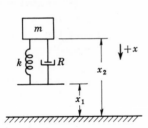

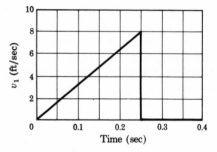

**Fig. 3.72-1** Computer with shock absorber.

**Fig. 3.72-2** Velocity profile of $v_1$.

Neglecting the dynamics of the vehicle, we would like to find the acceleration of the computer when the vehicle runs over a drop of one foot. It is assumed that the spring, mass, dashpot is at equilibrium before the drop begins and that all motion is in the vertical direction. The bottom of the spring and dashpot are attached to the vehicle, so $v_1$ is the vehicle velocity due to the acceleration of gravity which will be rounded off to 32 ft/sec². The velocity $v_1$ is that shown in Fig. 3.72-2.

The equations describing the system are

$$m\dot{v}_2 + R(v_2 - v_1) + k \int (v_2 - v_1) \, dt = mg \qquad (3.72\text{-}1)$$

$$
\begin{aligned}
v_1 &= gt, & 0 \le t \le 0.25 \text{ sec} \\
v_1 &= 0, & t \ge 0.25 \text{ sec}
\end{aligned}
\qquad (3.72\text{-}2)
$$

If numerical values are inserted, Eqs. (3.72-1) and (3.72-2) become

$$\tfrac{200}{32}\,\dot{v}_2 + 100(v_2 - v_1) + 400 \int (v_2 - v_1)\,dt = 200 \qquad (3.72\text{-}3)$$

$$
\begin{aligned}
v_1 &= 32t, & 0 \le t \le 0.25 \text{ sec} \\
v_1 &= 0, & t \ge 0.25 \text{ sec}
\end{aligned}
\qquad (3.72\text{-}4)
$$

Equation (3.72-3) reduces to

$$\dot{v}_2 + 16(v_2 - v_1) + 64 \int (v_2 - v_1)\,dt = 32 \qquad (3.72\text{-}5)$$

The transform of Eq. (3.72-5) is

$$sV_2 - v_2(0) + 16(V_2 - V_1)$$

$$+ \frac{64(V_2 - V_1)}{s} + \frac{64[x_2(0) - x_1(0)]}{s} = \frac{32}{s} \qquad (3.72\text{-}6)$$

The initial condition $v_2(0)$ is zero since the system was in equilibrium and the velocity of a mass cannot change instantaneously without an infinite acceleration. The initial condition $[x_2(0) - x_1(0)]$ must equal 0.5 since the spring constant of 400 lb/ft times this initial displacement must be equal to the computer weight of 200 lb. Using these initial conditions, $V_2$ is

$$V_2 = \frac{16(s + 4)}{s^2 + 16s + 64}\,V_1 \qquad (3.72\text{-}7)$$

The transform of $V_1$ is

$$
\begin{aligned}
v_1 &= \frac{32}{s^2}\,, & 0 \le t \le 0.25 \text{ sec} \\[2mm]
v_1 &= \frac{32}{s^2} - \frac{32}{s^2}\,\epsilon^{-0.25s} - \frac{8}{s}\,\epsilon^{-0.25s}, & t \ge 0.25 \text{ sec}
\end{aligned}
\qquad (3.72\text{-}8)
$$

Thus,

$$
\begin{aligned}
V_2 &= \frac{512(s + 4)}{s^2(s + 8)^2}\,, & 0 \le t \le 0.25 \text{ sec} \\[2mm]
V_2 &= \frac{512(s + 4)(1 - \epsilon^{-0.25s})}{s^2(s + 8)^2} - \frac{128\epsilon^{-0.25s}}{s(s + 8)^2}\,, & t \ge 0.25 \text{ sec}
\end{aligned}
\qquad (3.72\text{-}9)
$$

We are interested in $\dot{v}_2$ rather than $v_2$.

$$\dot{V}_2 = sV_2 - v_2(0) \qquad (3.72\text{-}10)$$

Since $v_2(0)$ is zero, $\dot{V}_2$ can be obtained by multiplying Eq. (3.72-9) by $s$, or

$$
\begin{aligned}
\dot{V}_2 &= \frac{512(s + 4)}{s(s + 8)^2}\,, & 0 \le t \le 0.25 \text{ sec} \\[2mm]
\dot{V}_2 &= \frac{512(s + 4)(1 - \epsilon^{-0.25s})}{s(s + 8)^2} - \frac{128\epsilon^{-0.25s}}{(s + 8)^2}\,, & t \ge 0.25 \text{ sec}
\end{aligned}
\qquad (3.72\text{-}11)
$$

By partial fraction expansion, $\dot{V}_2$ can be written as

$$\dot{V}_2 = \frac{32}{s} + \frac{256}{(s+8)^2} - \frac{32}{s+8}, \qquad 0 \le t \le 0.25 \text{ sec}$$

$$\dot{V}_2 = \left[ \frac{32}{s} + \frac{256}{(s+8)^2} - \frac{32}{s+8} \right] (1 - \epsilon^{-0.25s}) \tag{3.72-12}$$

$$- \frac{128\epsilon^{-0.25s}}{(s+8)^2}, \qquad t \ge 0.25 \text{ sec}$$

The inverse transform of Eq. (3.72-12) is

$$\dot{v}_2 = 32 + 256t\epsilon^{-8t} - 32\epsilon^{-8t}, \qquad 0 \le t \le 0.25 \text{ sec}$$

$$\dot{v}_2 = 32 + 256t\epsilon^{-8t} - 32\epsilon^{-8t} - [32 + 256(t - 0.25)\epsilon^{-8(t-0.25)} \tag{3.72-13}$$

$$- 32\epsilon^{-8(t-0.25)}] - 128(t - 0.25)\epsilon^{-8(t-0.25)}, \qquad t \ge 0.25 \text{ sec}$$

which can be simplified to

$$\dot{v}_2 = 32 + 256t\epsilon^{-8t} - 32\epsilon^{-8t}, \qquad 0 \le t \le 0.25 \text{ sec}$$

$$\dot{v}_2 = 256t\epsilon^{-8t} - 32\epsilon^{-8t} - 384t\epsilon^{-8(t-0.25)} \tag{3.72-14}$$

$$+ 128\epsilon^{-8(t-0.25)}, \qquad t \ge 0.25 \text{ sec}$$

A plot of $\dot{v}_2$ versus time is shown in Fig. 3.72-3. The maximum value of $\dot{v}_2$ is about 36 ft/sec or 1.1 g's. Had the spring and dashpot not been in the system, the value of $\dot{v}_2$ would theoretically have been infinite at 0.25 seconds.

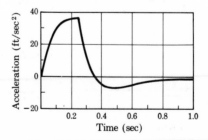

**Fig. 3.72-3** Computer acceleration.

## 3.73 MECHANICAL ROTATIONAL EXAMPLE

A missile is uncontrolled in roll. A torque is exerted on the missile owing to a misalignment of the fins. The missile is characterized by a moment of inertia about the roll axis $I_{zz}$ and roll damping $M_{\dot\phi}$. Note that the roll angle is designated by $\phi$. The equation that describes the roll behavior is

$$I_{zz}\ddot\phi + M_{\dot\phi}\dot\phi = T \tag{3.73-1}$$

The moment of inertia $I_{zz}$ is determined by application of the standard formula

$$I_{zz} = \int y^2 \, dm \tag{3.73-2}$$

The roll damping $M_{\dot\phi}$ is

$$M_{\dot\phi} = C_{1\dot\phi} \frac{qad^2}{2v} \tag{3.73-3}$$

where $C_{1\dot\phi}$ is the roll damping coefficient, $q$ is the dynamic pressure, $a$ is the reference area, $d$ is the reference length, and $v$ is the true air speed. The torque is

$$T = C_1 qad \tag{3.73-4}$$

where $C_1$ is the roll moment coefficient due to fin misalignment, $q$ is the dynamic pressure, $a$ is the reference area, and $d$ is the reference length. The dynamic pressure $q$ is a function of air density and missile velocity.

A typical air-launched missile has the following characteristics:

$I_{zz} = 2.5 \text{ lb-ft/sec}^2$,

$C_{1\dot\phi} = 15$,

$C_1 = 0.01$ (due to $0.1°$ fin misalignment)

$a = 0.785 \text{ ft}^2$ (body cross-sectional area)

$d = 1 \text{ ft}$ (body diameter)

It is launched at 10,000 feet altitude. The dynamic pressure is 5480 lb/ft$^2$ and the velocity is 2500 ft/second. Assuming that all conditions are constant, let us calculate the roll behavior. According to Eq. (3.73-3) $M_{\dot\phi}$ is

$$M_{\dot\phi} = \frac{15 \times 5480 \times 0.785 \times 1}{2 \times 2500} = 12.9 \ \frac{\text{ft-lb}}{\text{rad/sec}}$$

From Eq. (3.73-4),

$$T = 0.01 \times 5480 \times 0.785 \times 1 = 43.0 \text{ ft-lb}$$

The roll equation is then

$$2.5\ddot\phi + 12.9\dot\phi = 43 \tag{3.73-5}$$

The transform of Eq. (3.73-5) with $\dot{\phi}$ as the fundamental variable is

$$2.5s\dot{\Phi}(s) - 2.5\dot{\phi}(0) + 12.9\dot{\Phi}(s) = 43/s \qquad (3.73\text{-}6)$$

If the initial roll rate $\dot{\phi}(0)$ is zero, then

$$\dot{\Phi}(s) = \frac{17.2}{s(s + 5.16)} \qquad (3.73\text{-}7)$$

Equation (3.73-7) can be written in partial fraction form as

$$\dot{\Phi}(s) = \frac{3.33}{s} - \frac{3.33}{(s + 5.16)} \qquad (3.73\text{-}8)$$

The inverse transform of Eq. (3.73-8) is

$$\dot{\phi}(t) = 3.33(1 - \epsilon^{-5.16t}) \qquad (3.73\text{-}9)$$

This equation indicates that the steady-state roll rate is 3.33 radians per second and that it builds up to this value with a time constant of 1/5.16.

## 3.74 HYDRAULIC EXAMPLE

A chemical process consists of an autoclave which is maintained at a constant pressure of 25,000 psi or 3,600,000 lb/ft$^2$. An initiator dissolved in benzene is pumped in at a relatively low rate so that the flow is laminar. The benzene line is 66 feet long and $\frac{1}{16}$ inch in diameter. At this pressure the viscosity ($\mu$) of benzene is $0.672 \times 10^{-3}$ lb-sec/ft$^2$, its bulk modulus $B$ is $2.88 \times 10$ lb/ft$^2$, and its density is 50.6 lb/ft$^3$. We are interested in how long it takes a step change in pressure at the input to the benzene line to settle out in the reactor. To solve this problem we must first calculate the hydraulic resistance, capacitance, and inertance of the benzene line. According to Eq. (3.33-2),

$$R = \frac{0.78\mu l}{A^2} = \frac{0.78 \times 0.672 \times 10^{-3} \times 66}{\left[\frac{\pi}{4}\left(\frac{1}{16 \times 12}\right)^2\right]^2}$$

$$= 7.62 \times 10 \text{ lb-sec/ft}^3$$

From Eq. (3.33-6) for an inelastic container,

$$C = \frac{V}{B} = \frac{\frac{\pi}{4} \times \left(\frac{1}{16 \times 12}\right)^2 \times 66}{2.88 \times 10^7}$$

$$= 48.8 \times 10^{-12} \text{ ft}^5/\text{lb}$$

The inertance $M$ is found by applying Eq. (3.33-5),

$$M = \frac{\rho l}{gA} = \frac{50.6 \times 66}{32.2 \times \dfrac{\pi}{4}\left(\dfrac{1}{16 \times 12}\right)^2}$$

$$= 30 \times 10^5 \text{ lb-sec}^2/\text{ft}^5$$

Since the autoclave is at constant pressure it has the same effect as a battery in an electric circuit. The effects of the line can be represented by a T network. The problem is represented by the diagram of Fig. 3.74-1.

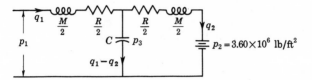

**Fig. 3.74-1** Circuit representation of autoclave problem.

The equations describing the behavior of Fig. 3.74-1 are

$$p_1 - \frac{M}{2}\frac{dq_1}{dt} - \frac{R}{2}q_1 - \frac{R}{2}q_2 - \frac{M}{2}\frac{dq_2}{dt} - p_2 = 0 \qquad (3.74\text{-}1)$$

$$\frac{1}{C}\int_0^t (q_1 - q_2)\,dt + p_3(0) = \frac{R}{2}q_2 + \frac{M}{2}\frac{dq_2}{dt} + p_2 \qquad (3.74\text{-}2)$$

where $p_3(0)$ is the pressure across $C$ at time equal zero. If the system is in the steady-state condition at the time the step change in pressure $\Delta p_1$ is applied, then the following conditions are true:

$$q_1(0) = q_2(0) \qquad (3.74\text{-}3)$$

$$p_3(0) = p_2 + q_2(0)(R/2) \qquad (3.74\text{-}4)$$

$$p_1 = \Delta p_1 + q_1(0)(R/2) + q_2(0)(R/2) + p_2 \qquad (3.74\text{-}5)$$

We now define $\Delta q_1$ and $\Delta q_2$ as

$$\Delta q_1 = q_1 - q_1(0), \quad \Delta q_2 = q_2 - q_2(0) \qquad (3.74\text{-}6)$$

Since $q_1(0)$ and $q_2(0)$ are constant,

$$\frac{d\Delta q_1}{dt} = \frac{dq_1}{dt} \qquad (3.74\text{-}7)$$

$$\frac{d\Delta q_2}{dt} = \frac{dq_2}{dt} \qquad (3.74\text{-}8)$$

If Eqs. (3.74-3) through (3.74-8) are used in Eqs. (3.74-1) and (3.74-2), the result is

$$\Delta p_1 - \Delta q_1 \frac{R}{2} - \frac{M}{2}\frac{d\Delta q_1}{dt} - \Delta q_2 \frac{R}{2} - \frac{M}{2}\frac{d\Delta q_2}{dt} = 0 \qquad (3.74\text{-}9)$$

$$\frac{1}{C}\int_0^t (\Delta q_1 - \Delta q_2)\,dt = \frac{R}{2}\Delta q_2 + \frac{M}{2}\frac{d\Delta q_2}{dt} \qquad (3.74\text{-}10)$$

If these equations are transformed and solved for $\Delta Q_2$, the result is

$$\Delta Q_2 = \frac{4\,\Delta p_1}{CM^2 s\left(s + \dfrac{R}{M}\right)\left(s^2 + \dfrac{Rs}{M} + \dfrac{4}{MC}\right)} \qquad (3.74\text{-}11)$$

If the numerical values of $R$, $M$, and $C$ are used,

$$\Delta Q_2 = \frac{9.12 \times 10^{-3}\,\Delta p_1}{s(s + 25.4)(s^2 + 25.4s + 2.73 \times 10^4)} \qquad (3.74\text{-}12)$$

By partial fraction expansion, $\Delta Q_2/\Delta p_1$ can be expressed as

$$\frac{\Delta Q_2}{\Delta p_1} = \frac{1.32 \times 10^{-8}}{s} - \frac{1.32 \times 10^{-8}}{s + 25.4} - \frac{33.4 \times 10^{-8}}{s^2 + 25.4s + 2.73 \times 10^4} \qquad (3.74\text{-}13)$$

If we complete the square of the denominator of the last term, we get

$$\frac{\Delta Q_2}{\Delta p_1} = \frac{1.32 \times 10^{-8}}{s} - \frac{1.32 \times 10^{-8}}{s + 25.4}$$

$$- \frac{33.4 \times 10^{-8}}{(s + 12.7)^2 + (1.65 \times 10^2)^2} \qquad (3.74\text{-}14)$$

The inverse transform of Eq. (3.74-14) is

$$\frac{\Delta q_2}{\Delta p_1} = 1.32 \times 10^{-8} - 1.32 \times 10^{-8}\epsilon^{-25.4t}$$

$$- 0.20 \times 10^{-8}\epsilon^{-12.7t}\sin (1.65 \times 10^2 t) \qquad (3.74\text{-}15)$$

For $t$ equal to 1 second, the exponential terms are $\epsilon^{-25.4}$ and $\epsilon^{-12.7}$, so the response to the step change is well settled out at the end of a second. The static sensitivity is

$$\frac{\Delta q_1}{\Delta p_1} = 1.32 \times 10^{-8}\,\frac{\text{ft}^3/\text{sec}}{\text{lb}/\text{ft}^2}$$

## 3.75 PNEUMATIC EXAMPLE

A missile has an altitude-sensing device. It consists of an orifice and of a tube 36 inches long and 0.3 inch in diameter feeding into a

chamber of 6 cubic inches. A cross section of the device is shown in
Figure 3.75-1. It is not to scale. We would like to know the response of
the system to a sudden change in altitude from 10,000 feet to 10,500 feet.
The equivalent circuit of the system is
shown in Figure 3.75-2.

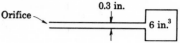

In Figure 3.75-2, $p_1$ is the atmospheric
pressure, $R_1$ is the orifice resistance, $M$
is the tubing inertance, $R_2$ is the tubing
resistance, $C_1$ is the tubing capacitance,

**Fig 3.75-1** Altitude sensing device.

$p_2$ is the pressure across the tubing capacitance, $C_2$ is the chamber capacitance, and $p_3$ is the pressure in the chamber. We will assume the system
is settled out before the change in altitude and therefore that

$$p_1(0) = p_2(0) = p_3(0) \quad \text{and} \quad q_1(0) = q_2(0) = 0$$

We can then work only with incremental values. Before setting up the
equations we will need the change in pressure and the values of $R_1$, $R_2$, $M$,
$C_1$, and $C_2$. At 10,000 feet altitude the pressure under standard conditions is

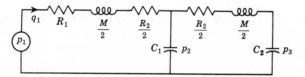

**Fig. 3.75-2** Equivalent circuit of altitude sensing device.

1512.7 lb/ft$^2$ and at 10,500 feet is 1483.8 lb/ft$^2$. The change in pressure
is therefore $-28.9$ lb/ft$^2$. The density $\rho$ of the air at 10,000 feet is 0.0565
lb/ft$^3$ and the viscosity is $3.54 \times 10^{-7}$ lb-sec/ft$^2$. $R_1$ requires experimental
data to calculate. We will assume that it has been found to be 100 lb-sec/ft$^5$.
The value of $R_2$ can be calculated from Eq. (3.34-1) which states

$$R_2 = \frac{0.78\mu l}{A^2} = \frac{0.78 \times 3.54 \times 10^{-7} \times 3}{\left(\dfrac{\pi \times 0.3^2}{4 \times 12^2}\right)^2} = 3.44 \text{ lb-sec/ft}^5$$

The inertance $M$ can be calculated from Eq. (3.34-4):

$$M = \frac{\rho l}{gA} = \frac{0.0565 \times 3}{32.2 \times \dfrac{\pi \times 0.3^2}{4 \times 12^2}} = 10.7 \text{ lb-sec}^2/\text{ft}^5$$

The capacitances $C_1$ and $C_2$ can be calculated using Eq. (3.34-5) which assumes an isothermal process:

$$C_1 = \frac{V_0}{p_0} - \frac{3 \times \dfrac{\pi \times 0.3^2}{4 \times 12^2}}{1513} = 0.974 \times 10^{-6} \text{ ft}^5/\text{lb}$$

$$C_2 = \frac{6/12^3}{1513} = 2.3 \times 10^{-6} \text{ ft}^5/\text{lb}$$

The orifice resistance $R_1$ is about 30 times the tubing resistance and therefore overbalances the effect of $R_2$. The resistance of restrictions such as orifices and valves is often an order of magnitude greater than other pneumatic resistances in the system.

The equations that describe the circuit of Fig. 3.75-2 are

$$p_1 - q_1 R_1 - \frac{M}{2}\frac{dq_1}{dt} - \frac{R_2}{2}q_1 - \frac{1}{C_1}\int (q_1 - q_2)\, dt = 0 \qquad (3.75\text{-}1)$$

$$\frac{1}{C_1}\int (q_1 - q_2)\, dt = q_2 \frac{R_2}{2} + \frac{M}{2}\frac{dq_2}{dt} + \frac{1}{C_2}\int q_2\, dt \qquad (3.75\text{-}2)$$

The transforms of these equations for incremental changes in $p_1$ with zero initial flows are

$$P_1 - Q_1\left(R_1 + \frac{sM}{2} + \frac{R_2}{2} + \frac{1}{C_1 s}\right) + \frac{Q_2}{C_1 s} = 0 \qquad (3.75\text{-}3)$$

$$\frac{Q_1}{C_1 s} - Q_2\left(\frac{1}{C_1 s} + \frac{1}{C_2 s} + \frac{R_2}{2} + \frac{sM}{2}\right) = 0 \qquad (3.75\text{-}4)$$

The solution for $Q_2$ from Eqs. (3.75-3) and (3.75-4) is

$$Q_2 = \frac{4sP_1}{C_1 M^2\left[s^4 + \left(\dfrac{2R_1}{M} + \dfrac{2R_2}{M}\right)s^3 + \left(\dfrac{4}{MC_1} + \dfrac{2}{MC_2} + \dfrac{2R_1 R_2}{M^2} + \dfrac{R_2^2}{M^2}\right)s^2 + h(s)\right]}$$

where

$$h(s) = \left(\frac{4R_2}{C_1 M^2} + \frac{4R_1}{C_1 M^2} + \frac{4R_1}{C_2 M^2} + \frac{2R_2}{C_2 M^2}\right)s + \frac{4}{C_1 C_2 M^2} \qquad (3.75\text{-}5)$$

If we now note that

$$P_3 = \frac{Q_2}{C_2 s} \qquad (3.75\text{-}6)$$

we can use Eq. (3.75-5) to write

$$P_3 = \cfrac{4P_1}{C_1 C_2 M^2 \left[ s^4 + \left( \dfrac{2R_1}{M} + \dfrac{2R_2}{M} \right) s^3 + \left( \dfrac{4}{MC_1} + \dfrac{2}{MC_2} + \dfrac{2R_1 R_2}{M^2} + \dfrac{R_2^2}{M^2} \right) s^2 + h(s) \right]}$$

where

$$h(s) = \left( \frac{4R_2}{C_1 M^2} + \frac{4R_1}{C_1 M^2} + \frac{4R_1}{C_2 M^2} + \frac{2R_2}{C_2 M^2} \right) s + \frac{4}{C_1 C_2 M^2} \qquad (3.75\text{-}7)$$

The transform $P_1$ is $\Delta p_1/s$ since it is a step change. If the transform $P_1$ with its numerical value is inserted along with the numerical values of the $R$'s, $C$'s, and $M$, Eq. (3.75-7) becomes

$$P_3 = \frac{(-28.9)(1.560 \times 10^{10})}{s(s^4 + 19.33s^3 + 4.65 \times 10^5 s^2 + 5.26 \times 10^6 s + 1.560 \times 10^{10})}$$

$$(3.75\text{-}8)$$

The denominator of Eq. (3.75-8) can be factored to yield

$$P_3 = \frac{(-28.9)(1.560 \times 10^{10})}{s[(s + 5.78)^2 + 190.3^2][(s + 3.89)^2 + 656^2]} \qquad (3.75\text{-}9)$$

By partial fraction expansion, Eq. (3.75-9) is

$$P_3 = \frac{-28.9}{s} + \frac{31.4(s + 5.78) + 0.906(190.3)}{(s + 5.78)^2 + 190.3^2}$$

$$- \frac{2.5(s + 3.89) + 0.025(656)}{(s + 3.89)^2 + 656^2} \qquad (3.75\text{-}10)$$

The inverse transform of Eq. (3.75-10) is

$$p_3 = -28.9 + 31.4\epsilon^{-5.78t} \cos 190.3t + 0.906\epsilon^{-5.78t} \sin 190.3t$$

$$- 2.5\epsilon^{-3.89t} \cos 656t + 0.025\epsilon^{-3.89t} \sin 656t \qquad (3.75\text{-}11)$$

Equation (3.75-11) indicates the response has two relatively high-frequency oscillations which are damped out fairly well in less than one second. The high-frequency oscillation with low damping results primarily from the low density and viscosity of the air. In actual practice these oscillations would be filtered by the other parts of the altitude system such as a diaphragm.

## 3.76 THERMODYNAMIC EXAMPLE

A thermistor is an electrical resistance that has a fairly high temperature coefficient of resistance. The variation of resistance with temperature makes it a useful temperature-sensing device. Once calibrated it does not require a reference temperature as does a thermocouple.

A thermistor is to be used as a temperature-sensing element in a chemical process. It is part of a temperature control system. To design the over-all control system it is necessary to calculate the dynamic response of the thermistor. The characteristics of the spherically shaped thermistor are as follows:

diameter of thermistor element—0.05 in. $= d_1$
outer diameter of glass—0.08 in. $= d_2$
thermistor element—silicon

To calculate the response of the thermistor to changes in the process temperature we will need the thermal resistances and capacitances of both the glass and the thermistor element as well as the configuration to represent it. Equation (3.35-1) states that the thermal resistance is

$$R = \frac{l}{kA}$$

where $R$ is the resistance in °F/(BTU/sec), $l$ is the length of the conduction path in ft, $k$ is the thermal conductivity in [(BTU/sec-ft²)/(°F/ft)], and $A$ is the cross-sectional area of the conduction path in ft². The thermal conductivity of the silicon is $1.68 \times 10^{-4}$ [(BTU/sec-ft²)/(°F/ft)]. We will assume that the effective value of $l$ is one-fourth of the diameter of the thermistor element or 0.0125 in. and that the effective area is $(d_1/2)^2$ or $1.96 \times 10^{-3}$ in.² The value of $R_t$ is

$$R_t = \frac{l}{kA}$$

$$= \frac{(0.0125 \text{ in.} \times \text{ft})/12 \text{ in.}}{1.68 \times 10^{-4} \text{ (BTU/sec-ft}^2)/(°\text{F/ft)} \times 1.96 \times 10^{-3} \text{ in.}^2 \times \text{ft}^2/144 \text{ in.}^2}$$

$$= \frac{0.0125 \times 12}{1.68 \times 10^{-4} \times 1.96 \times 10^{-3}} = 4.55 \times 10^5 \text{ °F/(BTU/sec)}$$

The thermal conductivity of the glass is $1.75 \times 10^{-4}$ [(BTU/sec-ft²)/(°F/ft)]. The effective length is the glass thickness or (0.08 in. − 0.05 in.)/2, which is 0.015 in. The effective area of the glass is assumed to be $\pi d_1 d_2$ or 0.0126 in.² The value of $R_g$ is

$$R_g = \frac{0.015/12}{1.75 \times 10^{-4} \times (1.26 \times 10^{-2})/144} = \frac{0.015 \times 12}{1.75 \times 10^{-4} \times 1.26 \times 10^{-2}}$$

$$= 8.16 \times 10^4 \text{ °F/(BTU/sec)}$$

The thermal capacitance, according to Eq. (3.35-4), is

$$C = shV\rho$$

where $C$ is the thermal capacitance in BTU/°F, *sh* is the specific heat in BTU/(lb-°F), $V$ is the volume in ft³, and $\rho$ is the density in lb/ft³.

The specific heat of the thermistor element is 0.210 BTU/(lb-°F), its volume is $\pi d_1^3/6$ or $6.54 \times 10^{-5}$ in.³ and its density is 138 lb/ft³. The capacitance is

$$C_t = 0.210 \, \frac{\text{BTU}}{\text{lb-°F}} \times \frac{6.54 \times 10^{-5} \, \text{in.}^3 \, \text{ft}^3}{12^3 \, \text{in.}^3} \times \frac{138 \, \text{lb}}{\text{ft}^3}$$

$$= 1.1 \times 10^{-6} \, \text{BTU/°F}$$

The specific heat of the glass is 0.199 BTU/(lb-°F), its volume is $(\pi d_2^2 - \pi d_1^2)/6$ or $2.03 \times 10^{-4}$ in.³ and its density is 162 lb/ft³. The thermal capacitance of the glass is

$$C_g = \frac{0.199 \times 2.03 \times 10^{-4}}{12^3} \times 162$$

$$= 3.79 \times 10^{-6} \, \text{BTU/°F}$$

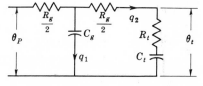

**Fig. 3.76-1** Thermal circuit of thermistor.

We now have the required thermal resistances and capacitances and must decide what circuit to represent the thermistor by. The thermal circuit of Fig. 3.76-1 represents the effect of the glass as a T element and the thermistor element as an L section. $\theta_p$ is the process temperature, $R_g$ the glass resistance, $C_g$ the glass capacitance, $R_t$ the thermistor element thermal resistance, $C_t$ the thermistor element capacitance, and $\theta_t$ the thermistor temperature. We are interested in the transfer function $\theta_t/\theta_p$. Initial conditions are assumed to be zero and the equations are written in the Laplace domain:

$$\theta_p - (Q_1 + Q_2) \frac{R_g}{2} - \frac{Q_1}{C_g s} = 0 \qquad (3.76\text{-}1)$$

$$Q_1 = \left( \frac{R_g}{2} + R_t \right) Q_2 + \frac{Q_2}{C_t s} \qquad (3.76\text{-}2)$$

Solving for $Q_2$, we get

$$Q_2 = \frac{\theta_p s}{C_g \left[ \left( \dfrac{R_g^2}{4} + \dfrac{R_g R_t}{2} \right) s^2 + \left( \dfrac{R_g}{C_g} + \dfrac{R_g}{2C_t} + \dfrac{R_t}{C_g} \right) s + \dfrac{1}{C_t C_g} \right]} \qquad (3.76\text{-}3)$$

But

$$\theta_t = \frac{Q_2}{C_t s} + Q_2 R_t \qquad (3.76\text{-}4)$$

so, using Eqs. (3.76-3) and (3.76-4),

$$\Theta_t = \frac{\Theta_p[R_t C_t s + 1]}{C_t C_g \left(\frac{R_g^2}{4} + \frac{R_g R_t}{2}\right) s^2 + \left(\frac{R_g}{C_g} + \frac{R_g}{2C_t} + \frac{R_t}{C_g}\right) s + \frac{1}{C_t C_g}} \tag{3.76-5}$$

If the numerical values previously calculated are put in Eq. (3.76-5), it becomes

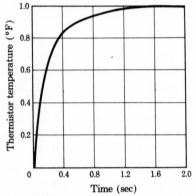

$$\Theta_t = \frac{11.83\Theta_p(0.5s + 1)}{s^2 + 8.83s + 11.83} \tag{3.76-6}$$

If we assume that $\Theta_p$ is a 1° step change in temperature and the denominator is factored, the equation for $\Theta_t$ is

$$\Theta_t = \frac{11.83(0.5s + 1)}{s(s + 1.64)(s + 7.19)} \tag{3.76-7}$$

By partial fraction expansion we can expand Eq. (3.76-7) to

**Fig. 3.76-2** Thermistor response to step change.

$$\Theta_t = \frac{1}{s} - \frac{0.23}{s + 1.64} - \frac{0.77}{s + 7.19} \tag{3.76-8}$$

The inverse transform is

$$\Theta_t = 1 - 0.23\epsilon^{-1.64t} - 0.77\epsilon^{-7.19t} \tag{3.76-9}$$

A plot of Eq. (3.76-9) is shown in Fig. 3.76-2. The thermistor reaches 90% of its final value in about 0.6 seconds.

## 3.80 PROBLEMS

1. A missile launcher must be trained rapidly to the proper firing direction. A torque source of 2500 lb-ft drives the launcher. The launcher has a moment of inertia of 5000 lb-ft-sec² and a rotational resistance of 2000 lb-ft-sec. Calculate $\ddot{\theta}$, $\dot{\theta}$, and $\theta$ as functions of time when the 2500 ft-lb of torque is applied as a step.

2. The network of Fig. 3.80-1 approximates a differentiating circuit. Calculate $e_2$ when the input is

$$e_1 = 100t, \qquad 0 \le t \le 1$$

$$e_1 = 0, \qquad t > 1$$

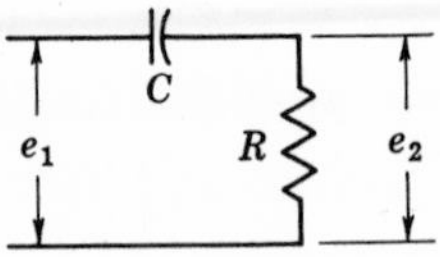

**Fig. 3.80-1**

$R$ is 10Ω and $C$ is 0.001 µf. How does the form of the output compare with the actual derivative of $e_1$?

3. The idealized vehicle shown in Fig. 3.80-2 travels at a uniform velocity of 45 ft/sec across a flat surface, traverses the hill $0.25[1 - \cos \pi x]$, and continues indefinitely along the flat surface. Let time be zero when the

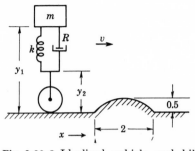

**Fig. 3.80-2** Idealized vehicle and hill.

vehicle encounters the hill at $x = 0$. Consider the vehicle in equilibrium before it encounters the hill. If the weight is 3200 lb, $k$ is 2500 lb/ft, and $R$ is 0.5 lb-sec/ft, calculate $y_1(t)$. Assume the horizontal velocity is constant.

4. Calculate the moment of inertia for a sphere of density $\rho$ about an axis through its center.

5. A chemical process uses water as a coolant. The water is at a temperature and pressure such that its bulk modulus is $6.75 \times 10^7$ lb/ft$^2$ and its density 65 lb/ft$^3$. It is fed into a reactor with a volume of 200 ft$^3$ through a circular pipe 0.25 ft in diameter and 50 ft long. The water exits from the reactor through a valve with resistance of $8.0 \times 10^6$ lb-sec/ft$^5$. Assuming the flow is laminar, calculate $C_1$, the capacitance of the line; $R_1$, the resistance of the line; $M$, the inertance of the line; and $C_2$, the capacitance of the reactor. Using these values and representing the line as a T network, calculate the response of the reactor pressure to a step change in pressure at the input to the line.

6. An iron-constantan thermocouple is used to measure the temperature of a flowing liquid. The area of the thermocouple junction is 0.001 ft$^2$. The film coefficient is 0.03 BTU/(sec-°F-ft$^2$). The average specific heat of the thermocouple is 0.1 BTU/(lb-°F) and the average density is 500 lb/ft$^3$. Its volume is $2.5 \times 10^{-6}$ ft$^3$. Neglecting the internal resistance of the thermocouple due to conductivity, calculate the response to a 1°F step change in temperature.

# ELECTRICAL ANALOGS

## 4.00 INTRODUCTION

The previous chapter demonstrated the similarities of the equations describing the behavior of the various systems and illustrated the equivalence among parameters and elements. In this chapter the concept of analogies will be expanded to include:

1. a method for designing scale models
2. a method for designing electrical models of other types of systems
3. electrical circuit analysis applied to other types of systems
4. transformer analogies

## 4.10 MODELS

Experimental analysis and design are often done more conveniently with scale models or with electrical models and in some cases with mechanical models. Sheer size of the actual design may be prohibitive economically for an experimental mechanical system. A model of smaller size is a desirable approach, but we must know how to scale the elements and parameters so that the performance of the smaller unit can be related directly to that of the larger unit.

Electrical models offer many advantages—economy, small size, availability of parts, availability of sources with a variety of waveforms, and ease of varying circuit values. A chemical process several hundred feet long may have its dynamic relationships between pressure and flow simulated by an electrical analog which occupies only a couple of square feet. Electrical analogs of thermodynamic systems offer another unique advantage in that the elements of heat systems are often such that it is difficult to separate thermal resistance from thermal capacitance and difficult to take separate measurements of the temperatures and heat flows.

## 4.11  NONDIMENSIONAL EQUATIONS AND ELECTRICAL ANALOGS

There are two widely used approaches to setting up numerical equivalents in scale models or analogs: (1) deduction of the equations which must be satisfied by writing nondimensional equations for all systems and (2) application of the $\pi$ theorem. The method of nondimensional equations will be used here. In order to make the method completely general, it is necessary that we choose equations which contain all the elements and parameters of each type of system as well as the parameter time. The parameter time will be introduced in derivatives and integrals. Although the parameter time appears in the forcing functions, they do not have the dimensions of time. An emf of the form $(e \sin \omega t)$ has the dimension of volts. The functional part, that is $\sin \omega t$, is nondimensional. The functional forms must be the same for all systems including the non-dimensionalizing coefficients of the parameter $t$. With respect to the time frame of each system the numerical values of the nondimensionalizing coefficients must be in a constant ratio from system to system. For example, if the forcing function for an electrical system were

$$5 \left[ \text{volts} \sin (3t_e) + 2 \frac{\text{volts}}{\text{sec}} t_e \right]$$

then the equivalent force in a rectilineal system would have to be

$$f_m \left[ \text{lb} \sin (3at_L) + 2a \frac{\text{lb}}{\text{sec}} t_L \right]$$

where $t_e$ is time in the electrical system, $f_m$ is the magnitude of the force, $t_L$ is time in the rectilineal system, and $a$ is any positive constant. What this amounts to is that time can be stretched from one system to an equivalent system but it must be stretched by the same factor everywhere it appears.

The second-order, single-degree-of-freedom systems of Figs. 4.11-1(a) through (e) satisfy the required conditions for electrical, mechanical rectilineal, mechanical rotational, hydraulic, and pneumatic systems; and the first-order, single-degree-of-freedom system of Fig. 4.11-1(f) satisfies the requirements for a thermodynamic system. Since some of the symbols occur in more than one system, the following subscripts are used to distinguish which system the symbol occurs in: $e$—electrical, $L$—rectilineal, $R$—rotational, $H$—hydraulic, $p$—pneumatic, and $\theta$—thermodynamic.

The equations that describe the configurations of Fig. 4.11-1 are

electrical:
$$L \frac{di}{dt_e} + R_e i + \frac{1}{C_e} \int i \, dt_e = e(t_e) \qquad (4.11\text{-}1)$$

rectilineal:
$$m \frac{dv}{dt_L} + R_L v + k \int v \, dt_L = f(t_L) \qquad (4.11\text{-}2)$$

rotational:
$$J \frac{d\omega}{dt_R} + B\omega + c \int \omega \, dt_R = T(t_R) \qquad (4.11\text{-}3)$$

hydraulic:
$$M_H \frac{dq_H}{dt_H} + R_H q_H + \frac{1}{C_H} \int q_H \, dt_H = p_H(t_H) \qquad (4.11\text{-}4)$$

pneumatic:
$$M_p \frac{dq_p}{dt_p} + R_p q_p + \frac{1}{C_p} \int q_p \, dt_p = p_p(t_p) \qquad (4.11\text{-}5)$$

thermodynamic:
$$R_\theta q_\theta + \frac{1}{C_\theta} \int q_\theta \, dt_\theta = \theta(t_\theta) \qquad (4.11\text{-}6)$$

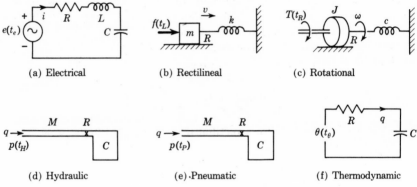

(a) Electrical          (b) Rectilineal          (c) Rotational

(d) Hydraulic          (e) Pneumatic          (f) Thermodynamic

**Figure 4.11-1**

Since the thermodynamic equation differs from the others, it will be treated separately. The first step in making these equations nondimensional is to divide by the coefficient of the leading term, resulting in

electrical:
$$\frac{di}{dt_e} + \frac{R_e}{L} i + \frac{1}{LC_e} \int i \, dt_e = \frac{1}{L} e(t_e) \qquad (4.11\text{-}7)$$

rectilineal:
$$\frac{dv}{dt_L} + \frac{R_L}{m} v + \frac{k}{m} \int v \, dt_L = \frac{1}{m} f(t_L) \qquad (4.11\text{-}8)$$

rotational:
$$\frac{d\omega}{dt_R} + \frac{B}{J} \omega + \frac{c}{J} \int \omega \, dt_R = \frac{1}{J} T(t_R) \qquad (4.11\text{-}9)$$

hydraulic:
$$\frac{dq_H}{dt_H} + \frac{R_H}{M_H} q_H + \frac{1}{M_H C_H} \int q_H \, dt_H = \frac{1}{M_H} p_H(t_H) \qquad (4.11\text{-}10)$$

pneumatic:
$$\frac{dq_p}{dt_p} + \frac{R_p}{M_p} q_p + \frac{1}{M_p C_p} \int q_p \, dt_p = \frac{1}{M_p} p_p(t_p) \qquad (4.11\text{-}11)$$

We now note that the dimensions of the terms in Eqs. (4.11-7) through (4.11-11) are as follows:

electrical:                    current/unit time

rectilineal:                   velocity/unit time

rotational:                    angular velocity/unit time

hydraulic:                     volumetric flow/unit time

pneumatic:                     volumetric flow/unit time

We therefore have to divide each of the terms by the appropriate dimension noted above and we will have a set of dimensionless equations. To accomplish this the following dimensional scale factors are introduced:

$$I = \frac{i}{\alpha_e}, \qquad \mathcal{T}_e = \beta_e t_e \qquad \qquad (4.11\text{-}12)$$

where $I$ is dimensionless, $\alpha_e$ is the current scale factor with the dimensions of current, $\mathcal{T}_e$ is dimensionless, and $\beta_e$ is the time scale factor with the dimensions of radians/unit time;

$$V = \frac{v}{\alpha_L}, \qquad \mathcal{T}_L = \beta_L t_L \qquad \qquad (4.11\text{-}13)$$

where $V$ is dimensionless, $\alpha_L$ is the velocity scale factor with the dimensions of velocity, $\mathcal{T}_L$ is dimensionless, and $\beta_L$ is the time scale factor with the dimensions of radians/unit time;

$$W = \frac{\omega}{\alpha_R}, \qquad \mathcal{T}_R = \beta_R t_R \qquad \qquad (4.11\text{-}14)$$

where $W$ is dimensionless, $\alpha_R$ is the angular velocity scale factor with the dimensions of radians/unit time, $\mathcal{T}_R$ is dimensionless, and $\beta_R$ is the time scale factor with the dimensions of radians/unit time (note that $\alpha_R$ and $\beta_R$ have the same dimensions, but $\alpha_R$ applies to the response function, $\beta_R$ to time $t$);

$$Q_H = \frac{q_H}{\alpha_H}, \qquad \mathcal{T}_H = \beta_H t_H \qquad \qquad (4.11\text{-}15)$$

where $Q_H$ is dimensionless, $\alpha_H$ is the volumetric flow scale factor with the dimensions of voluemtric flow, $\mathcal{T}_H$ is dimensionless, and $\beta_H$ is the time scale factor with the dimensions of radians/unit time;

$$Q_p = \frac{q_p}{\alpha_p}, \qquad \mathcal{T}_p = \beta_p t_p \qquad \qquad (4.11\text{-}16)$$

where $Q_p$ is dimensionless, $\alpha_p$ is the volumetric flow scale factor with the dimensions of volumetric flow, $\mathcal{T}_p$ is dimensionless, and $\beta_p$ is the time scale factor with the dimensions of radians/unit time. If the relations in

Eqs. (4.11-12) through (4.11-16) are used in Eqs. (4.11-7) through (4.11-11), the results are

electrical:

$$\alpha_e \beta_e \frac{dI}{d\mathcal{T}_e} + \alpha_e \frac{R_e}{L} I + \frac{\alpha_e}{\beta_e L C_e} \int I \, d\mathcal{T}_e = \frac{1}{L} e(t_e) \qquad (4.11\text{-}17)$$

rectilineal:

$$\alpha_L \beta_L \frac{dV}{d\mathcal{T}_L} + \alpha_L \frac{R_L}{m} V + \frac{\alpha_L k}{\beta_L m} \int V \, d\mathcal{T}_L = \frac{1}{m} f(t_L) \qquad (4.11\text{-}18)$$

rotational:

$$\alpha_R \beta_R \frac{dW}{d\mathcal{T}_R} + \frac{\alpha_R B}{J} W + \frac{\alpha_R c}{\beta_R J} \int W \, d\mathcal{T}_R = \frac{1}{J} T(t_R) \qquad (4.11\text{-}19)$$

hydraulic:

$$\alpha_H \beta_H \frac{dQ_H}{d\mathcal{T}_H} + \alpha_H \frac{R_H}{M_H} Q_H + \frac{\alpha_H}{\beta_H M_H C_H} \int Q_H \, d\mathcal{T}_H = \frac{1}{M_H} p_H(t_H) \qquad (4.11\text{-}20)$$

pneumatic:

$$\alpha_p \beta_p \frac{dQ_p}{d\mathcal{T}_p} + \frac{\alpha_p R_p}{M_p} Q_p + \frac{\alpha_p}{\beta_p M_p C_p} \int Q_p \, d\mathcal{T}_p = \frac{1}{M_p} p_p(t_p) \qquad (4.11\text{-}21)$$

If we divide each equation above by the appropriate $\alpha\beta$ product, the results are

electrical:

$$\frac{dI}{d\mathcal{T}_e} + \frac{R_e}{\beta_e L} I + \frac{1}{\beta_e^2 L C_e} \int I \, d\mathcal{T}_e = \frac{1}{\alpha_e \beta_e L} e(t_e) \qquad (4.11\text{-}22)$$

rectilineal:

$$\frac{dV}{d\mathcal{T}_L} + \frac{R_L}{\beta_L m} V + \frac{k}{\beta_L^2 m} \int V \, d\mathcal{T}_L = \frac{1}{\alpha_L \beta_L m} f(t_L) \qquad (4.11\text{-}23)$$

rotational:

$$\frac{dW}{d\mathcal{T}_R} + \frac{B}{\beta_R J} W + \frac{c}{\beta_R^2 J} \int W \, d\mathcal{T}_R = \frac{1}{\alpha_R \beta_R J} T(t_R) \qquad (4.11\text{-}24)$$

hydraulic:

$$\frac{dQ_H}{d\mathcal{T}_H} + \frac{R_H}{\beta_H M_H} Q_H + \frac{1}{\beta_H^2 M_H C_H} \int Q_H \, d\mathcal{T}_H = \frac{1}{\alpha_H \beta_H M_H} p_H(t_H) \qquad (4.11\text{-}25)$$

pneumatic:

$$\frac{dQ_p}{d\mathcal{T}_p} + \frac{R_p}{\beta_p M_p} Q_p + \frac{1}{\beta_p^2 M_p C_p} \int Q_p \, d\mathcal{T}_p = \frac{1}{\alpha_p \beta_p M_p} p_p(t_p) \qquad (4.11\text{-}26)$$

Equations (4.11-22) through (4.11-26) are a set of equivalent non-dimensional relations. To make their solutions exactly the same it is necessary only to make the coefficients of each corresponding term equal and to set the $\mathcal{T}$'s equal. The restrictions on the forcing functions have already been described but Eq. (4.11-30) states specifically that the stretch factor $a$ as previously referred to is the ratio of the $\beta$'s.

Setting these equal, we get

$$\frac{R_e}{\beta_e L} = \frac{R_L}{\beta_L m} = \frac{B}{\beta_R J} = \frac{R_H}{\beta_H M_H} = \frac{R_p}{\beta_p M_p} \tag{4.11-27}$$

$$\frac{1}{\beta_e^2 L C_e} = \frac{k}{\beta_L^2 m} = \frac{c}{\beta_R^2 J} = \frac{1}{\beta_H^2 M_H C_H} = \frac{1}{\beta_p^2 M_p C_p} \tag{4.11-28}$$

$$\frac{e}{\alpha_e \beta_e L} = \frac{f}{\alpha_L \beta_L m} = \frac{T}{\alpha_R \beta_R J} = \frac{p_H}{\alpha_H \beta_H M_H} = \frac{p_p}{\alpha_p \beta_p M_p} \tag{4.11-29}$$

$$\beta_e t_e = \beta_L t_L = \beta_R t_R = \beta_H t_H = \beta_p t_p \tag{4.11-30}$$

These four equations constitute a set of simultaneous equations in seven variables for each system. Therefore, we are free to—and in fact must— choose values for three of the variables in any system to solve for the other four variables in that system in terms of the variables in another system. The scale factors $\alpha$ and $\beta$ are logically two of the three variables to which we assign values. The third value we will choose is the energy storage element inductance or its equivalent. Other variables could be selected.

To demonstrate the application of Eqs. (4.11-27) through (4.11-30) we will derive the relations for an electrical analog of the mechanical system of Fig. 4.11-1(b). We will assume that we know all the values in the mechanical system and that both $\alpha_L$ and $\beta_L$ are equal to one. Under these assumptions, we can obtain the following from Eqs. (4.11-27) through (4.11-30):

$$\frac{R_e}{\beta_e L} = \frac{R_L}{m}, \quad \frac{1}{\beta_e^2 L C_e} = \frac{k}{m}, \quad \frac{e}{\alpha_e \beta_e L} = \frac{f}{m}, \quad \beta_e t_e = t_L \tag{4.11-31}$$

We now want to solve Eq. (4.11-31) for $R_e$, $C_e$, $e$, and $t_e$ in terms of $\alpha_e$, $\beta_e$, $L$, and the parameters of the mechanical system. They are given by

$$R_e = \frac{\beta_e L R_L}{m} \tag{4.11-32}$$

$$C_e = \frac{m}{\beta_e^2 L k} \tag{4.11-33}$$

$$e = \frac{\alpha_e \beta_e L f}{m} \tag{4.11-34}$$

$$t_e = \frac{t_L}{\beta_e} \tag{4.11-35}$$

Equations (4.11-32) through (4.11-35) explain how to set up the electrical analog but do not explain how to interpret the responses. The nondimensional equations were set up so that

$$I = V \qquad (4.11\text{-}36)$$

Since $I$ equals $i/\alpha_e$ and $v$ equals $V$ ($\alpha_L$ was assumed to be one),

$$v = \frac{i}{\alpha_e} \qquad (4.11\text{-}37)$$

All forces in the system can be obtained by solving Eq. (4.11-34) for $f$ and substituting the appropriate value of $e$ in the electrical circuit.

$$f = \frac{me}{\alpha_e \beta_e L} \qquad (4.11\text{-}38)$$

The preceding derivations were for a second-order, single-degree-of-freedom analog. They can be made applicable to any mechanical system by letting the ratio of any inductance to the equivalent mass equal to a constant factor $\gamma_e$, or

$$L_j = \gamma_e m_j \qquad (4.11\text{-}39)$$

where $L$ is the inductance in the electrical analog, $j$ is a subscript denoting corresponding elements in the electrical and mechanical systems, $\gamma_e$ is a constant scale factor with the units of inductance per unit mass, and $m$ is the mass in the mechanical system. Table 4.11-1 summarizes the method for calculating electrical analogs and interpreting results for the various other systems with the exception of thermodynamic. The values of $\alpha_e$,

**TABLE 4.11-1** METHOD FOR CALCULATING ELECTRIC ANALOGS

Choose $\alpha_e$, $\beta_e$, and $\gamma_e$

|  | Mechanical rectilineal | Mechanical rotational | Hydraulic | Pneumatic |
|---|---|---|---|---|
| Elements | $L_j = \gamma_e m_j$ | $L_j = \gamma_e J_j$ | $L_j = \gamma_e M_{Hj}$ | $L_j = \gamma_e M_{pj}$ |
|  | $R_{ej} = \beta_e \gamma_e R_{Lj}$ | $R_{ej} = \beta_e \gamma_e B_j$ | $R_{ej} = \beta_e \gamma_e R_{Hj}$ | $R_{ej} = \beta_e \gamma_e R_{pj}$ |
|  | $C_{ej} = \dfrac{1}{\beta_e{}^2 \gamma_e k}$ | $C_{ej} = \dfrac{1}{\beta_e{}^2 \gamma_e c}$ | $C_{ej} = \dfrac{C_{Hj}}{\beta_e{}^2 \gamma_e}$ | $C_{ej} = \dfrac{C_{pj}}{\beta_e{}^2 \gamma_e}$ |
| Forcing functions, responses, time, and initial conditions* | $*e_j = \alpha_e \beta_e \gamma_e f_j$ | $*e_j = \alpha_e \beta_e \gamma_e T_j$ | $*e_j = \alpha_e \beta_e \gamma_e p_{Hj}$ | $*e_j = \alpha_e \beta_e \gamma_e p_{pj}$ |
|  | $*i_j = \alpha_e v_j$ | $*i_j = \alpha_e \omega_j$ | $*i_j = \alpha_e q_{Hj}$ | $*i_j = \alpha_e q_{pj}$ |
|  | $t_e = \dfrac{t_L}{\beta_e}$ | $t_e = \dfrac{t_R}{\beta_e}$ | $t_e = \dfrac{t_H}{\beta_e}$ | $t_e = \dfrac{t_p}{\beta_e}$ |

* *Note:* Initial conditions of voltage and current corresponding to initial conditions of force and velocity, torque and angular velocity and pressure and volumetric flow are calculated by the same formulas.

$\beta_e$, and $\gamma_e$ are first chosen arbitrarily but actually with the idea of obtaining practical values.

As an example, consider the mechanical configuration of Fig. 4.11-2(a)

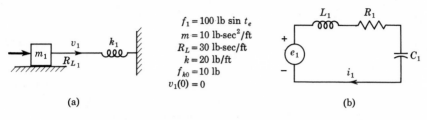

$$f_1 = 100 \text{ lb sin } t_e$$
$$m = 10 \text{ lb-sec}^2/\text{ft}$$
$$R_L = 30 \text{ lb-sec/ft}$$
$$k = 20 \text{ lb/ft}$$
$$f_{k0} = 10 \text{ lb}$$
$$v_1(0) = 0$$

(a)                                      (b)

**Fig. 4.11-2** Mechanical configuration and electrical analog.

and its electrical analog shown in Fig. 4.11-2(b). To calculate the equivalent values we will choose $\alpha_e$ equal to $10^{-2}$, $\beta_e$ equal to $10^5$, and $\gamma_e$ equal to $10^{-4}$. Then from Table 4.11-1,

$$L_1 = \gamma_e m_1 = 10^{-4} \times 10 = 1 \text{ mh}$$

$$R_{e_1} = \beta_e \gamma_e R_{L_1} = 10^5 \times 10^{-4} \times 30 = 300 \text{ ohms}$$

$$C_{e_1} = \frac{1}{\beta_e^2 \gamma_e k_1} = \frac{1}{10^{10} \times 10^{-4} \times 20} = 0.05 \ \mu\text{f}$$

$$e_1 = \alpha_e \beta_e \gamma_e f_j = 10^{-2} \times 10^5 \times 10^{-4} \times 100 \sin (10^5 t_e)$$
$$= 10 \sin (10^5 t_e)$$

$$e_{c_0} = \alpha_e \beta_e \gamma_e f_{k_0} = 10^{-2} \times 10^5 \times 10^{-4} \times 10 = 1 \text{ volt}$$

$$i_1(0) = \alpha_e v_1(0) = 10^{-2} \times 0 = 0$$

The equation describing the electrical circuit of Fig. 4.11-2(b) with the values above is

$$10^{-3} \frac{di_1}{dt_e} + 300 i_1 + \frac{1}{0.05 \times 10^{-6}} \int i_1 \, dt_e = 10 \sin (10^5 t_e) \qquad (4.11\text{-}40)$$

Taking the transform of Eq. (4.11-40) and applying the two initial conditions, we get

$$10^{-3} s I_1 + 300 I_1 + \frac{20 \times 10^6 I_1}{s} + \frac{1}{s} = 10 \frac{10^5}{s^2 + 10^{10}} \qquad (4.11\text{-}41)$$

Solving for $I_1$,

$$I_1 = \frac{10^9 s}{(s^2 + 10^{10})(s + 2 \times 10^5)(s + 1 \times 10^5)}$$

$$- \frac{10^3}{(s + 2 \times 10^5)(s + 1 \times 10^5)} \qquad (4.11\text{-}42)$$

The inverse transform is

$$i_1(t_e) = 10^{-2} \cos 10^5 t_e + 3 \times 10^{-2} \sin 10^5 t_e$$
$$+ 5 \times 10^{-2} \epsilon^{-2 \times 10^5 t_e} - 6 \times 10^{-2} \epsilon^{-10^5 t_e} \qquad (4.11\text{-}43)$$

If we now use the relations

$$v(t_L) = \frac{1}{\alpha_e} i(t_e) = 10^2 i(t_e) \qquad (4.11\text{-}44)$$

$$t_e = \frac{1}{\beta_e} t_L = 10^{-5} t_L \qquad (4.11\text{-}45)$$

in Eq. (4.11-43) it becomes for the mechanical system

$$v(t_L) = 10^2 \times 10^{-2} \cos (10^5 \times 10^{-5} t_L) + 10^2 \times 3 \times 10^{-2} \sin (10^5 \times 10^{-5} t_L)$$
$$+ 10^2 \times 5 \times 10^{-2} \epsilon^{-2 \times 10^5 \times 10^{-5} t_L} - 10^2 \times 6 \times 10^{-2} \epsilon^{-10^5 \times -10^{-5} t_L} \qquad (4.11\text{-}46)$$

or

$$v(t_L) = \cos t_L + 3 \sin t_L + 5 \epsilon^{-2 t_L} - 6 \epsilon^{-t_L} \qquad (4.11\text{-}47)$$

To demonstrate that Eq. (4.11-47) is the same as the solution obtained from solving the equation for Fig. 4.11-2(a) directly, we will write it in terms of the stated mechanical values:

$$10 \frac{dv}{dt_L} + 30v + 20 \int v \, dt_L = 100 \sin t_L$$

The transformed equation with the stated initial conditions is

$$10sV + 30V + \frac{20V}{s} + \frac{10}{s} = \frac{100}{s^2 + 1} \qquad (4.11\text{-}48)$$

Solving for $V$, we obtain

$$V = \frac{10s}{(s^2 + 1)(s + 2)(s + 1)} - \frac{1}{(s + 2)(s + 1)} \qquad (4.11\text{-}49)$$

The inverse transform of Eq. (4.11-49) is

$$v(t_L) = \cos t_L + 3 \sin t_L + 5 \epsilon^{-2 t_L} - 6 \epsilon^{-t_L} \qquad (4.11\text{-}50)$$

which is exactly the same as Eq. (4.11-47). Of course, when a model is made it is usually tested experimentally rather than being solved analytically; but the analytical solution demonstrates that the same results would be obtained if the experimental results of testing the electrical model were properly converted by application of Eqs. (4.11-44) and (4.11-45).

## 4.12 SCALE MODELS

Suppose now that we would like to test a system with a smaller model in the same system—for example, a smaller-scale mechanical model of a mechanical system. To do this it is only necessary to choose an $\alpha_m$, $\beta_m$, and $\gamma_m$ for the model system. The subscript $m$ represents model quantities; so $f_m$, $v_m$, $m_m$, $R_m$, and $k_m$ represent model quantities corresponding to the prototype quantities. Let us apply model design to the mechanical configuration of Fig. 4.11-2(a).

We would like the model to be a one-tenth scale model with respect to mass (and weight) so $\gamma_m$ must equal $\frac{1}{10}$. We want to speed up the response in the model so we choose $\beta_m$ as 10. $\alpha_m$ is chosen as $\frac{1}{10}$. With these values, the model values are

$$m_m = \gamma_m m_1 = 10^{-1} \times 10 = 1 \text{ lb-sec}^2/\text{ft}$$

$$R_m = \beta_m \gamma_m R_{L_1} = 10 \times 10^{-1} \times 30 = 30 \text{ lb-sec/ft}$$

$$k_m = \beta_m^2 \gamma_m k_1 = 100 \times 10^{-1} \times 20 = 200 \text{ lb/ft}$$

$$f_m = \alpha_m \beta_m \gamma_m f_1 = 10^{-1} \times 10 \times 10^{-1} \times 100 \sin(10t_m) = 10 \text{ lb} \sin(10t_m)$$

$$f_{mk_0} = \alpha_m \beta_m \gamma_m f_{k_0} = 10^{-1} \times 10 \times 10^{-1} \times 10 = 1 \text{ lb}$$

$$v_m(0) = \alpha_m v_1(0) = 10^{-1} \times 0 = 0$$

The equation describing the model system is

$$1 \frac{dv_m}{dt_m} + 30v_m + 200 \int v_m \, dt_m = 10 \sin(10t_m) \qquad (4.12\text{-}1)$$

With the stated initial conditions, the transformed equation is

$$sV_m + 30V_m + \frac{200V_m}{s} + \frac{1}{s} = \frac{100}{s^2 + 100} \qquad (4.12\text{-}2)$$

The solution for $V_m$ is

$$V_m = \frac{100s}{(s^2 + 100)(s + 20)(s + 10)} - \frac{1}{(s + 20)(s + 10)} \qquad (4.12\text{-}3)$$

The time solution of Eq. (4.12-3) is

$$v_m = 0.1 \cos 10t_m + 0.3 \sin 10t_m + 0.5\epsilon^{-20t_m} - 0.6\epsilon^{-10t_m} \qquad (4.12\text{-}4)$$

The conversions back to the prototype are

$$v_1(t_L) = \frac{v_m(t_m)}{\alpha_m} = 10v_m(t_m) \qquad (4.12\text{-}5)$$

and

$$t_m = \frac{t_L}{\beta_m} = 10^{-1}t_L \qquad (4.12\text{-}6)$$

Converting Eq. (4.12-4) to the prototype system, we obtain

$$v_1(t_L) = \cos t_L + 3 \sin t_L + 5\epsilon^{-2t_L} - 6\epsilon^{-t_L} \qquad (4.12\text{-}7)$$

which is exactly the same as Eq. (4.11-50), the direct solution for the proto-type system. The same approach can be used to scale any system. Scale models are useful in electrical circuits—particularly where high frequencies and short wavelengths are involved.

## 4.13 ELECTRIC ANALOGS OF THERMODYNAMIC SYSTEMS

Without proof, the method for determining the electric analogs of thermodynamic systems will be derived by assuming that both $L_e$ and $\gamma_e$ equal one. Table 4.13-1 can then be obtained from Table 4.11-1 by simply omitting the inductive storage element.

TABLE 4.13-1 METHOD FOR CALCULATING ELECTRICAL ANALOGS
OF THERMODYNAMIC SYSTEMS

Choose $\alpha_e$ and $\beta_e$

| Elements | |
|---|---|
| | $R_{ej} = \beta_e R_{\theta j}$ |
| | $C_{ej} = \dfrac{C_{\theta j}}{\beta_e^2}$ |
| Forcing function, response, time, and initial conditions | $e_j = \alpha_e \beta_e \theta_j$ |
| | $i_j = \alpha_e q_j$ |
| | $t_e = \dfrac{t_\theta}{\beta_e}$ |

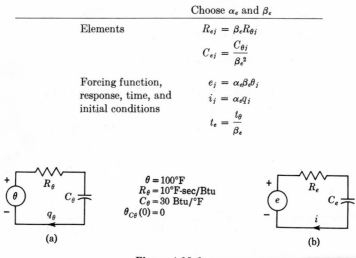

$\theta = 100°F$
$R_\theta = 10°F\text{-sec/Btu}$
$C_\theta = 30\ \text{Btu/°F}$
$\theta_{C\theta}(0) = 0$

(a)                                                              (b)

Figure 4.13-1

The thermodynamic circuit of Fig. 4.13-1(a) has the electric circuit of Fig. 4.13-1(b) as its analog. Using the equations of Table 4.13-1 after choosing $\alpha_e$ as $10^{-5}$ and $\beta_e$ as $10^4$, we obtain

$$R_e = \beta_e R_\theta = 10^4 \times 10 = 10^5 \text{ ohms}$$

$$C_e = \frac{C_\theta}{\beta_e^2} = \frac{30}{10^8} = 0.3 \ \mu f$$

$$e = \alpha_e \beta_e \theta = 10^{-5} \times 10^4 \times 100 = 10 \text{ volts}$$

$$e_{C_e}(0) = \alpha_e \beta_e \theta_{C\theta}(0) = 10^{-5} \times 10^4 \times 0 = 0$$

The equation for the circuit of Fig. 4.13-1 with these values is

$$10^5 i + \frac{1}{0.3 \times 10^{-6}} \int i \, dt_e = 10 \tag{4.13-1}$$

If the transform is taken using the initial conditions above, the result is

$$10^5 I + \frac{I}{0.3 \times 10^{-6} s} = \frac{10}{s} \tag{4.13-2}$$

The solution for $I$ is

$$I = \frac{10^{-4}}{\left( s + \dfrac{1}{3 \times 10^{-2}} \right)} \tag{4.13-3}$$

The time solution of (4.13-3) is

$$i(t_e) = 10^{-4} \epsilon^{-10^2 t_e / 3} \tag{4.13-4}$$

If it is now noted that

$$q_\theta = i / \alpha_e \tag{4.13-5}$$

and

$$t_e = t_\theta / \beta_e \tag{4.13-6}$$

Eq. (4.13-4) can be written for the thermodynamic system as

$$q_\theta(t_\theta) = \frac{10^{-4}}{10^{-5}} \epsilon^{-10^2 t_\theta / (3 \times 10^4)} \tag{4.13-7}$$

or

$$q_\theta(t_\theta) = 10 \epsilon^{-t_\theta / 300} \tag{4.13-8}$$

The equation for Fig. 4.13-1(a) is

$$10 q_\theta + \tfrac{1}{30} \int q_\theta \, dt_\theta = 100 \tag{4.13-9}$$

The transformed equation is

$$10 Q_\theta + \frac{Q_\theta}{30 s} = \frac{100}{s} \tag{4.13-10}$$

and $Q_\theta$ is then given by

$$Q_\theta = \frac{10}{s + \frac{1}{300}} \tag{4.13-11}$$

The time function corresponding to Eq. (4.13-11) is

$$q_\theta(t_\theta) = 10 \epsilon^{-t_\theta / 300} \tag{4.13-12}$$

which is exactly the same as Eq. (4.13-8)

## 4.20 THE IMPEDANCE CONCEPT

In Chap. 2 the method of substituting $(j\omega)$ for $s$ to determine the steady-state response to a sinusoidal forcing function was discussed. This section will show the application of this method by introducing the concept of impedances in the various systems. In addition it will be shown that impedance methods can be used to determine the complete transform provided initial conditions are zero.

### 4.21 DEFINITION OF IMPEDANCE

An impedance $z$ is defined as the complex coefficient which relates the voltage across an element to the current through it when the forcing function is sinusoidal according to the equation

$$zi = e \qquad (4.21\text{-}1)$$

If the following equations are transformed when all initial conditions are zero,

$$e = L\frac{di}{dt} \qquad (4.21\text{-}2)$$

$$e = Ri \qquad (4.21\text{-}3)$$

$$e = \frac{1}{C}\int i\,dt \qquad (4.21\text{-}4)$$

they become

$$E = sLI \qquad (4.21\text{-}5)$$

$$E = RI \qquad (4.21\text{-}6)$$

$$E = \frac{I}{Cs} \qquad (4.21\text{-}7)$$

It is these equations which give the basic impedances for inductances, resistances, and capacitances. If we use the form of Eq. (4.21-1) and substitute $j\omega$ for $s$, then we can interpret the transformed equations given in Eqs. (4.21-5) through (4.21-7) as

inductance:        $z_L = j\omega L$                            (4.21-8)

resistance:        $z_R = R$                              (4.21-9)

capacitance:        $z_C = \dfrac{1}{j\omega C}$                  (4.21-10)

These equations define the impedances of electric circuits.

To illustrate the application of this concept to a series circuit, let us consider the circuit of Fig. 4.21-1. Impedances in series add directly, so the total impedance is

$$z_t = R + j\omega L + \frac{1}{j\omega C} = 100 + j \times 10^3 \times 10^{-1} + \frac{1}{j \times 10^3 \times 5 \times 10^{-6}}$$

or

$$z_t = 100 + j100 + \frac{200}{j}$$

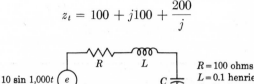

| | R = 100 ohms |
| 10 sin 1,000t | L = 0.1 henries |
| | C = 5 μf |

**Figure 4.21-1**

Since $(1/j)$ is equal to $(-j)$, $z_t$ is

$$z_t = 100 + j100 - j200 = 100 - j100$$

If we convert $z_t$ to polar form, it is

$$z_t = 100\sqrt{2} \underline{/-45°}$$

We then write $e \sin (1000t)$ in polar form as

$$e = 10\underline{/0°}$$

Using the polar forms of $e$ and $z_t$ in Eq. (4.21-1) we obtain

$$100\sqrt{2} \underline{/-45°} \, i = 10\underline{/0°}$$

If we divide by $100\sqrt{2} \underline{/-45°}$, we get

$$i = \frac{10\underline{/0°}}{100\sqrt{2} \underline{/-45°}} = \frac{0.1}{\sqrt{2}}\underline{/45°}$$

which is interpreted as the steady-state response to the sinusoidal forcing function $(10 \sin 1000t)$ and is a current of magnitude $(0.1/\sqrt{2})$ and a phase angle of 45°, or

$$i = 0.0707 \sin (1000t + 45°) \qquad (4.21\text{-}11)$$

To illustrate that the same response is obtained by transform methods, the differential equation of the circuit can be solved. It is

$$L\frac{di}{dt} + Ri + \frac{1}{C} \int i \, dt = e \sin \omega t \qquad (4.21\text{-}12)$$

The transformed equation with zero initial conditions is

$$LsI + RI + \frac{I}{Cs} = \frac{e\omega}{s^2 + \omega^2} \qquad (4.21\text{-}13)$$

or

$$I = \frac{e\omega s}{L(s^2 + \omega^2)\left(s^2 + \frac{R}{L}s + \frac{1}{LC}\right)} \qquad (4.21\text{-}14)$$

If the given values are substituted, the result is

$$I = \frac{10 \times 10^3 s}{10^{-1}(s^2 + 10^6)\left(s^2 + \dfrac{10^2}{10^{-1}}s + \dfrac{1}{10^{-1} \times 5 \times 10^{-6}}\right)}$$

or

$$I = \frac{10^5 s}{(s^2 + 10^6)(s^2 + 10^3 s + 2 \times 10^6)} \qquad (4.21\text{-}15)$$

By partial fraction expansion, Eq. (4.21-15) can be stated as

$$I = \frac{5 \times 10^{-2}s + 5 \times 10}{(s^2 + 10^6)} + \frac{5 \times 10^{-2}s - 10^2}{(s^2 + 10^3 s + 2 \times 10^6)} \qquad (4.21\text{-}16)$$

The inverse transform of the term involving $(s^2 + 10^6)$ in Eq (4.21-16) is

$$i(t) = 5 \times 10^{-2} \cos 1000t + 5 \times 10^{-2} \sin 1000t \qquad (4.21\text{-}17)$$

The term involving $(s^2 + 10^3 s + 2 \times 10^6)$ has been omitted because it represents the transient response. Now

$$A \cos \omega t + B \sin \omega t = \sqrt{A^2 + B^2} \sin (\omega t + \tan^{-1} A/B)$$

For the values in Eq. (4.21-17),

$$\sqrt{A^2 + B^2} = \sqrt{(0.5 \times 10^{-2})^2 + (0.5 \times 10^{-2})^2} = 0.5 \times 10^{-2}\sqrt{2} = 0.0707$$

and

$$\tan^{-1} A/B = \tan^{-1} (0.5 \times 10^{-2})/(0.5 \times 10^{-2}) = \tan^{-1} 1 = 45°$$

so Eq. (4.21-17) can be written as

$$i(t) = 0.0707 \sin (1000t + 45°) \qquad (4.21\text{-}18)$$

which is the same as Eq. (4.21-11).

## 4.22 SUMMARY OF IMPEDANCES

Table 4.22-1 summarizes the impedances to sinusoidal forcing functions for the various systems.

**TABLE 4.22-1** SUMMARY OF IMPEDANCES

| System | Basic equation | Storage element 1 | Storage element 2 | Dissipative element | Impedance unit |
|---|---|---|---|---|---|
| Electrical | $i = \dfrac{e}{z_e}$ | $z = j\omega L$ | $z = \dfrac{-j}{\omega C_e}$ | $z = R_e$ | ohms |
| Rectilineal | $v = \dfrac{f}{z_L}$ | $z = j\omega m$ | $z = \dfrac{-jk}{\omega}$ | $z = R_L$ | lb-sec/ft |
| Rotational | $\omega = \dfrac{T}{z_R}$ * | $z = j\omega_f J$* | $z = \dfrac{-jc}{\omega_f}$* | $z = B$ | lb-ft-sec |
| Hydraulic | $q_H = \dfrac{p_H}{z_H}$ | $z = j\omega M_H$ | $z = \dfrac{-j}{\omega C_H}$ | $z = R_H$ | lb-sec/ft$^5$ |
| Pneumatic | $q_p = \dfrac{p_p}{z_p}$ | $z = j\omega M_p$ | $z = \dfrac{-j}{\omega C_p}$ | $z = R_p$ | lb-sec/ft$^5$ |
| Thermodynamic | $q_\theta = \dfrac{\theta}{z_\theta}$ | | $z = \dfrac{-j}{\omega C_\theta}$ | $z = R_\theta$ | °F-sec/Btu |

*Note:* The subscript $f$ is used to distinguish the forcing function angular velocity from the response parameter angular velocity.

## 4.23 RULES FOR COMBINING IMPEDANCES

There are two basic rules for combining impedances: (1) impedances in series are added directly to obtain a single equivalent impedance and (2) impedances in parallel can be replaced by a single equivalent impedance equal to the product of the individual impedances divided by the sum of the partial products of the impedances. For any number of impedances $n$ in a series, the total impedance $z_t$ is thus

$$z_t = z_1 + z_2 + z_3 + z_4 + \cdots + z_n \qquad (4.23\text{-}1)$$

For $n$ impedances in parallel, the total equivalent impedance $z_t$ is

$$z_t = \frac{z_1 z_2 z_3 z_4 \cdots z_n}{z_1 z_2 z_3 z_4 \cdots z_{n-1} + z_1 z_2 z_3 z_4 \cdots z_{n-2} z_n + \cdots + z_2 z_3 z_4 z_5 \cdots z_n} \qquad (4.23\text{-}2)$$

The denominator of Eq. (4.23-2) is simply the sum of all possible products of individual $z$'s with one missing. As written, $z_n$ is missing from the first term of the denominator, $z_{n-1}$ from the second, and so on down to the last term from which $z_1$ is missing. If there are only two impedances, Eq. (4.23-2) becomes

$$z_t = \frac{z_1 z_2}{z_1 + z_2} \qquad (4.23\text{-}3)$$

or for two impedances in parallel, the equivalent single impedance is the product of the two impedances divided by the sum of the two impedances. If there are three,

$$z_t = \frac{z_1 z_2 z_3}{z_1 z_2 + z_1 z_3 + z_2 z_3}$$ (4.23-4)

## 4.24 RECTANGULAR AND POLAR FORMS

An impedance is represented by a complex number of the form $a + jb$ where $a$ is the real part, $b$ is the imaginary part, and $j$ is the square root of minus one. There are two ways an impedance can be expressed: (1) in simple complex number form as $a + jb$ or (2) as a vector with a magnitude and reference angle as $c\underline{/\phi}$ where $c$ is the magnitude and $\phi$ is the reference angle. The two forms are related by

$$c = \sqrt{a^2 + b^2}$$ (4.24-1)

$$\phi = \tan^{-1} b/a$$ (4.24-2)

$$a + jb = c(\cos \phi + j \sin \phi)$$ (4.24-3)

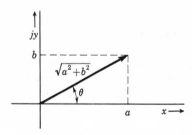

**Fig. 4.24-1** Rectangular and polar forms of complex numbers.

The relation of the rectangular and polar forms is demonstrated by the complex plane plot of Fig. 4.24-1. Both forms are useful in manipulating impedances. Nyquist plots, discussed in Chap. 6, are simply polar plots of magnitude versus phase angle as the frequency varies. In other words they are plots of the tips of the vectors $(\sqrt{a^2 + b^2}\underline{/\phi})$ as the frequency or angular velocity changes. Single impedances can never have a phase angle greater than $+90°$ or less than $-90°$. The maximum positive phase shift for any transfer function is $(+n \times 90°)$, where $n$ is the order of the system and the maximum negative phase shift is $(-n \times 90°)$.

The forms of Eqs. (4.23-1), (4.23-2), (4.23-3), and (4.23-4) indicate that products, sums, and quotients of impedances must be obtained to combine impedances into single equivalent impedances. Sums and differences must be taken in rectangular form, although they can be indicated in polar form. To add two numbers,

$$C_1 \underline{\phi_1} + C_2 \underline{\phi_2} = C_1 \cos \phi_1 + jC_1 \sin \phi_1 + C_2 \cos \phi_2 + jC_2 \sin \phi_2$$

$$= (C_1 \cos \phi_1 + C_2 \cos \phi_2) + j(C_1 \sin \phi_1 + C_2 \sin \phi_2)$$

$$= (a_1 + a_2) + j(b_1 + b_2)$$

$$= \sqrt{(a_1 + a_2)^2 + (b_1 + b_2)^2}\underline{/\tan^{-1} (b_1 + b_2)/(a_1 + a_2)}$$

On the other hand, it is more convenient to multiply and divide in polar form. To multiply in polar form,

$$C_1\underline{/\phi_1} \times C_2\underline{/\phi_2} = C_1C_2\underline{/\phi_1 + \phi_2}$$

or the product of two vectors in polar form is a vector with magnitude equal to the product of the magnitudes of the two at an angle equal to the sum of the two angles. To divide,

$$\frac{C_1\underline{/\phi_1}}{C_2\underline{/\phi_2}} = \frac{C_1}{C_2}\underline{/\phi_1 - \phi_2}$$

or the quotient of two vectors is a vector with magnitude equal to the quotient of the magnitudes of the two at an angle equal to the difference of the two angles. Multiplication of two vectors in rectangular form is more complicated as demonstrated below:

$$(a_1 + jb_1)(a_2 + jb_2) = (a_1a_2 - b_1b_2) + j(a_1b_2 + a_2b_1)$$

To divide in rectangular coordinates, the denominator must be multiplied by its conjugate.

$$\frac{a_1 + jb_1}{a_2 + jb_2} = \frac{(a_1 + jb_1)(a_2 - jb_2)}{(a_2 + jb_2)(a_2 - jb_2)} = \frac{(a_1a_2 + b_1b_2) - j(a_1b_2 + a_2b_1)}{a_2^2 + b_2^2}$$

Manipulation of impedances in rectangular and polar form will be demonstrated in Sec. 4.26.

## 4.25 EQUIVALENT CIRCUITS

The methods for calculating electric analog values have been given, and the impedance concept has been introduced. To use the impedance concept it is necessary to be able to draw the diagrams of mechanical rectilineal, mechanical rotational, hydraulic, pneumatic, and thermo-dynamic systems in the same form as their electric equivalents. The basic steps are

1. Establish the basic reference level for the forcing function whether it be voltage, force, torque, pressure, or temperature.
2. Starting with the forcing function, trace all flow or velocity paths. The following special rules apply to the branching of flows or velocities:
   (a) Electrical: any type of element or any voltage source can be used either in series or shunt, so a current branch point can be introduced.
   (b) Mechanical rectilineal: a velocity branch point is introduced by each dashpot and spring unless one side is tied to the refer-

ence for velocity (usually the earth). A pure mass, being a rigid body, cannot introduce a velocity branch point because all parts must be at the same velocity.

(c) Mechanical rotational: an angular velocity branch point is introduced by each rotational dashpot and spring unless one side is tied to the reference for angular velocity. A pure inertia cannot introduce a velocity branch point.

(d) Hydraulic and pneumatic: flow branch points can be introduced by the simple insertion of a "T" in the plumbing. Hydraulic and pneumatic capacitances must be shunt elements unless they have an inlet only, in which case they can be series elements but at the end of the flow path. In other words, if they have both an inlet and outlet flow, flow branch points are introduced by the capacitances.

(e) Thermodynamic: all thermodynamic capacitances must be shunt elements and therefore introduce a heat flow branch point unless they represent the terminating element. Furthermore, all shunt branches must contain a capacitance. If these rules did not hold, the impossible situation of steady-state differences in temperatures with constant-temperature heat sources would result.

3. Insert all elements into the appropriate flow or velocity paths.

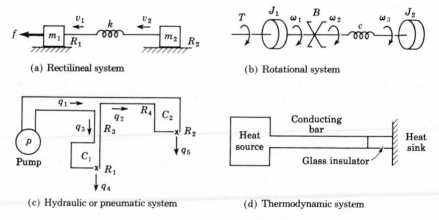

(a) Rectilineal system                    (b) Rotational system

(c) Hydraulic or pneumatic system        (d) Thermodynamic system

**Fig. 4.25-1** Example systems.

To illustrate the application of these three rules and special conditions, let us examine the configurations of Fig. 4.25-1.

The mechanical rectilineal system of Figure 4.25-1(a) has a single forcing function $f$. We establish it as the reference and indicate the posi-

tive direction for force, velocity, and displacement to the left. We next
note that two velocities can exist because the spring $k$ is not connected to
ground. We now draw the force $f$ as we would a voltage as shown in Fig.
4.25-2(a). From the force $f$ must "flow" the velocity $v_1$ since the force is

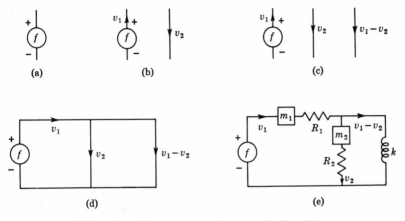

Fig. 4.25-2 Steps in setting up equivalent circuit of rectilineal system.

acting directly on the mass $m_1$ which is moving at velocity $v_1$. The second
velocity is $v_2$, so we add a $v_2$ path as shown in (b). We next note that the
spring force is a function of $(v_1 - v_2)$ so we add a $(v_1 - v_2)$ path in (c). We
now have all of the velocity effects, so we now connect them so that
Kirchhoff's current law applies to the velocities as shown in (d). The last
step of adding in the elements affected by each velocity is shown in (e).

For the rotational system of Fig. 4.25-1(b), we note that the angular
velocity $\omega_1$ must "flow" out of it because that is the velocity of the inertia
$J_1$. Both the dashpot and the spring introduce branch points since neither
is grounded. We next note that the velocities that affect elements are

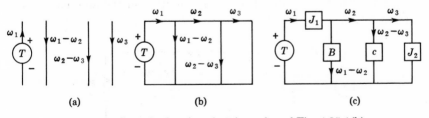

Fig. 4.25-3 Steps in drawing electric analog of Fig. 4.25-1(b).

$J_1$, $\omega_1$; $B$, $(\omega_1 - \omega_2)$; $c$, $(\omega_2 - \omega_3)$; and $J_2$, $\omega_3$. The required velocities and
torque are shown in Fig. 4.25-3(a). The angular velocities are next con-
nected to give a circuit consistent with Kirchhoff's current law as shown

in (b). Note that it was necessary to introduce $\omega_2$ as an entity to complete the connections. Each element is now introduced into the appropriate angular velocity path and the circuit is completed as shown in (c).

The same approach can be used in the hydraulic or pneumatic system of Fig. 4.25-1(c). A pump brings the fluid above the reference pressure level and pumps it through a header. It then divides at the "T" and part of the flow goes into one reactor and out through a letdown valve to refer-

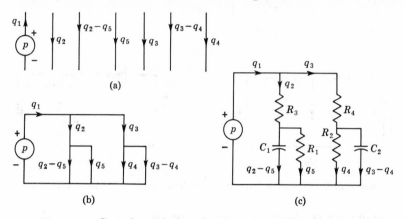

(a)

(b)                       (c)

**Fig. 4.25-4** Steps in setting up electric analog of Fig. 4.25-1(c).

ence pressure. The other flow goes through the same sequence through another reactor. It is assumed that the resistance, capacitance, and inertance of the header can be neglected. When the flow divides there is a resistance in each line before the capacitance of the reactor. The flow $q_1$ comes from the pump giving pressure $p$, and $q_1$ divides at the "T" to $q_2$ and $q_3$. The flows determining pressure drops are $q_2$, $q_3$, $q_3 - q_4$, $q_2 - q_5$, $q_4$ and $q_5$. In Fig. 4.25-4(a) are drawn the flow lines and the pressure source. In (b) the flow lines are connected to correspond to Kirchhoff's current law, and in (c) the elements are inserted in the appropriate flow path to complete the circuit.

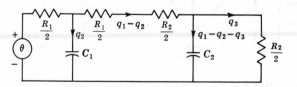

**Fig. 4.25-5** Analog of thermodynamic system of Fig. 4.25-1(d).

The thermodynamic system of Fig. 4.25-1(d) consists of a heat source at a temperature $\theta$ above that of the heat sink reference. Heat flows through a conducting bar as well as into the thermal capacitance of the bar. The conduction flow then goes into the insulator where part of it goes into the thermal capacitance and part flows through it to the heat sink. We choose to represent both the conductor and insulator as "T" networks. If the thermal resistance of the bar is $R_1$ and its capacitance $C_1$, and the thermal resistance of the insulator is $R_2$ and its capacitance $C_2$, the electric circuit representation is as shown in Fig. 4.25-5.

## 4.26 CIRCUIT ANALYSIS BY IMPEDANCE METHODS

If the forcing function in a system is of the form $A(\sin \omega t)$, we can use the relations developed in the preceding paragraphs of Sec. 4.20 to determine the steady-state response. Let us assume that the forcing function of Fig. 4.25-2(e) is $f(\sin \omega t)$ and that we want to determine $v_1 - v_2$. The first step is to combine the parallel impedances $(k/j\omega)$ and $(R_2 + j\omega m_2)$.

$$z_p = \frac{z_1 z_2}{z_1 + z_2} = \frac{(k/j\omega)(R_2 + j\omega m_2)}{R_2 + j\omega m_2 - j(k/\omega)}$$

The next step is to add this equivalent series impedance to the impedance $(R_1 + j\omega m_1)$.

$$\begin{aligned}
z_t &= \frac{(k/j\omega)(R_2 + j\omega m_2)}{R_2 + j\omega m_2 - jk/\omega} + R_1 + j\omega m_1 \\
&= \frac{(-jk/\omega)(R_2 + j\omega m_2) + (R_1 + j\omega m_1)(R_2 + j\omega m_2 - jk/\omega)}{R_2 + j\omega m_2 - jk/\omega}
\end{aligned}$$

$z_t$ is now the total series impedance and the velocity $v_1$ is

$$v_1 = \frac{f}{z_t} = \frac{f(R_2 + j\omega m_2 - jk/\omega)}{(-jk/\omega)(R_2 + j\omega m_2) + (R_1 + j\omega m_1)(R_2 + j\omega m_2 - jk/\omega)}$$

If we multiply $v_1$ by the equivalent series impedance of the parallel branch, we get the force across the parallel branch.

$$\begin{aligned}
f_p = v_1 z_p &= \frac{f(R_2 + j\omega m_2 - jk/\omega)}{(-jk/\omega)(R_2 + j\omega m_2) + (R_1 + j\omega m_1)(R_2 + j\omega m_2 - jk/\omega)} \\
&\qquad\qquad\qquad\qquad\qquad \times \frac{(k/j\omega)(R_2 + j\omega m_2)}{(R_2 + j\omega m_2 - jk/\omega)} \\
&= \frac{f(k/j\omega)(R_2 + j\omega m_2)}{(-jk/\omega)(R_2 + j\omega m_2) + (R_1 + j\omega m_1)(R_2 + j\omega m_2 - jk/\omega)}
\end{aligned}$$

The force across the parallel branch $f_p$ can now be divided by the impedance of the spring to get the velocity $(v_1 - v_2)$.

$$v_1 - v_2 = \frac{f_p}{k/j\omega} = \frac{f(R_2 + j\omega m_2)}{(-jk/\omega)(R_2 + j\omega m_2) + (R_1 + j\omega m_1)(R_2 + j\omega m_2 - jk/\omega)}$$

There are short-cuts which can be applied. For example, the procedure above could have been shortened by recognizing that the current flowing into a two-path parallel branch divides according to the relation

$$i = \frac{z_1}{z_1 + z_2} i + \frac{z_2}{z_1 + z_2} i$$

where the first term on the right is the current through $z_2$ and the second term is the current through $z_1$. In other words, if $z_1$ and $z_2$ are two impedances in parallel and $i$ is the total current flowing into the parallel combination, then the current through $z_1$ is the total current times the *other* impedance $z_2$ divided by the sum of the two impedances.

To illustrate the manipulation of complex numbers, the following values will be assigned to the parameters and elements of Fig. 4.25-2(e).

$$f = 100 \sin t, \qquad k = 20 \text{ lb/ft}$$
$$R_1 = 20 \text{ lb-sec/ft}, \qquad R_2 = 30 \text{ lb-sec/ft}$$
$$m_1 = 20 \text{ lb-sec}^2/\text{ft}, \qquad m_2 = 10 \text{ lb-sec}^2/\text{ft}$$
$$\omega = 1 \text{ rad/sec.}$$

Then

$$R_1 + j\omega m_1 = 20 + j20 = 28.3\underline{/45^\circ}$$
$$R_2 + j\omega m_2 = 30 + j10 = 31.6\underline{/18.4^\circ}$$
$$-jk/\omega = -j20 = 20\underline{/-90^\circ}$$
$$R_2 + j\omega m_2 - jk/\omega = 30 + j10 - j20 = 30 - j10 = 31.6\underline{/-18.4^\circ}$$

Using these values in the expression for $(v_1 - v_2)$,

$$v_1 - v_2 = \frac{100\underline{/0^\circ} \times 31.6\underline{/18.4^\circ}}{20\underline{/-90^\circ} \times 31.6\underline{/18.4^\circ} + 28.3\underline{/45^\circ} \times 31.6\underline{/-18.4^\circ}}$$

$$= \frac{316\underline{/18.4^\circ}}{632\underline{/-71.6^\circ} + 893\underline{/26.6^\circ}}$$

$$= \frac{316\underline{/18.4^\circ}}{200 - j600 + 790 + j396}$$

$$= \frac{316\underline{/18.4^\circ}}{990 - j204}$$

$$= \frac{316\underline{/18.4^\circ}}{1010\underline{/-11.65^\circ}}$$

$$= 0.313\underline{/30.0^\circ}$$

or

$$v_1 - v_2 = 0.313(\text{ft/sec}) \sin (t + 30^\circ)$$

Note that in solving for $(v_1 - v_2)$ it was necessary or convenient to switch back and forth between polar and rectangular forms.

Sometimes it is easier to write the impedances as $z$'s and combine them in that form rather than writing the impedances as explicit functions of $\omega$. For example, the circuit of Fig. 4.25-3(c) can be drawn as shown in Fig. 4.26-1. The angular velocity of the forcing torque function is denoted

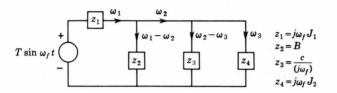

**Fig. 4.26-1** General impedance form of Fig. 4.25-3(a).

by the subscript $f$ to distinguish it from the response angular velocities. To find the angular velocity $\omega_3$, the first step is to combine the parallel impedances $z_2$, $z_3$, and $z_4$ into a single equivalent $z_p$.

$$z_p = \frac{z_2 z_3 z_4}{z_2 z_3 + z_2 z_4 + z_3 z_4}$$

The total series impedance $z_t$ is

$$z_t = z_1 + z_p = z_1 + \frac{z_2 z_3 z_4}{z_2 z_3 + z_2 z_4 + z_3 z_4}$$

$$= \frac{z_1 z_2 z_3 + z_1 z_2 z_4 + z_1 z_3 z_4 + z_2 z_3 z_4}{z_2 z_3 + z_2 z_4 + z_3 z_4}$$

If we divide the torque by the total impedance we get the velocity $\omega_1$:

$$\omega_1 = \frac{T}{z_t}$$

If we multiply $\omega_1$ by $z_p$ the result is the torque across the parallel branch.

$$T_p = z_p \omega_1 = z_p \frac{T}{z_t}$$

The angular velocity $\omega_3$ is $T_p$ divided by $z_4$.

$$\omega_3 = \frac{T_p}{z_4} = T \cdot \frac{z_p}{z_t z_4}$$

Using the expressions above for $z_p$ and $z_t$,

$$\omega_3 = T \frac{\dfrac{z_2 z_3 z_4}{z_2 z_3 + z_2 z_4 + z_3 z_4}}{\dfrac{z_1 z_2 z_3 + z_1 z_2 z_4 + z_1 z_3 z_4 + z_2 z_3 z_4}{z_2 z_3 + z_2 z_4 + z_3 z_4}} \frac{1}{z_4}$$

$$= T \frac{z_2 z_3}{z_1 z_2 z_3 + z_1 z_2 z_4 + z_1 z_3 z_4 + z_2 z_3 z_4}$$

The functions of $\omega_f$ given for $z_1$, $z_2$, $z_3$, and $z_4$ can now be used to get the expression for $\omega_3$ as a function of $\omega_f$.

## 4.27 GENERAL RESPONSE WITH ZERO INITIAL CONDITIONS

The previously described impedance method for obtaining steady-state response has another useful application. If all initial conditions are zero (no energy stored initially), the impedance concept can be used to

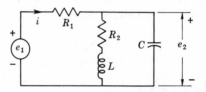

Fig. 4.27-1 Electric circuit.

derive transforms or transfer functions. Simply replace $j\omega$ with $s$ in the equations for impedance and solve for the desired unknown. The circuit of Fig. 4.27-1 will be used to illustrate this application.

The parallel impedance in terms of $s$ is

$$z_p(s) = \frac{(R_2 + sL)(1/sC)}{R_2 + sL + (1/sC)} = \frac{R_2 + sL}{1 + sCR_2 + LCs^2}$$

The total impedance is

$$z_t = R_1 + z_p(s) = R_1 + \frac{R_2 + sL}{1 + sCR_2 + LCs^2}$$

$$= \frac{R_1 + R_2 + (CR_1R_2 + L)s + R_1LCs^2}{1 + sCR_2 + s^2LC}$$

If we divide $E_1(s)$ by $z_t(s)$, the result is $I_1(s)$.

$$I_1(s) = \frac{E_1(s)}{z_t(s)} = \frac{E_1(s)[1 + sCR_2 + LCs^2]}{R_1 + R_2 + (CR_1R_2 + L)s + R_1LCs^2}$$

$E_2(s)$ is the product of $I_1(s)$ and $z_p(s)$.

$$E_2(s) = I_1(s)z_p(s) = \frac{E_1(s)[1 + sCR_2 + LCs^2]}{R_1 + R_2 + (CR_1R_2 + L)s + R_1LCs^2}$$

$$\times \frac{R_2 + sL}{1 + sCR_2 + LCs^2}$$

$$= E_1(s)\frac{R_2 + sL}{R_1 + R_2 + (CR_1R_2 + L)s + R_1LCs^2}$$

If $e_1(t)$ is a unit step function,

$$E_2(s) = \frac{R_2 + sL}{s[R_1 + R_2 + (CR_1R_2 + L)s + R_1LCs^2]}$$

The ratio $E_2(s)/E_1(s)$ is known as a *transfer function*. In the $s$ domain it describes the characteristics of the system relating the output to the input.

## 4.30  CIRCUIT THEOREMS

There are many useful circuit theorems. The discussion here will be limited to two: (1) the superposition theorem and (2) Thevenin's theorem.

THE SUPERPOSITION THEOREM: If a system has two or more source functions in it, the value of any response function is the sum of the responses obtained by considering the sources one at a time while the other sources are replaced by their internal impedances.

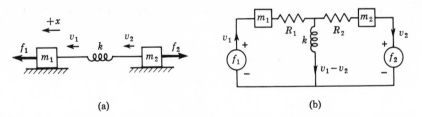

(a)                                              (b)

**Fig. 4.30-1** Mechanical system with two-source functions.

To illustrate this theorem let us consider the rectilineal configuration of Fig. 4.30-1(a) and its electrical form in (b). To solve for $v_2$ by the superposition theorem we first solve for $v_{21}$, the part of $v_2$ due to $f_1$, by simply omitting $f_2$ since it has zero internal impedance. By impedance methods,

$$v_{21} = \frac{-j(k/\omega)f_1}{(R_1 + j\omega m_1)(R_2 + j\omega m_2) - j(k/\omega)(R_1 + R_2 + j\omega m_1 + j\omega m_2)}$$

The next step is to solve for $v_{22}$, the part of $v_2$ due to $f_2$, by simply omitting $f_1$. By impedance methods,

$$v_{22} = \frac{-f_2(R_1 + j\omega m_1 - jk/\omega)}{(R_1 + j\omega m_1)(R_2 + j\omega m_2) - j(k/\omega)(R_1 + R_2 + j\omega m_1 + j\omega m_2)}$$

then

$$v_2 = v_{21} + v_{22}$$

$$= \frac{f_1(-jk/\omega) - f_2(R_1 + j\omega m_1 - jk/\omega)}{(R_1 + j\omega m_1)(R_2 + j\omega m_2) - (jk/\omega)(R_1 + R_2 + j\omega m_1 + j\omega m_2)}$$

If the transform with zero initial conditions is desired, $s$ replaces $j\omega$. The superposition theorem holds true for nonzero initial conditions as well, but the impedance method cannot be used.

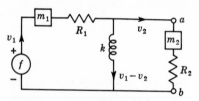

**Fig. 4.30-2** Mechanical circuit.

THEVENIN'S THEOREM: If a circuit has a sinusoidal forcing function, the current through any impedance can be obtained by replacing the sinusoidal forcing function with a value equal to the open-circuit value at the terminals of that impedance and inserting a series impedance equal to the impedance looking back into the network at the terminals of that impedance.

The mechanical circuit of Fig. 4.30-2 will illustrate the application of Thevenin's theorem. To find the open-circuit force across the terminals

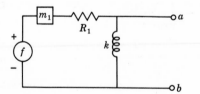

**Fig. 4.30-3** Open circuit at terminals $a$-$b$.

$a$-$b$, the circuit of Fig. 4.30-3 applies. The open-circuit force at terminals $a$-$b$ is

$$f_{a-b} = \frac{f(-jk/\omega)}{R_1 + j\omega m_1 - jk/\omega}$$

The impedance looking into the terminals $a$-$b$ (with the source shorted) is simply the parallel combination of the spring with the mass and resistance in series, or

$$z_{a-b} = \frac{(-jk/\omega)(R_1 + j\omega m_1)}{R_1 + j\omega m_1 - jk/\omega}$$

so the equivalent circuit so far as $v_2$ is concerned is that shown in Fig. 4.30-4.

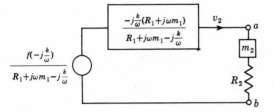

**Fig. 4.30-4** Thevenin's theorem equivalent circuit of Fig. 4.30-2.

## 4.40 TRANSFORMER ANALOGS

In electrical, mechanical rectilineal, mechanical rotational, hydraulic, and pneumatic systems there are devices which act as transformers. As ideal devices they change the parameters of voltage and current, force and velocity, torque and angular velocity, or pressure and flow so that the product of the two in each case remains constant. Thus if force were multiplied by the constant $a$, the velocity would be multiplied by $1/a$. The actual devices are never ideal and usually have both unwanted dissipative effects and energy storage effects. The physical arrangements of the devices or the physical phenomena which result in the transformation are such that the forcing functions most usefully applied to these devices are sinusoidal. The discussion here will be devoted primarily to steady-state sinusoidal responses, so impedance concepts will be used.

## 4.41 ELECTRICAL TRANSFORMERS

If two electrical inductances are placed close together, some of the magnetic flux due to the current in one will cut the conductors of the other and thereby induce a voltage in the other. A current in the other

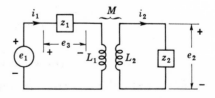

**Fig. 4.41-1** Ideal transformer circuit.

will induce a voltage in the first. This phenomenon leads to the concept of *mutual inductance* denoted by the letter $M$. The circuit of Fig. 4.41-1 shows an ideal transformer connecting a voltage source $e_1$ with series

internal impedance $z_1$ and a load of impedance $z_2$. The impedances will be
treated as transfer functions so that the behavior of the circuit can be
described by differential equations and their transforms. The equation in
the time domain can be written as

$$e_1 - e_3(i_1, z_1) - L_1 \frac{di_1}{dt} \mp M \frac{di_2}{dt} = 0 \qquad (4.41\text{-}1)$$

$$L_2 \frac{di_2}{dt} \pm M \frac{di_1}{dt} + e_2(i_2, z_2) = 0 \qquad (4.41\text{-}2)$$

where $e_3(i_1, z_1)$ shows that the voltage drop across $z_1$ is a function of the
current $i_1$ and its particular combination of elements, and similarly for
$e_2(i_2, z_2)$; $M$ is the mutual inductance; $e_1$ is the forcing function; and $L_1$
and $L_2$ are respectively the self-inductances of the primary and secondary
windings of the transformer. The sign connected with the mutual inductance $M$ depends upon whether the voltage across it is in the same or
opposite direction as the voltage of self-induction. In other words, if the
voltages $L(di_1/dt)$ and $M(di_2/dt)$ are in the same direction $M$ is positive.
The sign of $M$ is always the same for effects with respect to both $L_1$ and
$L_2$. An easy way to think of how $M$ can change sign is to consider the
effect when the terminals of the secondary are reversed. The direction of
flow of $i_2$ through the winding $L_2$ is reversed and thus the voltage it induces
in the primary winding $L_1$ is reversed. In analyzing circuits with mutual
inductance it will be carried in all equations as a positive quantity. Then
when numerical values are substituted, the correct sign can be used based
on whether the mutual inductance is aiding or opposing.

If initial conditions are assumed to be zero, the transformed versions
of Eqs. (4.41-1) and (4.41-2) are

$$E_1 - Z_1 I_1 - sL_1 I_1 - sM I_2 = 0 \qquad (4.41\text{-}3)$$

$$sL_2 I_2 + sM I_1 + Z_2 I_2 = 0 \qquad (4.41\text{-}4)$$

The solutions for $I_1$ and $I_2$ are

$$I_1 = \frac{E_1}{Z_1 + sL_1 - s^2 M^2 / (Z_2 + sL_2)} \qquad (4.41\text{-}5)$$

$$I_2 = \frac{-E_1 sM}{(Z_1 + sL_1)(Z_2 + sL_2) - s^2 M^2} \qquad (4.41\text{-}6)$$

If Eqs. (4.41-5) and (4.41-6) are taken as the steady-state solutions with
sinusoidal forcing functions, several observations can be made. The effect
of the mutual coupling introduces an effective impedance into the primary
equal to

$$Z_{1R} = - \frac{Z_m^2}{Z_2 + j\omega L_2} = + \frac{\omega^2 M^2}{Z_2 + j\omega L_2} \qquad (4.41\text{-}7)$$

where $Z_{1R}$ is the impedance reflected into the primary from the secondary, $Z_m$ is the mutual impedance equal to $(j\omega M)$, $Z_2$ is the load impedance in series with the secondary winding, and $j\omega L_2$ is the impedance of the second-ary winding. Equation (4.41-5) can be represented by the circuit of Fig. 4.41-2. Since the numerator of the reflected impedance is squared, it will be positive whether $M$ is aiding or opposing. Since the total series imped-ance of the secondary $(Z_2 + j\omega L_2)$ appears in the denominator of the reflected impedance term, the reactive part of the reflected impedance will

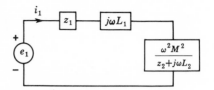

**Fig. 4.41-2** Steady-state representa-tion of Eq. (4.41-5).

always be of the opposite sign to that of the reactive part of the total secondary impedance. Thus if $Z_2$ had a net capacitive reactance larger than $j\omega L_2$, inductive reactance (plus resistance) would be reflected into the primary. If $(Z_2 + j\omega L_2)$ has a net inductive reactance, the impedance reflected into the primary is capacitive reactance (plus resistance).

The value of $M$ depends on the values of $L_1$ and $L_2$ and the parts of the flux due to the current in one winding that cuts the other winding. The mutual inductance is

$$M = k\sqrt{L_1 L_2} \qquad (4.41\text{-}8)$$

where $M$ is the mutual inductance, $k$ is the coefficient of coupling and is a measure of the part of the flux due to $i_1$ that cuts the windings of $L_2$ and vice versa, and $L_1$ and $L_2$ are the self-inductances. Note that $k$ will be $+$ or $-$ depending on the sign of $M$. $k$ can approach 1 for practical pur-poses in some iron-core transformers but is usually much lower for air-core transformers.

The self-inductance of some types of windings varies as the square of the number of turns. If $a$ is defined as

$$a = N_1/N_2 \qquad (4.41\text{-}9)$$

where $N_1$ and $N_2$ are the number of turns of the primary and secondary windings, then

$$L_1/L_2 = a^2 \qquad (4.41\text{-}10)$$

and

$$M = k\sqrt{L_1 L_2} = k\sqrt{L_1 L_1/a^2} = kL_1/a = kaL_2 \qquad (4.41\text{-}11)$$

In the circuit of Fig. 4.41-1 the self voltage $e_4$ across the primary wind-ing for steady-state sinusoidal conditions is

$$e_4 = j\omega L i$$

The self voltage $e_5$ across the secondary winding is, from Eq. (4.41-4),

$$e_5 = j\omega L_2 i_2 = -j\omega L_2 \frac{j\omega M}{z_2 + j\omega L_2} i_1 \qquad (4.41\text{-}12)$$

The ratio of the secondary to primary voltage is

$$\frac{e_5}{e_4} = \frac{-j\omega L_2 \dfrac{j\omega M}{z_2 + j\omega L_2} i_1}{j\omega L_1 i_1} = -\frac{L_2}{L_1} \frac{j\omega M}{z_2 + j\omega L_2} \qquad (4.41\text{-}13)$$

But $M = (kL_1/a)$; then

$$\frac{e_5}{e_4} = -\frac{L_2}{L_1} \frac{j\omega(kL_1/a)}{z_2 + j\omega L_2} = \frac{-k}{a} \frac{j\omega L_2}{z_2 + j\omega L_2} \qquad (4.41\text{-}14)$$

For the load $z_2$ equal to zero, Eq. (4.41-14) reduces to

$$\frac{e_5}{e_4} = -\frac{k}{a} \qquad (4.41\text{-}15)$$

which states that the voltage induced in the secondary is directly proportional to the coefficient of coupling $k$ and inversely proportional to the turns ratio $a$.

From Eq. (4.41-4), the ratio of the currents is

$$\frac{i_2}{i_1} = -\frac{j\omega M}{z_2 + j\omega L_2} \qquad (4.41\text{-}16)$$

Substituting the relation $M = k\sqrt{L_1 L_2}$, we get

$$\frac{i_2}{i_1} = \frac{-j\omega k\sqrt{L_1 L_2}}{z_2 + j\omega L_2} \qquad (4.41\text{-}17)$$

In terms of the turns ratio, Eq. (4.41-17) can be rewritten as

$$\frac{i_2}{i_1} = \frac{-j\omega k\sqrt{a^2 L_2 L_2}}{z_2 + j\omega L_2} = \frac{-j\omega k a L_2}{z_2 + j\omega L_2} \qquad (4.41\text{-}18)$$

If $z_2$ is zero, Eq. (4.41-18) reduces to

$$\frac{i_2}{i_1} = \frac{-j\omega k a L_2}{j\omega L_2} = -ka \qquad (4.41\text{-}19)$$

If Eqs. (4.41-15) and (4.41-19) are multiplied together, the result is

$$\frac{e_5 i_2}{e_4 i_1} = \left(-\frac{k}{a}\right)(-ka) = k^2 \qquad (4.41\text{-}20)$$

which states that for zero load or short-circuit conditions the product of secondary voltage and secondary current is equal to the square of the coupling coefficient times the product of primary voltage and primary current. If the coefficient of coupling is unity, then for zero load on the secondary,

$$e_5 i_2 = e_4 i_1 \qquad (4.41\text{-}21)$$

and

$$e_5 = e_4/a \qquad (4.41\text{-}22)$$

and

$$i_2 = a i_1 \qquad (4.41\text{-}23)$$

Equations (4.41-22) and (4.41-23) demonstrate a fundamental characteristic of transformers, that when the voltage is stepped down the current is stepped up.

The next characteristic of electrical transformers to be introduced is the departure from an ideal transformer. An ideal transformer has no dissipative elements and no capacitance. In practice there is usually a resistance associated with the actual ohmic resistance of the winding and there is a leakage resistance associated with leakage currents to the transformer case. There is a capacitive effect because the individual turns of the winding are in close proximity to each other. The complete equivalent circuit of a transformer can be represented by Fig. 4.41-3.

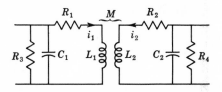

**Fig. 4.41-3** Equivalent circuit of non-ideal transformer.

In this figure, $R_1$ is the resistance of the primary winding, $C_1$ is the shunt capacitance of the primary winding, $R_3$ is the leakage resistance of the primary, $L_1$ is the primary self-inductance, $M$ is the mutual inductance, $R_2$ is the resistance of the secondary winding, $C_2$ is the shunt capacitance of the secondary, $R_4$ is the leakage resistance of the secondary, and $L_2$ is the secondary self-inductance. The circuit of Fig. 4.41-3 can be represented also by

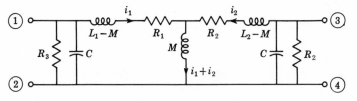

**Fig. 4.41-4** Transformer equivalent circuit.

the circuit of Fig. 4.41-4. The equations describing the circuit of this figure are exactly the same as those describing the circuit of Fig. 4.41-3. Whatever else is in a transformer circuit is then drawn with the correct connections to terminals 1, 2, 3, and 4. In many applications, particularly those for low frequencies, the shunt capacitances and leakage resistances can be neglected, and in some applications even the series resistances $R_1$ and $R_2$ can be neglected.

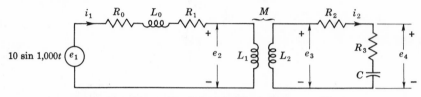

**Fig. 4.41-5** Example of electrical transformer problem.

EXAMPLE: A 1000 rad/sec generator with internal impedance contributed by a 10-ohm resistance and a 4-millihenry inductance supplies a transformer with load as shown in Fig. 4.41-5. The shunt resistances and capacitances of the transformer can be neglected. With the values given in the diagram, calculate $i_1$, $e_2$, $e_3$, $i_2$, and $e_4$.

$$R_0 = 10\ \Omega, \qquad L_0 = 5\ \text{mh}, \qquad e_1 = 10 \sin 1000t$$
$$R_1 = 5\ \Omega, \qquad L_1 = 25\ \text{mh}, \qquad M = 25\ \text{mh}$$
$$R_2 = 10\ \Omega, \qquad L_2 = 100\ \text{mh},$$
$$R_3 = 10\ \Omega, \qquad C = 5\ \mu\text{f}.$$

The various impedances are

$$R_0 = 10, \qquad j\omega L_0 = j5$$
$$R_1 = 5, \qquad j\omega L_1 = j25$$
$$R_2 = 10, \qquad j\omega L_2 = j100$$
$$R_3 = 10, \qquad 1/j\omega C = -j200 \qquad 10 - j200 = 200\underline{/-87.1°}$$
$$j\omega M = j25$$

The current $i_1$ is

$$i_1 = \cfrac{e_1}{R_0 + j\omega L_0 + R_1 + j\omega L_1 + \cfrac{\omega^2 M^2}{R_2 + j\omega L_2 + R_3 + 1/j\omega C}}$$

$$= \cfrac{10}{10 + j5 + 5 + j25 + \cfrac{25^2}{10 + j100 + 10 - j200}}$$

$$= \cfrac{10}{15 + j30 + \cfrac{625}{20 - j100}} = \cfrac{10}{15 + j30 + \cfrac{625}{102\underline{/-78.7°}}}$$

$$= \frac{10}{15 + j30 + 6.13\underline{/78.7^\circ}} = \frac{10}{15 + j30 + 1.202 + j6.01} = \frac{10}{16.2 + j36.0}$$

$$= \frac{10}{39.4\underline{/65.7^\circ}} = 0.254\underline{/-65.7^\circ} \text{ amps}$$

$$e_2 = j\omega L_1 i_1 = 25\underline{/90^\circ} \times 0.254\underline{/-65.7^\circ}$$

$$= 6.35\underline{/24.3^\circ}$$

$$i_2 = \frac{-j\omega M i_1}{R_2 + j\omega L_2 + R_3 + 1/j\omega C} = \frac{-j25 \times 0.254\underline{/-65.7^\circ}}{6.13\underline{/-78.7^\circ}}$$

$$= 1.04\underline{/-77.0^\circ}.$$

$$e_3 = j\omega L_2 i_2 = 100\underline{/90^\circ} \times 1.04\underline{/-77^\circ}$$

$$= 104\underline{/13^\circ}$$

$$e_4 = (R_3 + 1/j\omega C)i_2 = 200\underline{/-87.1^\circ} \times 1.04\underline{/-77.0^\circ}$$

$$= 208\underline{/-164.1^\circ}$$

## 4.42 MECHANICAL RECTILINEAL TRANSFORMERS

The rectilineal equivalent of an ideal electrical transformer is shown in Fig. 4.42-1. It is not a true analog because it holds only for very small displacements. For large displacements an appreciable departure from

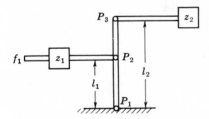

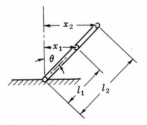

**Fig. 4.42-1** Ideal mechanical rectilineal transformer.

**Fig. 4.42-2** Pivot arm relationships.

rectilineal motion occurs. The transformer consists of a rigid rod with frictionless bearings at points $p_1$, $p_2$, and $p_3$. When a displacement of $p_2$ occurs a larger displacement of $p_3$ occurs. This fact can be illustrated by reference to Fig. 4.42-2. From this figure,

$$x_1 = l_1 \sin \theta \qquad (4.42\text{-}1)$$

$$x_2 = l_2 \sin \theta \qquad (4.42\text{-}2)$$

Therefore it follows that

$$\frac{x_1}{x_2} = \frac{l_1}{l_2} \qquad (4.42\text{-}3)$$

or

$$x_1 = \frac{l_1}{l_2} x_2 \qquad (4.42\text{-}4)$$

If $f_{p_2}$ is the force at $p_2$ and $f_{p_3}$ is the force at $p_3$, then

$$f_{p_2}\, dx_1 = f_{p_3}\, dx_2 \qquad (4.42\text{-}5)$$

since there is no energy lost or stored in the pivot arm. If we take the differential of both sides of Eq. (4.42-4) and substitute the result in Eq. (4.42-5), we can obtain

$$f_{p_2} = \frac{l_2}{l_1} f_{p_3} \qquad (4.42\text{-}6)$$

If the derivatives of both sides of Eq. (4.42-4) are taken with respect to time, the result is

$$\frac{dx_1}{dt} = \frac{l_1}{l_2} \frac{dx_2}{dt} \qquad (4.42\text{-}7)$$

or

$$v_1 = \frac{l_1}{l_2} v_2 \qquad (4.42\text{-}8)$$

If $l_1/l_2$ is defined as $a$, Eqs. (4.42-6) and (4.42-8) can be revised as

$$\frac{f_{p_3}}{f_{p_2}} = a \qquad (4.42\text{-}9)$$

and

$$\frac{v_2}{v_1} = \frac{1}{a} \qquad (4.42\text{-}10)$$

which are analogous to Eqs. (4.41-15) and (4.41-23) with the transformation ratio inverted.

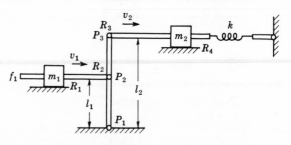

**Fig. 4.42-3** Rectilineal transformer configuration.

The only departure from the ideal rectilineal transformer which will be considered here is the presence of viscous friction at the pivot points. If it exists to an appreciable amount, it is simply added in with the series mechanical impedance in each leg of the pivot arm. Figure 4.42-3 shows a mechanical configuration with mechanical impedances in both legs as well as viscous friction at the pivot points. If $f_2$ is the force at $p_2$ and $f_3$ the force at $p_3$, the equations describing the configuration of Fig. 4.42-3 are

$$f_1 = m_1\dot{v}_1 + (R_1 + R_2)v_1 + f_2 \tag{4.42-11}$$

$$f_3 = m_2\dot{v}_2 + (R_3 + R_4)v_2 + k \int v_2 \, dt \tag{4.42-12}$$

$$f_3 = af_2 \tag{4.42-13}$$

$$v_2 = v_1/a \tag{4.42-14}$$

From Eqs. (4.42-12) and (4.42-13),

$$f_2 = \frac{1}{a}[m_2\dot{v}_2 + (R_3 + R_4)v_2 + k \int v_2 \, dt] \tag{4.42-15}$$

Using Eq. (4.42-14) in Eq. (4.42-15),

$$f_2 = \frac{1}{a^2}[m_2\dot{v}_1 + (R_3 + R_4)v_1 + k \int v_1 \, dt] \tag{4.42-16}$$

If $f_2$ as given by Eq. (4.42-16) is substituted in Eq. (4.42-11), the result is

$$f_1 = m_1\dot{v}_1 + (R_1 + R_2)v_1 + \frac{1}{a^2}[m_2\dot{v}_1 + (R_3 + R_4)v_1 + k \int v_1 \, dt] \tag{4.42-17}$$

If we take the transform of Eq. (4.42-17), assuming initial conditions are zero, we obtain

$$F_1 = (sm_1 + R_1 + R_2)V_1 + \frac{1}{a^2}\left[sm_2 + R_3 + R_4 + \frac{k}{s}\right]V_1 \tag{4.42-18}$$

If we now define the functions of $s$ as

$$z_1 = sm_1 + R_1 + R_2 \tag{4.42-19}$$

and

$$z_2 = sm_2 + R_3 + R_4 + \frac{k}{s} \tag{4.42-20}$$

and substitute them in Eq. (4.42-18), the result is

$$F_1 = z_1V_1 + \frac{z_2}{a^2}V_1 \tag{4.42-21}$$

If the forcing function $f_1$ is sinusoidal, $z_1$ and $z_2$ can be treated as rectilineal impedances and Eq. (4.42-21) becomes

$$f_1 = \left(z_1 + \frac{z_2}{a^2}\right) v_1 \tag{4.42-22}$$

or

$$v_1 = \frac{f_1}{z_1 + z_2/a^2} \tag{4.42-23}$$

Equation (4.42-23) indicates that the equivalent series impedance $z_2$ in the secondary of the rectilineal transformer is reflected into the primary multiplied by the factor $1/a^2$. From Eqs. (4.42-15) and (4.42-23),

$$v_2 = \frac{f_1/a}{z_1 + z_2/a^2} \tag{4.42-24}$$

or

$$v_2 = \frac{af_1}{a^2 z_1 + z_2} \tag{4.42-25}$$

EXAMPLE: The mechanical configuration of Fig. 4.42-4 has the following values:

$$m_1 = 50 \text{ lb-sec}^2/\text{ft}, \quad m_2 = 10 \text{ lb-sec}^2/\text{ft}, \quad m_3 = 10 \text{ lb-sec}^2/\text{ft}$$

$$k_1 = 100 \text{ lb/ft}, \quad k_2 = 10 \text{ lb/ft}, \quad R_3 = 10 \text{ lb-sec/ft}$$

$$R_1 = 20 \text{ lb-sec/ft}, \quad R_2 = 10 \text{ lb-sec/ft}, \quad f_1 = 1 \sin t$$

$$l_1 = 1 \text{ ft}, \quad l_2 = 2 \text{ ft}.$$

Find the velocities $v_0$, $v_1$, $v_2$, and $v_3$ and the forces $f_2$ and $f_3$.

To understand the configuration we will first draw an equivalent circuit for both the primary and secondary as shown in Fig. 4.42-5(a) and (b). The impedance $z_2$ is the equivalent series impedance at the terminals $a$-$b$ in the secondary. It is

$$z_2 = R_2 + j\omega m_2 + \frac{(R_3 + j\omega m_3) - jk/\omega}{R_3 + j\omega m_3 - jk/\omega}$$

$$= 10 + j10 + \frac{(10 + j10)(-j10)}{10 + j10 - j10} = 10 + j10 + 10 - j10$$

$$= 20$$

$$a = l_1/l_2 = \tfrac{1}{2}$$

$$\frac{z_2}{a^2} = \frac{20}{(\tfrac{1}{2})^2} = 80$$

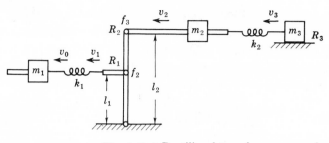

**Fig. 4.42-4** Rectilineal transformer example.

The impedance which $f_1$ sees is

$$z_0 = j\omega m_1 + \frac{\left(R_1 + \dfrac{z_2}{a^2}\right)\left(-j\dfrac{k_1}{\omega}\right)}{R_1 + \dfrac{z_2}{a^2} - j\dfrac{k_1}{\omega}} = j70.7 + \frac{(80 + 20)(-j100)}{80 + 20 - j100}$$

$$= j50 + \frac{100\ \underline{/-45°}}{\sqrt{2}} = j50 + 50 - j50 = 50$$

Then
$$v_0 = \frac{f_1}{z_0} = \tfrac{1}{50} = 0.02\underline{/0°}\ \text{ft/sec}$$

$$v_1 = \frac{v_0\left(-j\dfrac{k}{\omega}\right)}{R_1 + \dfrac{z_2}{a^2} - j\dfrac{k}{\omega}} = \frac{0.02(-j100)}{100 - j100} = \frac{0.02\underline{/-90°}}{\sqrt{2}\underline{/-45°}}$$

$$= 0.01414\underline{/-45°}\ \text{ft/sec}$$

Since $v_1$ is the velocity of the point $p_2$ on the lever arm and $v_2$ is the velocity of the point $p_3$,

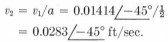

$$v_2 = v_1/a = 0.01414\underline{/-45°}/\tfrac{1}{2}$$
$$= 0.0283\underline{/-45°}\ \text{ft/sec}.$$

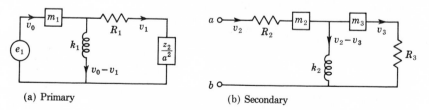

(a) Primary          (b) Secondary

**Fig. 4.42-5** Equivalent circuits of Fig. 4.42-4.

The force $f_3$ is equal to $v_2$ times the equivalent series impedance $z_2$, or

$$f_3 = v_2 z_2 = 0.0283 \underline{/-45°} \times 20\underline{/0°}$$
$$= 0.566 \ -45° \text{ lb}$$

The force $f_2$ is $(1/a)$ times $f_3$, or

$$f_2 = \frac{0.566 \ \underline{/-45°}}{\frac{1}{2}} = 1.13 \ \underline{/-45°} \text{ lb}$$

The velocity $v_3$ is

$$v_3 = v_2 \frac{-jk_2/\omega}{R_3 + j\omega m_3 - jk_2/\omega} = \frac{0.0283 \ \underline{/-45°} \times 10 \ \underline{/-90°}}{10 + j10 - j10}$$
$$= 0.0283 \underline{/-135°}$$

## 4.43  MECHANICAL ROTATIONAL TRANSFORMERS

Interlocking circular gears are rotational transformers. The diagram of Fig. 4.43-1 shows interlocking gears with shafts coupled to rotational loads. We will assume that the gears are inertialess, frictionless, perfectly

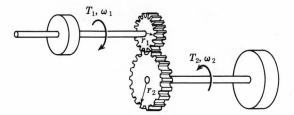

Fig. 4.43-1  Gear transformer.

rigid, and mesh perfectly. Under these conditions, the distance the meshing point moves along the circumferences of the two gears must be the same. For any circumferential distance $x$ moved, the following equation must be true:

$$r_1\theta_1 = x = r_2\theta_2 \tag{4.43-1}$$

Taking the derivative of both sides of Eq. (4.43-1), we get

$$r_1\omega_1 = r_2\omega_2 \tag{4.43-2}$$

or
$$\omega_2 = r_1\omega_1/r_2 \tag{4.43-3}$$

The angular velocities are inversely proportional to the ratio of the two radii. If we define the ratio of the radii as $a$, Eq. (4.43-3) becomes

$$\omega_2 = a\omega_1 \tag{4.43-4}$$

The torques at the shafts of the gears are transformed by the inverse ratio of the radii

$$T_2 = \frac{r_2}{r_1} T_1 \qquad (4.43\text{-}5)$$

or

$$T_2 = \frac{1}{a} T_1 \qquad (4.43\text{-}6)$$

Equations (4.43-4) and (4.43-5) can be used to show that the equivalent series rotational impedance at the secondary appears in the primary as

$$z_{1R} = a^2 z_2 \qquad (4.43\text{-}7)$$

Gear trains do not have the same mechanical limits as do the rectilineal transformers since they can continue to rotate without hitting a stop. Fluid transformers also have limit stops.

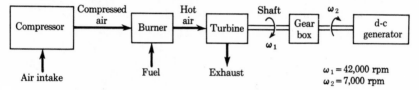

**Fig. 4.43-2** Simplified gas turbine.

As an example of a rotational transformer, let us consider the diagram of Fig. 4.43-2. It is a simplified gas turbine. Air at atmospheric pressure is drawn into the compressor chamber and compressed. The high-pressure air is then passed into a combustion chamber where it is heated. The hot air passes over the turbine blades and rotates the drive shaft. The drive shaft is connected to a load through a gear box with an angular velocity stepdown ratio of 7:1. The inertia of the primary drive shaft is 0.01 ft-lb-sec² and the rotational spring constant is 480 ft-lb/rad. The load on the secondary is 0.1 ft-lb-sec² and a d-c generator which develops an equiva-

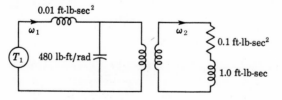

**Fig. 4.43-3** Electrical analog of gas turbine.

lent viscous friction of 1.0 ft-lb-sec. We would like to know what torque the hot air must exert at the turbine blades in order to maintain a steady angular velocity of 10 radians/second at the d-c motor.

Since the problem is analogous to a d-c problem in electrical engineering, the inertias and rotational spring constant do not affect the problem. The equivalent torque at the secondary is

$$T_2 = \omega_2 B = 10 \times 1.0 = 10 \text{ ft-lb}$$

According to Eq. (4.43-6),

$$T_1 = aT_2 = \tfrac{1}{7} \times 10 = 1.43 \text{ ft-lb}$$

which is the torque the hot air must supply at the turbine blades.

## 4.44 FLUID TRANSFORMERS

In both hydraulics and pneumatics, pistons act as the equivalent of transformers. Since the equations are identical for both liquid and gas systems, they will be treated as one. The methods for calculating some of the constants do differ as explained in Chap. 3.

Figure 4.44-1 shows a piston with areas $A_1$ and $A_2$. The force at $A_1$ must equal the force at $A_2$ since the piston is a rigid body. Since force is equal to pressure times area,

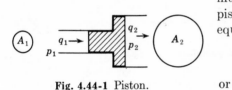

$$p_1 A_1 = p_2 A_2 \qquad (4.44\text{-}1)$$

**Fig. 4.44-1** Piston.         or

$$\frac{p_1}{p_2} = \frac{A_2}{A_1} \qquad (4.44\text{-}2)$$

The lineal velocity must be the same for both piston faces.

$$\frac{\Delta x_1}{\Delta t} = \frac{\Delta x_2}{\Delta t} \qquad (4.44\text{-}3)$$

Since the velocity is flow divided by area,

$$\frac{q_1}{A_1} = \frac{q_2}{A_2} \qquad (4.44\text{-}4)$$

or

$$\frac{q_1}{q_2} = \frac{A_1}{A_2} \qquad (4.44\text{-}5)$$

Equations (4.44-2) and (4.44-5) describe the basic transformer action of pistons. The pressures at the faces are inversely proportional to the areas, and the flows are directly proportional to the areas. If the ratio of areas is defined as

$$a = A_1/A_2 \qquad (4.44\text{-}6)$$

then

$$p_1/p_2 = 1/a \qquad (4.44\text{-}7)$$

and

$$q_1/q_2 = a \qquad (4.44\text{-}8)$$

The application of these equations is the same as for the analogous ones in the other systems.

EXAMPLE: A chemical process operates at a pressure of 25,000 psi. Small amounts of a certain chemical dissolved in benzene must be injected into the process. The large volume of the reactor is maintained automatically at a constant pressure, so the small amount of benzene has no effect on reactor pressure. The reactor can therefore be treated as the equivalent of a battery. Figure 4.44-2 shows a simplified diagram of the benzene

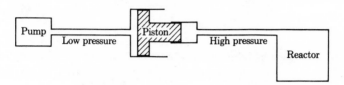

Fig. 4.44-2 Simplified benzene injection system.

injection system. Necessary valves have been omitted. On the high-pressure side the inertance of the line is $30 \times 10^5$ lb-sec$^2$/ft$^5$, the line capacitance is $48.8 \times 10^{-12}$ ft$^5$/lb, and the line resistance is $7.62 \times 10^7$ lb-sec/ft$^3$. The ratio of the piston areas $A_1/A_2$ is 100/1, where $A_1$ is the low-pressure side area and $A_2$ the high-pressure side. The piston moves at the rate of 10 strokes per second. We would like to know the impedance at 10 cps the high-pressure side reflects into the low-pressure side.

The first step is to draw the equivalent circuit. It is shown in Fig. 4.44-3. The high-pressure line is represented as a T-network, the process as a battery. Since we are interested in a-c impedance, the battery will not enter into the calculations although it does affect the values of the line elements because of its effect on total pressure.

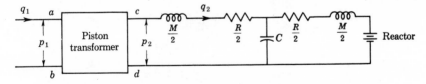

Fig. 4.44-3 Equivalent circuit of high pressure slide.

At the terminals $a$-$b$, the impedance $z_1$ is $p_1/q_1$ and at $c$-$d$ the impedance $z_2$ is $p_2/q_2$. From Eqs. (4.44-7) and (4.44-8), the ratio of $z_1$ to $z_2$ is

$$\frac{z_1}{z_2} = \frac{p_1/p_2}{q_1/q_2} = \frac{1/a}{a} \qquad (4.44\text{-}9)$$

or

$$z_1 = z_2/a^2 \qquad (4.44\text{-}10)$$

We must then calculate $z_2$ and divide by the square of the piston area ratio. $z_2$ is the impedance at 10 cps of the circuit of Fig. 4.44-4 looking into the terminals $c$-$d$.

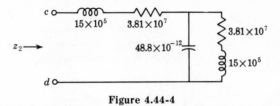

**Figure 4.44-4**

$$z_2 = \frac{(3.81 \times 10^7 + j6.28 \times 10 \times 15 \times 10^5)\,[-j/(6.28 \times 10 \times 48.8 \times 10^{-12})]}{3.81 \times 10^7 + j6.28 \times 10 \times 15 \times 10^5 - j/(6.28 \times 10 \times 48.8 \times 10^{-12})}$$
$$+\,3.81 \times 10^7 + j6.28 \times 10 \times 15 \times 10^5$$

$$= \frac{(3.81 \times 10^7 + j9.42 \times 10^7)(-j32.6 \times 10^7)}{3.81 \times 10^7 + j9.42 \times 10^7 - j32.6 \times 10^7} + 3.81 \times 10^7 + j9.42 \times 10^7$$

$$= \frac{10.16 \times 10^7 \underline{/68.0^\circ} \times 32.6 \times 10^7 \underline{/-90^\circ}}{3.81 \times 10^7 - j23.2 \times 10^7} + j3.81 \times 10^7 + j9.42 \times 10^7$$

$$= \frac{10.16 \times 10^7 \underline{/68.0^\circ} \times 32.6 \times 10^7 \underline{/-90^\circ}}{23.5 \times 10^7 \ \underline{-80.7^\circ}} + j3.81 \times 10^7 + j9.42 \times 10^7$$

$$= 14.08 \times 10^7 \underline{/58.7^\circ} + j3.81 \times 10^7 + j9.42 \times 10^7$$

$$= 7.30 \times 10^7 + j12.02 \times 10^7 + j3.81 \times 10^7 + j9.42 \times 10^7$$

$$= 11.11 \times 10^7 + j21.5 \times 10^7 = 24.2 \times 10^7 \underline{/62.7^\circ}$$

The impedance $z_1$ is $z_2/a^2$ or

$$z_1 = z_2/(100)^2 = 11.11 \times 10^3 + j21.5 \times 10^3$$

$$= 24.2 \times 10^3 \underline{/62.7^\circ}$$

To find the impedance presented to the pump the low-pressure line impedance would then be combined with the reflected impedance $z_1$.

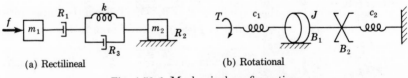

(a) Rectilineal                  (b) Rotational

**Fig. 4.50-1** Mechanical configurations.

## 4.50 PROBLEMS

1. Draw the equivalent circuits of the mechanical configurations shown in Fig. 4.50-1, write the describing equations from the equivalent circuits, and compare the results with those obtained from applying D'Alembert's principle to the original configurations.

2. The electric circuit shown in Fig. 4.50-2 is a compensating network used to introduce positive phase shift in control systems. Calculate the transfer function $e_2/e_1$ as a function of frequency. Plot the amplitude and phase response on a normalized basis.

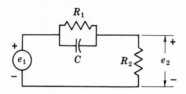

**Fig. 4.50-2** Lead network.

3. The mechanical configuration of Fig. 4.50-3(a) is a low-pass filter; that is, it transmits low frequencies with relatively little attenuation but provides a high attenuation for high frequencies. For a dashpot load as shown in Fig. 4.50-3(b) calculate $v_2(\omega)/f(\omega)$.

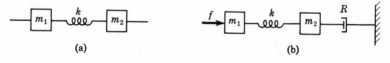

(a)                              (b)

**Fig. 4.50-3** Low-pass mechanical filter.

4. In the example given in Sec. 4.44, the low-pressure line has the following values:

$$R = 1.20 \times 10^4 \text{ lb-sec/ft}^5$$
$$M = 5 \times 10^2 \text{ lb-sec}^2/\text{ft}^5$$
$$C = 6 \times 10^{-9} \text{ ft}^5/\text{lb}$$

If the low-pressure line is represented as a T-network and the impedance reflected from the high side is

$$z_1 = 11.11 \times 10^3 + j21.5 \times 10^3 \text{ lb-sec/ft}^5$$

what is the impedance at the input to the line at 10 cps?

5. Design an electric model of the pressure device described in Sec. 3.75.

6. A radar antenna with a moment of inertia of 10 lb-ft-sec² is on a shaft with a spring constant of 3000 lb-ft/rad. The damping resistance is 1 lb-ft-sec. The antenna searches back and forth over 120°. It is to make a complete

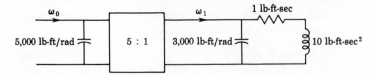

**Fig. 4.50-4** Equivalent circuit of radar antenna drive.

search cycle in 15 seconds. If it is coupled through gears with a stepdown ratio of 5:1 in angular velocity and the input shaft has a spring constant of 5000 lb-ft/rad, calculate the load on the driving motor. The equivalent circuit is shown in Fig. 4.50-4.

# CHAPTER FIVE

# BLOCK DIAGRAM ANALYSIS

## 5.00 INTRODUCTION

Block diagrams are useful tools in systems engineering. They have applications in both synthesis and analysis and, regardless of the particular use, help to illustrate graphically the system makeup and functional inter-relationships. This chapter will discuss the use of block diagrams for determining over-all transfer functions.

## 5.10 DETERMINATION OF OVER-ALL TRANSFER FUNCTIONS

When we wish to examine the behavior of a system, we ultimately must determine how some output varies with some input or disturbance. We want a mathematical expression directly relating the output to the input or the disturbance. One method for obtaining this expression is to define the system by its block diagram—and then to reduce the block diagram by standard techniques.

There are four basic arithmetic processes that can be described in the blocks: addition, subtraction, multiplication, and division. In practice this number is reduced to two by treating subtraction as negative addition and by treating division as multiplication by a reciprocal. In many cases the factors manipulated may represent operations but are manipulated as algebraic quantities. As explained in Chap. 2, for example, multiplication by $1/s$ in the Laplace domain represents integration in the time domain. The symbology of block diagrams is simple and straightforward, although it may be confusing at first glance to a believer in Kirchhoff's laws when he sees the same current shown branching off into several paths so that the sum of the currents leaving the point is greater than the sum of those entering. There is, of course, no contradiction or paradox but simply a difference in the meaning of the symbol. The first basic rule of block diagrams is that all signal flows are unidirectional. In this sense, a voltage, force, pressure, or any other physical quantity can flow. The reason for this rule is obvious from consideration of the block diagrams for Ohm's law or the special case of Newton's second law. The block diagrams of these laws are shown in Fig. 5.10-1. The

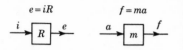

$$e = iR \qquad\qquad f = ma$$

arrows indicate the direction of flow, the box indicates that the quantity flowing into it (the box) is multiplied by the factor in the box to produce the quantity flowing out of the box. If the flow were not unidirectional, it would lead to the *untrue* statements that voltage times resistance equals current and force times mass equals acceleration. In these simple cases there is an obvious reciprocal relation that could be invoked, but in other cases involving operational factors rather than constants the reciprocal relation would not always hold true.

**Fig. 5.10-1** Block diagrams of Ohm's law and Newton's second law.

The preceding example illustrates the symbology of multiplication by simple quantities (no dynamics) as well as the unilateral flow in block diagrams. The same box with different symbols inside is used to represent operations. What the nomenclature means is that there is some functional relationship between the output and input. The functional relationship may or may not be known. In Fig. 5.10-2 are listed some typical relationships. They are given in both the time and Laplace domains.

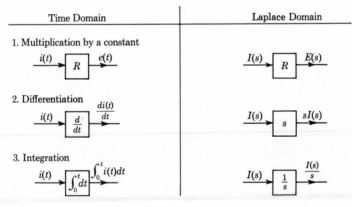

**Fig. 5.10-2** Block diagram operations.

The next symbol to illustrate is that for addition and subtraction. By convention the symbol for a summation point is a circle with an inscribed "X" as shown in Fig. 5.10-3(a), the block diagram for the division of current at a branch point. The equation implied by this diagram is $i_3 = i_1 - i_2$. A summation symbol can represent up to three inputs and one output. If more than three inputs are to be summed, two or more summation points are often used as in Fig. 5.10-3(b). A positive addition is implied unless the appropriate section of the circle is shaded to indicate a

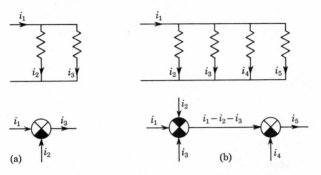

**Fig. 5.10-3** Examples of summation point symbology.

negative addition. As demonstrated it is the summation point by which we express Kirchhoff's law symbolically.

Another important symbol is that for pickoff points. The requirement for pickoff points arises when a quantity must be used in more than one place in a flow diagram. The basic rule for a pickoff point is that all lines

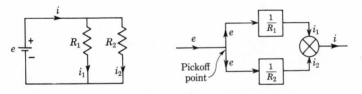

**Fig. 5.10-4** Illustration of pickoff point.

leaving a point carry the same quantity as the line entering the point. A pickoff point (and summation point) are shown in Fig. 5.10-4.

The last symbol to complete the basic building units of block diagrams is the multiplication point representing the product of two variables. Since the symbol "X" usually reserved for multiplication has been allocated to the summation point, we shall use an asterisk inside a circle to represent multiplication of variables. For example, instantaneous power can be expressed as the product of voltage and current as shown in Fig. 5.10-5. Since the Laplace operational calculus cannot handle products of

**Fig. 5.10-5** Symbol for multiplication of variables.

variables because this represents either a nonlinear system or a linear system with nonconstant coefficients, special methods must be used to linearize the product variable before the diagram can be represented in the Laplace domain. A common method is illustrated in this chapter under "Reduction Techniques," and it is covered more completely in Chap. 7.

## 5.20 BLOCK DIAGRAMS OF PHYSICAL SYSTEMS

Now that we have learned the rules and symbology of block diagrams, we must learn how to assemble them to describe physical systems. Let us first examine some common electric circuits. Figure 5.20-1 shows a

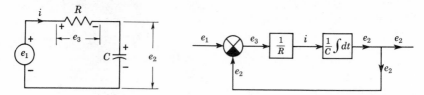

**Fig. 5.20-1** Series $R\text{-}C$ circuit and its block diagram.

series $R\text{-}C$ circuit with a voltage source $e_1$. The block diagram can be explained by considering that the summation symbol represents the equation

$$e_3 = e_1 - e_2 \tag{5.20-1}$$

The output from the summation point is then multiplied by $1/R$ to represent the equation

$$i = e_3/R \tag{5.20-2}$$

The current $i$ is then operated on by $\int dt$ and multiplied by $1/C$ to give the output voltage

$$e_2 = \frac{1}{C} \int i \, dt \tag{5.20-3}$$

Since the output voltage $e_2$ was used at the summation point to represent

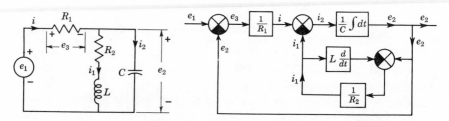

**Fig. 5.20-2** Series-parallel circuit and its block diagram.

Eq. (5.20-1), we must have a pickoff point after the integration block and draw a line back to the summation point. This line completes the block diagram.

A more complicated electric circuit is the series-parallel combination of Fig. 5.20-2. The first step in forming the block diagram is to note that

$$e_3 = e_2 - e_1 \qquad (5.20\text{-}4)$$

so we must have a summation point to represent the subtraction. The current $i$ is defined by

$$i = e_3/R_1 \qquad (5.20\text{-}5)$$

so a block to multiply $e_3$ by $1/R_1$ is indicated. At the parallel branch the current divides according to the equation

$$i_2 = i - i_1 \qquad (5.20\text{-}6)$$

so another summation point is required. If the current $i_2$ is now operated on by $(1/C) \int dt$, the result is $e_2$, and a block is drawn to represent this operation. The diagram is not yet complete because $e_2$ appears in two places and $i_1$ has simply been left dangling as an input to the second summation point. A pickoff point from $e_2$ back to the first summation is drawn because it is the same quantity. To complete the block diagram we now must observe that

$$i_1 = \frac{e_2 - L \dfrac{di_1}{dt}}{R_2} \qquad (5.20\text{-}7)$$

If we take a pickoff point from $i_1$ and operate on it with $L(d/dt)$ we have the second piece of the numerator of Eq. (5.11-7). This quantity subtracted from $e_2$ is the numerator, so a summation point with a plus for $e_2$ and a minus for $L(di_1/dt)$ is required to generate the numerator. An additional pickoff point for $e_2$ to the summation is required. If the output of this summation point is multiplied by $1/R_2$, the result is $i_1$ and it is the input line to the $i_1$ pickoff point. The diagram is now complete.

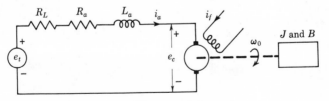

**Fig. 5.20-3** Diagram of d-c motor.

Physical systems which convert energy from one form to another present interesting examples of block diagrams because they contain multiple signal paths with different kinds of quantities in the various paths. Such a system is the d-c motor characterized by the diagram of Fig. 5.20-3.

In the diagram, the symbols have the following meanings: $e_t$, applied voltage, $R_L$, source resistance; $R_a$, armature winding resistance; $L_a$, armature winding inductance; $i_a$, armature current; $e_c$, motor back emf; $i_f$, motor field current; $\omega$, angular velocity of motor; $J$, motor moment of inertia; and $B$, motor viscous friction. If it is assumed that the field current is constant, the following equations describe the system behavior:

$$e_t = i_a(R_L + R_a) + L_a \frac{di_a}{dt} + e_c \qquad (5.20\text{-}8)$$

$$T = K_t i_a \qquad (5.20\text{-}9)$$

$$T = B\omega + \frac{1}{J} \int \omega \, dt \qquad (5.20\text{-}10)$$

$$e_c = K_c \omega \qquad (5.20\text{-}11)$$

where $T$ is the motor torque and $K_t$ and $K_c$ are constants of proportionality.

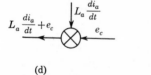

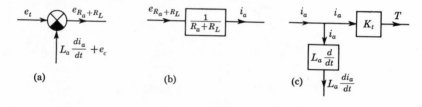

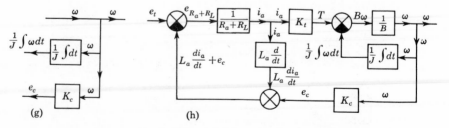

**Fig. 5.20-4** Synthesis of block diagram of d-c motor.

From Eq. (5.20-8) we see that we can at least start the block diagram with a summation point having $e_t$ and $-(L_a(di_a/dt) + e_c)$ as inputs as indicated in Fig. 5.20-4(a). The output of this summation is the voltage across $(R_a + R_L)$, so multiplication of this voltage by $1/(R_a + R_L)$ yields $i_a$ as shown in Fig. 5.20-4(b). $i_a$ is now needed in two places—to get the torque $T$ and to get the voltage across $L_a$; so a pickoff point is required as shown in Fig. 5.20-4(c). The quantity $L_a(di_a/dt)$ can now be added to $e_c$ at a summation point to produce that particular input to the first summation point. The torque $T$ is now run to a summation point and the quantity $(1/J) \int \omega\, dt$ subtracted from it, which according to Eq. (5.20-10) gives us $B\omega$. If we now multiply $B\omega$ by $1/B$ the output is $\omega$. A pickoff point is needed because $\omega$ must be integrated to get the torque component across the inertia and must be multiplied by $K_c$ to get the back emf. If all of the pieces are now fitted together, Fig. 5.20-4(h) results and gives the complete block diagram of the d-c motor with constant field current.

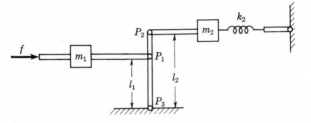

**Fig. 5.20-5** Mechanical transformer.

Let us next construct the block diagram of a mechanical rectilineal system. In Fig. 5.20-5 is shown the diagram of a mechanical system which is the analog of an ideal transformer. A force is applied to a mass-viscous friction combination which is coupled to a spring-mass-viscous friction combination. The coupling element is a perfectly rigid rod with zero mass and frictionless bearings at the pivot points $p_1$, $p_2$, and $p_3$. Actually there is some degree of curvilinear motion, but for small displacements the system can be treated as rectilineal. If we consider only the pivot arm as shown in Fig. 5.20-6, we see that the following relations are true:

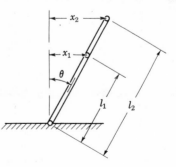

$$x_1 = l_1 \sin \theta$$
$$x_2 = l_2 \sin \theta$$
(5.20-12)

Therefore it follows that

$$x_1/x_2 = l_1/l_2 \qquad (5.20\text{-}13)$$

or

$$x_1 = (l_1/l_2)x_2 \qquad (5.20\text{-}14)$$

**Fig. 5.20-6** Pivot arm relationships.

If $f_1$ is defined as the force at $p_1$ and $f_2$ as the force at $p_2$, then

$$f_1\, dx_1 = f_2\, dx_2 \tag{5.20-15}$$

since there is no energy loss or storage in the lever arm. If the differential of both sides of Eq. (5.20-14) is taken the result is

$$dx_1 = \frac{l_1}{l_2}\, dx_2 \tag{5.20-16}$$

Substituting this expression for $dx_1$ in Eq. (5.20-15) and canceling the $dx_2$, we obtain

$$f_1 \frac{l_1}{l_2} = f_2 \tag{5.20-17}$$

Together with those in Eqs. (5.20-14) and (5.20-17), the following relations describe the system behavior:

$$f - m_1\ddot{x}_1 - R_1\dot{x}_1 \quad = f_1 \tag{5.20-18}$$

$$m_2\ddot{x}_2 + R_2\dot{x}_2 + k_2x_2 = f_2 \tag{5.20-19}$$

We can get our first step in formulating the block diagram from Eq. (5.20-18) by setting up a summation point with $f$ and $-(m_1\ddot{x}_1 + R_1\dot{x}_1)$ as inputs and $f_1$ as the output. This summation is shown in Fig. 5.20-7(a). By rearranging Eq. (5.20-19), we see that we can use $f_2$ and $-(m_2\ddot{x}_2 + R_2\dot{x}_2)$ as inputs to a summation point and get $k_2x_2$ as the output as shown in Fig. 5.20-7(c). If we now multiply $k_2x_2$ by $1/k_2$, the result is $x_2$. This operation is illustrated in Fig. 5.20-7(d). We need $x_2$ to obtain both $\dot{x}_2$ and $x_1$ as stated in Eq. (5.20-14), so a pickoff point with two operations performed is indicated in Fig. 5.20-7(e). Similarly in the next figure two operations are performed on $\dot{x}_2$ to obtain $\ddot{x}_2$ and $R_2\dot{x}_2$. In Fig. 5.20-7(g), $\ddot{x}_2$ is multiplied by $m_2$ and summed with $R_2\dot{x}_2$ to get the other input to the summation point of Fig. 5.20-7(c). We have now taken care of all dangling lines involving $x_2$ and its derivatives, so we must now go back to $x_1$ which was left hanging. In Fig. 5.20-7(h), $x_1$ is differentiated to get $\dot{x}_1$. Next $\dot{x}_1$ by virtue of a pickoff point is differentiated in one path and multiplied by $R_1$ in another. In Fig. 5.20-7(j), $\ddot{x}_1$ is multiplied by $m_1$, then summed with $(R_1\dot{x}_1)$ to produce $(m_1\ddot{x}_1 + R_1\dot{x}_1)$ which is also one of the inputs to the original summation. The loop is now complete. If we connect the lines identified by corresponding numbers in Figs. 5.20-7(a) through (j), we have the complete block diagram of Fig. 5.20-7(k).

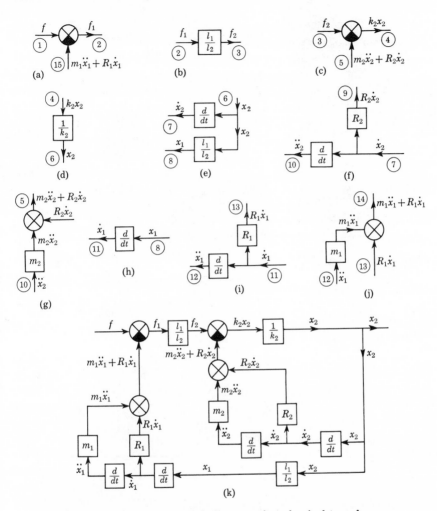

**Fig. 5.20-7** Synthesis of block diagram of mechanical transformer.

## 5.30 OPERATIONAL NOTATION IN BLOCK DIAGRAMS

In Fig. 5.10-2 are shown several equivalent blocks in the time and Laplace domains. Since we can in the Laplace domain treat differentiation as multiplication by the operator $s$ and integration as multiplication by the reciprocal of the operator $s$, it is usually more convenient to work in the Laplace domain rather than the time domain. The basic restrictions on the problems which can be represented in the Laplace domain are: (1) the system must be characterized by linear differential equations with constant coefficients and (2) all forcing functions must be Laplace transformable. There will be many systems that do not meet these criteria but can be represented by linear approximations that do. Let us examine

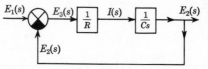

(a) Laplace domain diagram of Fig. 5.20-1

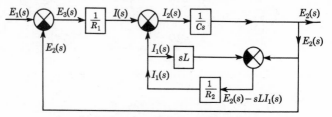

(b) Laplace domain diagram of Fig. 5.20-2

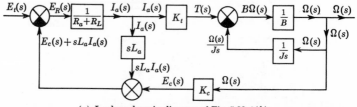

(c) Laplace domain diagram of Fig. 5.20-4(h)

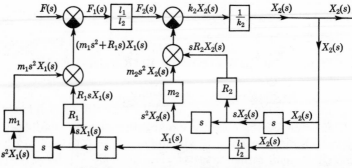

(d) Laplace domain diagram of Fig. 5.20-7(k)

Fig. 5.30-1 Block diagrams in Laplace domain.

the operational version of some of the block diagrams previously set up in the time domain.

The block diagram of Fig. 5.20-1 can be transformed to the Laplace domain by noting that multiplication by $1/s$ corresponds to integration in the time domain. The time-dependent variables are then represented as functions of $s$ as shown in Fig. 5.30-1(a). The other diagrams in Fig. 5.30-1 represent the Laplace versions of previously described diagrams in the time domain. In each case the time-varying quantities have been replaced by the appropriate function of $s$, differentiation with respect to $t$ has been replaced by multiplication by the operator $s$ and integration by $1/s$. *All initial conditions were assumed to be zero.* Had initial conditions other than zero existed, the block diagrams would have been different as explained in the next section.

## 5.31 NONZERO INITIAL CONDITIONS IN OPERATIONAL BLOCK DIAGRAMS

If we take the Laplace transform of each term in Eq. (5.20-19) and regroup the terms, the result is

$$X_2(s) = \frac{F_2(s)}{m_2 s^2 + R_2 s + k_2} + \frac{m_2 s x_2(0) + m_2 \dot{x}_2(0) + R_2 x_2(0)}{m_2 s^2 + R_2 s + k_2} \qquad (5.31\text{-}1)$$

If we choose to make the initial conditions described as $x_2(0)$ and $\dot{x}_2(0)$ both zero, then the operational block diagram of Fig. 5.31-1(a) results. If the initial conditions are not zero, the block diagram must be modified. The method for modifying it is indicated by the form of Eq. 5.31-1. The terms involving the initial conditions are multiplied by the same reciprocal relation as is $F_2(s)$, and the terms are in fact additive to it. This suggests a summation point with $F_2(s)$ and the terms containing the initial conditions as inputs to the operational box containing $1/(m_2 s^2 + R_2 s + k_2)$; so the diagram of Fig. 5.31-1(a) is revised as shown in Fig. 5.31-1(b). The

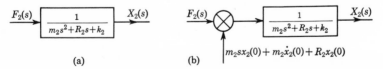

(a)                                    (b)

**Fig. 5.31-1** Operational block diagram with and without zero initial conditions.

initial conditions are equivalent mathematically to a disturbance in the system. If nonzero initial conditions must be used, it is advisable to write the time equations relating the output of a given operational block to its input, then to take the transformed equations and solve for the output in terms of the input and the initial conditions. For example, if the time equations describing the behavior of the circuit in Fig. 5.20-2 are transformed and $E_2(s)$ is solved for in terms of $E_1(s)$ and the initial conditions, the following equation results:

$$E_2(s) = E_1(s) \frac{sL + R_2}{R_1LCs^2 + (R_1R_2C + L)s + R_1 + R_2}$$
$$+ \frac{R_1Ce_2(0)(sL + R_2)}{R_1LCs^2 + (R_1R_2C + L)s + R_1 + R_2}$$
$$- \frac{R_1i_1(0)}{R_1LCs^2 + (R_1R_2C + L)s + R_1 + R_2} \qquad (5.31\text{-}2)$$

In order to use the two terms containing initial conditions as inputs to the box operating on $E_1(s)$, it is obviously necessary that they be operated on by the same function as $E_1(s)$. The factor $(sL + R_2)$ is missing from the numerator of the last term of Eq. (5.31-2) and so must be revised to include it. We can make the required inputs most clear by simply factoring out the multiplier of $E_1(s)$ as indicated in Eq. (5.31-3).

$$E_2(s) = \frac{sL + R_2}{R_1LCs^2 + (R_1R_2C + L)s + R_1 + R_2}$$
$$\times \left[ E_1(s) + R_1Ce_2(0) - \frac{R_1Li_1(0)}{sL + R_2} \right] \qquad (5.31\text{-}3)$$

The block diagram representing the circuit of Fig. 5.20-2 in the Laplace domain is shown in Fig. 5.31-2.

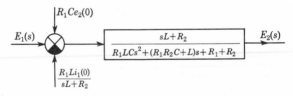

**Fig. 5.31-2** Block diagram of Eq. 5.31-3.

For many applications we can neglect initial conditions, and we usually omit them in analyzing linear systems with continuous forcing functions. When we analyze nonlinear systems for stability we must include initial conditions because some nonlinear systems can be stable or unstable depending on initial conditions. Stability of linear systems is independent of initial conditions. In predicting the time response of linear systems with discontinuous forcing functions we usually must carry the initial conditions. An example of a system which may be linear to a reasonable approximation but has a discontinuous input is a "bang-bang" missile control system. This is one in which commands are sent to the fins intermittently and the fins are, except for short transition times, either in the hardover position or in the neutral position. If a new command is sent during the transition period, the exact initial conditions must be considered to get the exact time response of the fins.

## 5.40  REDUCTION OF BLOCK DIAGRAMS

As mentioned earlier we usually are interested in how some output or dependent parameter varies with some input or independent parameter. The input may be either a forcing function or a disturbance. In terms of block diagrams this desired relationship, called the *transfer function*, is expressed by having only a single block between the input and the output. The transfer function can be derived by solving the system equations or it can be obtained by reducing the block diagram. It is the purpose of this section to illustrate the rules for manipulating block diagrams. An early developer of these rules was T. D. Graybeal.*

*Rule 1 Superposition.* The principle of superposition applies to linear systems, so the response to a given forcing function or disturbance can be obtained by assuming all other forcing functions or disturbances to be zero. The output is then the summation of the responses to the individual forcing functions and disturbances.

EXAMPLE

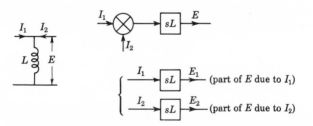

---

* T. D. Graybeal, "Transformation of Block Diagram Networks," AIEE Paper No. 51-298.

*Rule 2 Combination of cascaded elements.* Cascaded elements can be combined by multiplying them together. In the process the identity of the parameter between the two elements is lost.

EXAMPLE

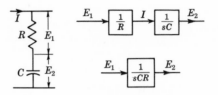

Note that the identity of $I$ has been lost.

*Rule 3 Interchange of cascaded elements.* Cascaded elements can be interchanged without affecting the input and output parameters but the parameter between the two elements is changed.

EXAMPLE

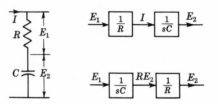

Note that $I$ is no longer the parameter between elements.

*Rule 4 Moving element forward past summation.* An element can be moved past a summation in the direction of flow provided the reciprocal of the element is inserted in each leg of the other inputs to the summation.

EXAMPLE

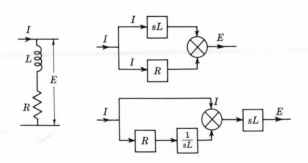

*Rule 5 Moving element backward past summation.* An element can be moved past a summation against the direction of flow provided it is inserted in every leg that represents an input to the summation.

EXAMPLE

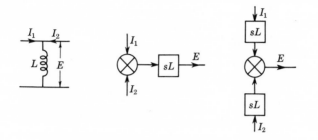

*Rule 6 Interchange of summation points.* Summation points with no element or pickoff point between them can be interchanged. In so doing the quantity flowing between the summation points is changed.

EXAMPLE

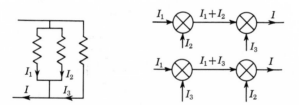

*Rule 7 Combination of summation points.* Summation points with no element or pickoff point between them can be combined. In the process the quantity flowing between them is lost as an identity.

EXAMPLE

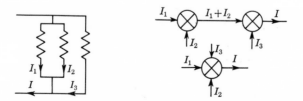

*Rule 8  Moving element forward past pickoff point.* An element can be moved forward past a pickoff point provided it is placed in each branch leading away from the pickoff point.

EXAMPLE

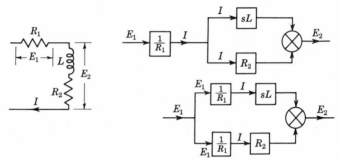

*Rule 9  Moving element backward past a pickoff point.* An element can be moved backward past a pickoff point provided its reciprocal is inserted in all branches other than the one it originated in.

EXAMPLE

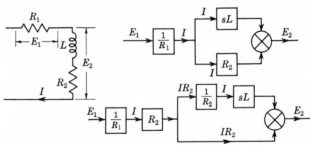

*Rule 10  Moving a summation point forward past a pickoff point.* A summation point can be moved forward past a pickoff point by inserting the summation point in all branches leaving the pickoff point.

EXAMPLE

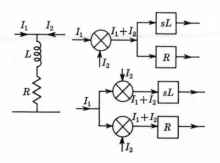

*Rule 11 Moving a summation point backward past a pickoff point.* A summation point can be moved backwards past a pickoff point provided a new summation point removing the extra parameters is introduced into all legs leaving the pickoff point except the leg originally containing the summation point.

EXAMPLE

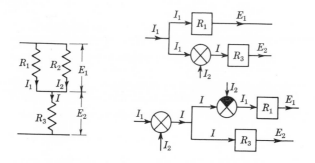

*Rule 12 Combination of parallel paths.* Parallel paths containing no pickoff points or summations between a pickoff point and a summation point can be combined into a single path whose element is the sum of the elements in the individual paths.

EXAMPLE

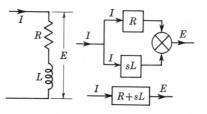

*Rule 13 Removal of feedback loop.* A feedback loop with forward transfer function $F_1(s)$ and feedback transfer function $F_2(s)$ can be replaced by a single element equal to $F_1(s)/[1 \mp F_1(s)F_2(s)]$. The minus sign is used when the feedback is additive, the plus sign when the feedback is subtractive.

Special cases, sometimes listed separately, occur when either $F_1(s)$ or $F_2(s)$ is equal to one.

EXAMPLES

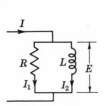

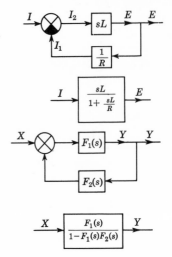

Note: No passive circuit will produce the conditions for the diagram at the right

*Rule 14 Replacing element with feedback loop.* (Inverse of Rule 14.) An element with transfer function $F_1(s)$ can be replaced by a feedback loop with forward element equal to $F_1(s)/[1 - F_1(s)]$ and feedback element equal to one. That this is true can be shown by performing the inverse operation by Rule 13.

EXAMPLE

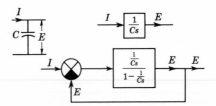

*Rule 15 Replacing multiplication point for small signal variation.* A multiplication point can be replaced by a summation point when the two variables change only a small amount around their nominal values by working only with the incremental values. If $z(t)$ is the product of $x(t)$ and $y(t)$, and $x_0$ and $y_0$ are the nominal values of $x$ and $y$, then the product of the two independent parameters can be written as $(x_0 + \Delta x)(y_0 + \Delta y)$ which is equal to $(x_0 y_0 + x_0\,\Delta y + y_0\,\Delta x + \Delta x\,\Delta y)$. We can immediately discard the term $(\Delta x\,\Delta y)$ because it is a second-order increment. When we are interested only in the dynamics of the system, we can discard the

term $x_0 y_0$ and define new variables $\Delta x$ and $\Delta y$ representing the variations around the nominal value. The multiplication point can then be replaced by a summation with $\Delta x y_0$ and $\Delta y x_0$ as inputs. The transform is then taken of the incremental values. The linearization must be made in the time domain, so the block diagrams in the example are given for both the time and Laplace domains.

EXAMPLE

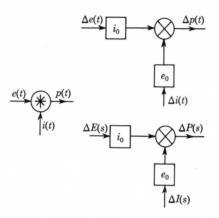

## 5.41 EXAMPLES OF BLOCK DIAGRAM REDUCTION

The rules for reducing block diagrams have been covered, but the examples given involved only one rule each. We will now examine some diagrams which involve increasingly more steps in the reduction process. As our first example, let us take the circuit of Fig. 5.20-1 whose block

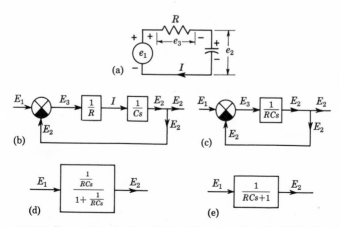

Fig. 5.41-1 Steps in reducing block diagram of series $R$-$C$ circuit.

diagram in the Laplace domain is shown in Fig. 5.30-1(a). Both figures are repeated in Fig. 5.41-1 so that the step-by-step procedure will be clear without having to refer back to other figures. We first invoke the rule for combining cascaded elements (Rule 2) and in so doing reduce the diagram to that shown in Fig. 5.41-1(c). This diagram now represents a simple feedback loop with $F_1(s)$ equal to $1/RCs$ and $F_2(s)$ equal to one. According to Rule 13 for removing a feedback loop, the single element relating $E_2$ to $E_1$ is equal to $(1/RCs)/(1 + 1/RCs)$ as shown in Fig. 5.41-1(d).

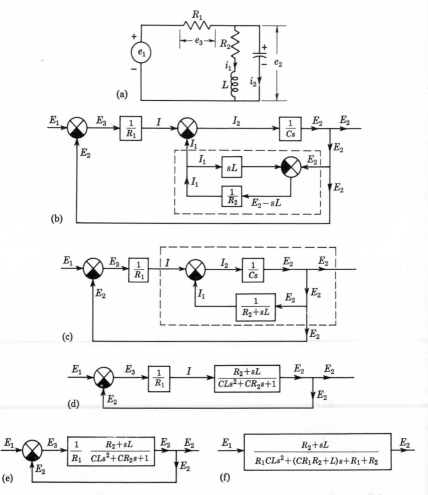

**Fig. 5.41-2** Steps in reducing block diagram of series-parallel circuit.

Since the transfer function is more usable when the numerator and denominator are cleared of fractions, the form of the transfer function in Fig. 5.41-1(e) represents standard practice.

A more complicated block diagram describes the series-parallel circuit of Fig. 5.20-2. The steps in reducing it are shown in Fig. 5.41-2. Examination of the portion of Fig. 5.41-2(b) enclosed in the dotted lines shows that it is a feedback loop with $E_2$ as the input, $I_1$ as the output, $1/R_2$ as $F_1(s)$ and $(sL)$ as $F_2(s)$. Our first step then is to apply Rule 13 for removal of a feedback loop and clear of fractions. The result is shown in Fig. 5.41-2(c). Again we can enclose a feedback loop, this time with $I$ as the input, $E_2$ as the output, $1/Cs$ as $F_1(s)$, and $1/(R_2 + sL)$ as $F_2(s)$. If we again apply Rule 13 and clear of fractions, we get the diagram of Fig. 5.41-2(d). In the forward loop two elements are cascaded, so by Rule 2 for combining cascaded elements we get the diagram of Fig. 5.41-2(e). Since this is a single feedback loop, we now make the last step of applying Rule 13 and clearing of fractions to get the composite transfer function relating $E_2$ to $E_1$. Comparison of the transfer function in Fig. 5.41-2(f) with the first term of Eq. (5.31-2) shows that solution of the circuit equations and reduction of the block diagram do indeed give the same answer when initial conditions are the same, in this case zero.

## 5.50 REDUCTION OF THERMISTOR BRIDGE BLOCK DIAGRAM

We have discussed several simple examples of block diagram reduction in which manipulation of the equations was perhaps easier than going through the steps of block diagram reduction. We will now discuss a problem in which the comparison is less in favor of manipulating the equations. Furthermore, the illustrative problem is one that indicates the types of answers we may be seeking in applying these techniques.

The circuit of Fig. 5.50-1 is part of a temperature control system. The portion shown is a thermistor bridge which has an output proportional to the temperature to be controlled, the setpoint bridge which has an output proportional to the temperature to be maintained by the controller, and the mixing network which combines the outputs of the two

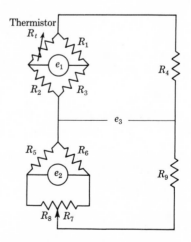

**Fig. 5.50-1** Thermistor bridge circuit diagram.

bridges to produce a signal proportional to the temperature error. Fig. 5.50-2 shows the block diagram of the circuit. The block diagram describes a nonlinear system as indicated by the multiplication points. In addition,

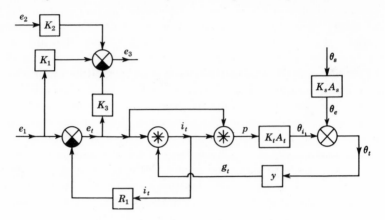

**Fig. 5.50-2** Block diagram of thermistor bridge circuit.

the function $y$, which relates thermistor conductance to temperature, is nonlinear. The following equations apply to or are implied by the block diagram:

$$e_3 = K_1e_1 - K_2e_2 - K_3e_t \tag{5.50-1}$$

$$e_t = e_1 - i_tR_1 \tag{5.50-2}$$

$$i_t = e_tg_t \tag{5.50-3}$$

$$p = e_ti_t \tag{5.50-4}$$

$$\theta_i = K_tA_ip \tag{5.50-5}$$

$$\theta_e = K_sA_s\theta_s \tag{5.50-6}$$

$$\theta_t = \theta_i + \theta_e \tag{5.50-7}$$

$$g_t = y(\theta_t) \tag{5.50-8}$$

where $e_1$ is the thermistor bridge supply voltage

$e_2$ is the setpoint bridge supply voltage

$e_3$ is the output voltage proportional to temperature error

$K_1$ is a network constant equal to $R_2R_9/[(R_2 + R_3)(R_4 + R_9)]$

$K_2$ is a network constant equal to $[R_4/(R_4 + R_9)]\{[R_5/(R_5 + R_6)]$
$- [R_8/(R_7 + R_8)]\}$

$K_3$ is a network constant equal to $R_9/(R_4 + R_9)$

$e_t$ is the thermistor voltage

$i_t$ is the thermistor current

$g_t$ is the thermistor conductance

$p$ is the thermistor power dissipation

$K_tA_t$ is the transfer function relating thermistor temperature to power dissipation

$K_sA_s$ is the transfer function relating thermistor temperature to external temperature

$\theta_s$ is the process temperature which is to be controlled

$\theta_i$ is the component of thermistor temperature due to internal heating

$\theta_e$ is the component of thermistor temperature due to external heating

$\theta_t$ is the total thermistor temperature

$y$ is the function relating thermistor conductance to temperature

It has been assumed that the mixing network does not load the bridges and that the bridges are isolated from each other.

We are interested primarily in two transfer functions: $e_3/\theta_s$, the sensitivity to changes in the controlled temperature, and $e_3/e_1$, the sensitivity to changes in the supply voltage. The ratio $e_3/\theta_s$ influences the design of the rest of the control system. For example, the required amplification in the controller will depend on this sensitivity, how accurately temperature is to be controlled, and other considerations. Changes in the supply voltage $e_1$ represent disturbances, and the function $e_3/e_1$ together with $e_3/\theta_s$ can be used to determine the degree of regulation necessary for the power source to introduce negligible disturbances.

The first step in reducing the block diagram of Fig. 5.50-2 is to linearize it. We have two multiplication points which can be replaced with summation points by applying Rule 15 of Sec. 5.40. If we apply this rule to Eq. (5.50-3), the result is

$$\Delta i_t = \Delta e_t g_{t_0} + \Delta g_t e_{t_0} \quad (5.50\text{-}9)$$

The same rule applied to Eq. (5.50-4) results in

$$\Delta p = \Delta e_t i'_{t_0} + \Delta i_t e_{t_0} \quad (5.50\text{-}10)$$

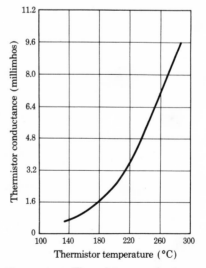

**Fig. 5.50-3** Thermistor conductance *vs.* temperature.

The other function which must be linearized is thermistor conductance, which is a nonlinear function of thermistor temperature. Since we will be concerned only with incremental quantities once we apply Eqs. (5.50-9)

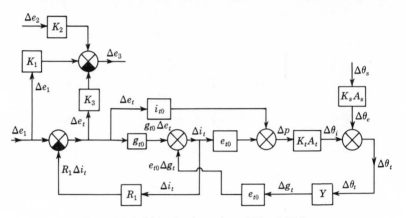

Fig. **5.50-4** Linearized version of Fig. 5.50-2.

and (5.50-10), we can replace $g_t$ by its incremental value by making the multiplier in the box relating $\Delta g_t$ to $\Delta \theta_t$ simply the slope at the static operating point. A curve of thermistor conductance versus temperature is shown in Fig. 5.50-3. In Fig. 5.50-4 is shown the linearized version of the block diagram of Fig. 5.50-2. We next transform to the Laplace domain as denoted by the upper-case letters in Fig. 5.50-5. The diagram could not be transformed before it was linearized.

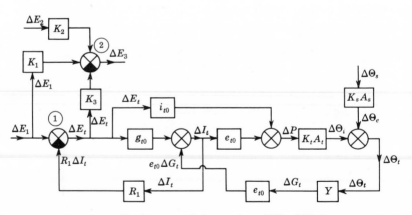

Fig. **5.50-5** Laplace transform version of Fig. 5.50-4.

Let us now go through the steps to determine the transfer function $\Delta E_3 / \Delta \theta_t$. Since the diagram has been made linear, the principle of superposition holds. We then make our first reduction by assuming that both

$\Delta E_1$ and $\Delta E_2$ are zero. When we make this assumption the summation points denoted by the numbers ① and ② in Fig. 5.50-5 become meaningless because each has only one input. However, we must note that in both cases the remaining input is subtracted, so we must introduce a

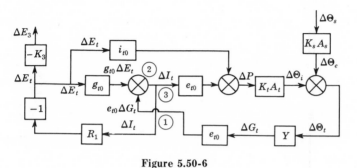

**Figure 5.50-6**

block containing $-1$ in both signal paths when we eliminate the meaningless summation points. In one case it is combined with $K_3$. The result is illustrated in Fig. 5.50-6.

The next thing we would like to do to make the diagram appear more normal is to eliminate the nonconnected crossover line at point ① of Fig. 5.50-6. We can accomplish this by applying Rule 10 for moving a summation point forward past a pickoff point. The summation point is indicated by ② and the pickoff point by ③ in Fig. 5.50-6. Application of Rule 10 results in the diagram of Fig. 5.50-7. Note that we now have two summation points (tagged as ① and ②) with $g_{t_0} \Delta E_t$ and $e_{t_0} \Delta G_t$ as inputs and with $\Delta I_t$ as the output.

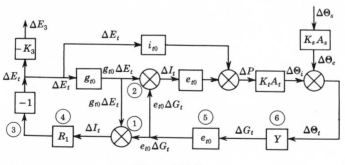

**Figure 5.50-7**

The next simplifications are perhaps the easiest. We can combine two sets of cascaded elements marked as ③ and ④ and ⑤ and ⑥ in Fig. 5.50-7. We will now perform two operations on the diagram of Fig. 5.50-8. The element $g_{t_0}$ denoted by ① will be moved backward past the pickoff point ② according to Rule 9, and the element $e_{t_0}$ denoted by ③ will be moved forward past the summation point ④ according to Rule 4. Since both of these operations introduce an element into the branch containing $i_{t_0}$ marked ⑤, they are immediately combined as cascaded elements. The revised diagram is shown in Fig. 5.50-9.

The element at point ① of Fig. 5.50-9 is equal to $i_{t_0}/(g_{t_0}e_{t_0})$. Since the product $g_{t_0}e_{t_0}$ is $i_{t_0}$, the element is simply equal to 1. This change is shown

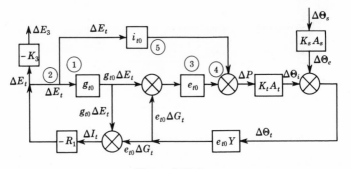

Figure 5.50-8

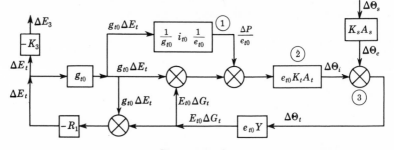

Figure 5.50-9

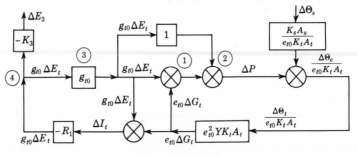

Figure 5.50-10

in Fig. 5.50-10. A second change that appears in this figure results from having moved the element marked ② in Fig. 5.50-9 forward past the summation point marked ③. This operation is performed under Rule 4.

In Fig. 5.50-10 we can combine summation points numbered ① and ② by application of Rule 7. At the same time to get to Fig. 5.50-11 we

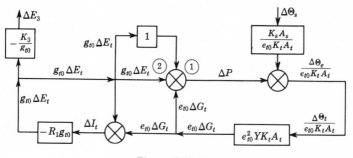

**Figure 5.50-11**

apply Rule 9 and move the element $g_{t_0}$ marked ③ backward past the pickoff point numbered ④ in Fig. 5.50-10. We next observe that the summation point with inputs ① and ② can be simplified because they represent simple parallel paths. In this case the multiplier in each path is 1, so the combination of the two parallel paths gives a sum equal to 2 as shown in Fig. 5.50-12.

To clarify the next step in our reduction process we redraw Fig. 5.50-12 by simply moving the pickoff point at ① over to point ②. We can make

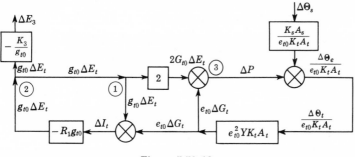

**Figure 5.50-12**

this shift since the same quantities flow in both places. At the same time we can combine the summation points numbered ③ and ④ by applying Rule 7. The result of these changes is shown in Fig. 5.50-13. We now observe that loop number ① is a feedback loop with an input of $e_{t_0} \Delta G_t$, an output of $g_{t_0} \Delta E_t$, a forward gain of $-R_1 g_{t_0}$ and unity feedback. The

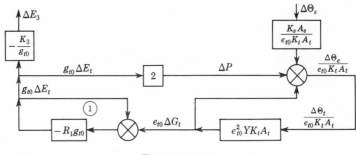

**Figure 5.50-13**

loop can be eliminated by applying Rule 13 and the diagram of Fig. 5.50-14 results.

We can now use the same rule to eliminate the feedback loop numbered ① in Fig. 5.50-14. The inputs are $\Delta P$ and $\Delta\Theta_e/(e_{t_0}K_tA_t)$, the output is

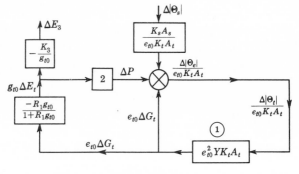

**Figure 5.50-14**

$e_{t_0}\Delta G_t$, the forward loop gain is $e_{t_0}^2 YK_tA_t$, and the feedback gain is unity. The revised diagram is shown in Fig. 5.50-15. We are now down to a relatively simple diagram consisting of one feedback loop containing two

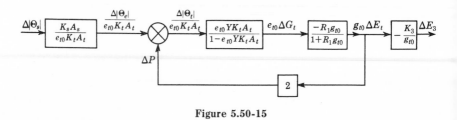

**Figure 5.50-15**

cascaded elements in the forward loop and a feedback gain of 2. If we eliminate this feedback loop after combining the cascaded elements in the

**Figure 5.50-16**

forward path, we get the diagram of Fig. 5.50-16 which contains only elements in cascade. When we combine these elements in cascade and simplify we have the transfer function $\Delta E_3/\Delta\Theta_s$ as shown in Fig. 5.50-17.

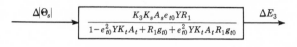

**Figure 5.50-17**

## 5.51 NUMERICAL EXAMPLE OF THERMISTOR BRIDGE SENSITIVITY

Now that we have derived the transfer function relating the change in output voltage $\Delta E_3$ to the change in process temperature $\Delta\Theta_s$, let us examine its meaning in a specific numerical example. We will take an actual set of values of parameters in the transfer function $\Delta E_3/\Delta\Theta_s$ to calculate the static sensitivity. The block diagram of Fig. 5.50-17 states that the transfer function is

$$\frac{\Delta E_3}{\Delta\Theta_s} = \frac{K_3 K_s A_s e_{t_0} Y R_1}{1 - e_{t_0}^2 Y K_t A_t + R_1 g_{t_0} + e_{t_0}^2 Y K_t A_t R_1 g_{t_0}} \tag{5.51-1}$$

The values of the resistances of Fig. 5.50-1 required to calculate $K_1^*$ and $K_3$ as defined after Eq. (5.50-8) and $\Delta E_3/\Delta\Theta_s$ are as follows:

$$R_1 = 124\ \Omega, \qquad R_2 = 16.3\ \Omega, \qquad R_3 = 8.5\ \Omega$$

$$R_4 = 9750\ \Omega, \qquad R_9 = 17{,}000\ \Omega$$

The values of $K_1$ and $K_3$ resulting from these resistances are respectively 0.417 and 0.636. The value of $Y$ was obtained from the slope of the curve shown in Fig. 5.50-3 at a static operating point of 225°C. The slope at that point is 77 $\mu$mho/°C. The value of $g_{t_0}$ is 4.22 millimhos. The static operating voltage $e_{t_0}$ was measured as 3.48 volts.

For the static case the function $K_s A_s$ was assumed to equal one. This assumption implies that the thermistor puts a completely negligible heat load on the process and that after a long enough period of time the thermistor would reach the process temperature if there were no internal

---

* $K_1$ does not appear in $\Delta E_3/\Delta\Theta_s$.

heating. The value of $K_t$ was assumed to be the ratio of the temperature gradient across the glass of the thermistor to the heat flowing through the glass; i.e.,

$$K_t = \frac{\Delta\theta}{q} = \frac{\Delta x}{kA} \tag{5.51-2}$$

where $\Delta\theta$ is the temperature drop across the glass covering the thermistor element, $q$ is the power input to the thermistor, $\Delta x$ is the thickness of the glass enclosing the thermistor element, $k$ is the thermal conductivity of the glass, and $A$ is the effective area of the glass. For the particular thermistor used $K_t$ was calculated to be 43.0°C/watt. $A_t$ was assumed to equal 1 for the static case. To summarize the values of the parameters to be used in Eq. (5.51-1), they are repeated below:

$$e_{t_0} = 3.48 \text{ v}, \qquad Y = 77 \times 10^{-6} \text{ mhos/°C},$$

$$K_3 = 0.636, \qquad R_1 = 124 \ \Omega$$

$$K_s G_s = 1°C/°C, \quad g_{t_0} = 4.22 \times 10^{-3} \text{ mhos},$$

$$K_t = 43.0°C/w, \quad G_t = 1$$

If we substitute these values in Eq. (5.51-1), we find that the static sensitivity $\Delta E_3/\Delta\Theta_s$ is 14.1 millivolts/°C.

Let us now examine the specific effect of internal heating. If we let $K_t A_t$ equal zero, we assume that internal heating has no effect. Under this assumption Eq. (5.51-1) becomes

$$\frac{\Delta E_3}{\Delta\Theta_s} = \frac{K_3 K_s A_s e_{t_0} Y R_1}{1 + R_1 g_{t_0}} \tag{5.51-3}$$

If we substitute the same numerical values of the parameters in Eq. (5.51-3), we get 13.9 millivolts/°C as the static sensitivity. The two values of static sensitivities are within the accuracy of the calculations, so the more complicated expression of Eq. (5.51-1) is not justified. The value of $K_t$ can be used, however, to estimate the error in temperature level introduced by the internal heating of the thermistor. With $e_{t_0}$ equal to 3.48 volts and $g_{t_0}$ equal to 4.22 millimhos, the power dissipation is about 0.05 watts. For $K_t$ equal to 43.0°C/watt, this power dissipation corresponds to about 2°C error in temperature level. Since the heat capacity of the thermistor is small, the value of $A_t$ would have little effect at low frequencies.

## 5.60 PROBLEMS

1. Draw the block diagram of the mechanical system shown in Fig. 5.60-1.

2. By reducing the block diagram of Fig. 5.30-1(c), find the transfer function $\Omega(s)/E_t(s)$.

3. By reducing the block diagram of Fig. 5.30-1(d), find the transfer function $X_2(s)/F(s)$.

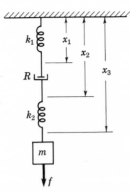

**Fig. 5.60-1** Mechanical system.

4. Write the equations for the rotational system of Fig. 5.60-2, transform them, and draw the block diagram of the system including initial conditions.

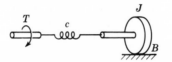

**Fig. 5.60-2** Rotational system.

5. By reducing the block diagram of Fig. 5.50-5 under the assumptions that $\Delta E_2$ and $\Delta \Theta_s$ are zero, show that the transfer function $\Delta E_3/\Delta E_1$ is

$$\frac{\Delta E_3}{\Delta E_1} = K_1 - \frac{K_3}{1 + R_1 g_{t_0} \dfrac{1 + e_{t_0}^2 Y K_t A_t}{1 - e_{t_0}^2 Y K_t A_t}} \qquad (5.60\text{-}1)$$

6. (a) Using the numerical values given in Sec. 5.51, calculate the static sensitivity for $\Delta E_3/\Delta E_1$.

   (b) Using the static sensitivity for $\Delta E_3/\Delta \Theta_s$ calculated in Sec. 5.51 and the static sensitivity for $\Delta E_3/\Delta E_1$ from (a) above, calculate the regulation required to keep the power supply $e_1$ from causing no more than 0.01°C error.

   (c) Calculate the static sensitivity $\Delta E_3/\Delta E_1$ neglecting thermistor internal heating effects and compare with the results of (a) above.

# CHAPTER SIX

# CONTROL SYSTEMS

## 6.00 DEFINITION OF A CONTROL SYSTEM

A logical definition of a control system can be derived from a physical system as shown in Fig. 6.00-1. Here in schematic form is shown the action of a man steering a ship. A compass indicates the difference between the desired heading and the actual heading. The helmsman positions the rudder an amount proportional to this difference. The force of the water against the rudder produces a turning moment that causes the ship to

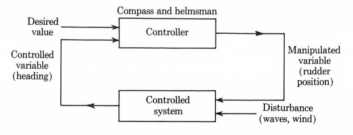

**Fig. 6.00-1** A typical control system.

rotate. The wind acts as a restraining force to prevent this action. As the ship rotates, the heading is altered and the helmsman starts the cycle again by changing the rudder position. This simple system contains all the elements of a control system and will now serve as a model for our development.

In Chaps. 2 and 5 the reader was introduced to two powerful tools for the system engineer, the Laplace transform and block diagrams. By these two tools any physical system which can be characterized by a set of linear differential equations with constant coefficients can be represented as in Fig. 6.00-2 by a block containing a constant $K$ and a function $G(s)$ which is the ratio of two polynomials in $s$.

Now let us return to our system in Fig. 6.00-1. The difference between the desired heading and actual heading as measured by the compass can be represented by a summer as in Fig. 6.00-3. The input to the summer

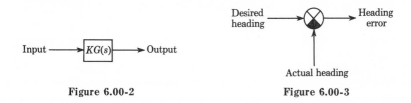

Figure 6.00-2                                                Figure 6.00-3

due to the actual heading is negative. This shows that the helmsman must know the phase of the heading error as well as the magnitude and must position the rudder in an opposite phase to that of the error. The relationship among heading error, rudder position, and turning moment can be represented by a differential equation and hence a ratio of two polynomials in $s$. Thus the block diagram now becomes as shown in Fig. 6.00-4.

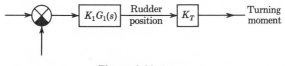

Figure 6.00-4

Since the wind acts as a retarding force, the total turning moment applied to the ship is the difference between these two moments. The relationship between the heading and turning moment can also be described by a differential equation, and hence the final block diagram of the system has the form as shown in Fig. 6.00-5.

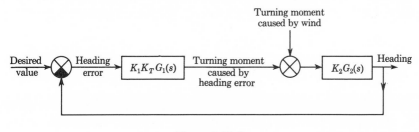

Figure 6.00-5

It is the presence of the error that distinguishes our definition of a control system: "a control system is one in which the manipulated variable is actuated in response to some linear function of the difference between the controlled variable and some desired value."

With the disturbance constant, the response of the system to a change in the desired value is termed the *servo response* and the system is said to be a *servomechanism*. With the desired value constant, the response of the system to a change in the disturbance is termed the *regulator response* and the system is said to be a *regulator*. Most systems act as both a regulator and servomechanism, and a compromise must be made in designing both responses.

## 6.10 ELEMENTS OF A CONTROL SYSTEM

It is usual to represent a control system by the block diagram and terminology as shown in Fig. 6.10-1. Since the feedback to the summer is negative, this system is said to have *negative feedback*. The ratio $\dfrac{C}{E}$ $(s)$ is termed the *open loop response*. It can be related to the *closed loop response* $\dfrac{C}{R}$ $(s)$ as follows:

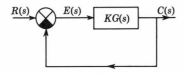

**Fig. 6.10-1** A system with negative feedback.

$$\frac{C}{E}(s) = KG(s) \qquad (6.10\text{-}1)$$

But

$$E(s) = R(s) - C(s) \qquad (6.10\text{-}2)$$

Hence

$$\frac{C}{R-C}(s) = KG(s) \qquad (6.10\text{-}3)$$

and

$$\frac{C}{R}(s) = \frac{KG(s)}{1 + KG(s)} \qquad (6.10\text{-}4)$$

Now in general the open loop response $KG(s)$ is a ratio of two polynomials and hence has poles and zeros. From Eq. (6.10-4) we see that the zeros of the open loop response and closed loop response are the same but the poles of the closed loop response are in general different from those of the open loop response.

A standard classification procedure for control systems or closed loop systems—as they are often called—is to base the classification on the order of the open loop pole at the origin. Hence a Type 0 system has *no* poles at the origin. The classification can be shown as in Table 6.10-1.

**TABLE 6.10-1** CLASSIFICATION OF CONTROL SYSTEMS

| Class | Open loop response |
|-------|--------------------|
| Type 0 | $KG(s)$ |
| Type 1 | $\dfrac{K}{s} G(s)$ |
| Type 2 | $\dfrac{K}{s^2} G(s)$ |

The final concept to be discussed in this section is that of the error constants called the *positional, velocity,* and *acceleration constants.* These can be defined as limits, viz.,

$$K_p = \lim_{s \to 0} KG(s) \tag{6.10-5}$$

$$K_v = \lim_{s \to 0} sKG(s) \tag{6.10-6}$$

$$K_a = \lim_{s \to 0} s^2 KG(s) \tag{6.10-7}$$

$K_p$, the positional constant, is a measure of the steady-state error that will exist with a constant input. This can be shown by considering the open loop system as being a Type 0 system. Hence

$$\frac{E}{C}(s) = \frac{1}{KG(s)} \tag{6.10-8}$$

For $C(s)$ a unit step input

$$E(s) = \frac{1}{s} \times \frac{1}{KG(s)} \tag{6.10-9}$$

The steady-state error $E_{\text{s.s.}}$ can be obtained by use of the final-value theorem. Thus

$$E_{\text{s.s.}} = \lim_{s \to 0} \left[ s \times \frac{1}{sKG(s)} \right] \tag{6.10-10}$$

and by Eq. (6.10-5),

$$E_{\text{s.s.}} = \frac{1}{K_p} \tag{6.10-11}$$

The gain of the Type 0 system, $K$, determines the positional constant $K_p$, and the larger this gain the smaller the steady-state error. Thus an engineer wishes to have a control system with the maximum possible gain. (The factors that limit the magnitude of this gain will be discussed presently.) It should be clear now that a Type 0 system will have a finite $K_p$ and a zero $K_v$ and $K_a$.

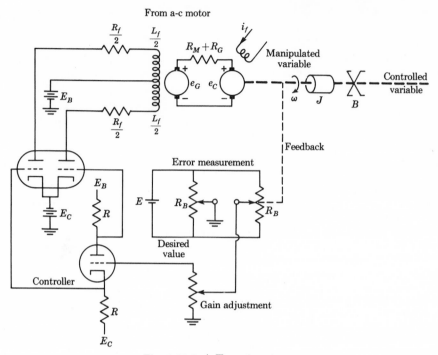

Fig. 6.10-2 A Type 1 system.

These error constants can be conviently shown as in Table 6.10-2.

TABLE 6.10-2 ERROR CONSTANTS

| Type system | $K_p$ | $K_v$ | $K_a$ |
|:-----------:|:-----:|:-----:|:-----:|
| 0 | $K$ | 0 | 0 |
| 1 | $\infty$ | $K$ | 0 |
| 2 | $\infty$ | $\infty$ | $K$ |

In Fig. 6.10-2 is shown a simple Type 1 system consisting of a Ward-Leonard motor-generator set. The field of the generator is supplied by a

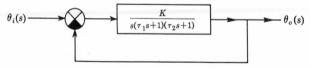

Fig. 6.10-3 Block diagram of Fig. 6.11-1.

push-pull amplifier whose signal is generated by a d-c bridge. The block diagram is shown in Fig. 6.10-3. If the input arm were suddenly rotated a certain number of degrees this would be a step input to the system. Since this is a Type 1 system we would expect the other arm of the bridge to be rotated by the motor until it had turned exactly the same number of degrees. ($K_p$ is ∞ for a Type 1 system.) However, owing to the nonlinearities such as constant friction there will always be a small error existing in physical systems. The theoretical response to a step and velocity input is shown in Fig. 6.10-4.

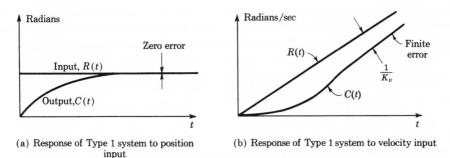

(a) Response of Type 1 system to position input

(b) Response of Type 1 system to velocity input

**Fig. 6.10-4** Response of a Type 1 system.

## 6.20 STABILITY

Section 6.10 emphasized the desirability of having the open loop gain of a system as large as possible. However, the effect of this increased gain upon the transient response will be the limiting factor in the choice.

It has been stated previously that the poles of the open loop response are different from those of the closed loop response. This can be shown by considering the closed loop response, which is

$$\frac{C}{R}(s) = \frac{KG(s)}{1 + KG(s)} \tag{6.20-1}$$

The poles of Eq. (6.20-1) are the zeros of the so-called characteristic equation

$$1 + KG(s) = 0 \tag{6.20-2}$$

For purposes of illustration let us choose a Type 0 system; hence

$$KG(s) = K\frac{(s + a_1)(s + a_2)\cdots(s + a_n)}{(s + b_1)(s + b_2)\cdots(s + b_m)} \tag{6.20-3}$$

Substituting Eq. (6.20-3) into (6.20-1),

$$\frac{C}{R}(s) = K\frac{(s + a_1)(s + a_2)\cdots(s + a_n)}{(s + b_1)(s + b_2)\cdots(s + b_m) + K(s + a_1)\cdots(s + a_n)} \tag{6.20-4}$$

Now if the denominator of Eq. (6.20-4) is factored into its roots and expanded by the Heaviside's expansion theorem,

$$C(s) = R(s)\left[\frac{K_1}{s + c_1} + \frac{K_2}{s + c_2} + \cdots + \frac{K_m}{s + c_m}\right] \qquad (6.20\text{-}5)$$

These poles of Eq. (6.20-4), $c_1, \cdots, c_m$, are varied as the gain $K$ is varied. From the final-value theorem we know that if the poles of Eq. (6.20-4) are negative ($c_1$ is a positive value) or have a negative real part ($c_k = \alpha_k + j\beta_k$) then the time response of Eq. (6.20-4) is bounded. In this case the system is said to be *stable*. If some poles are pure imaginary, the system is said to be *neutrally stable*.

Since we can increase the gain of our system only while the roots of Eq. (6.20-2) (poles of Eq. (6.20-1)) have negative real parts, there exists the need for an engineering method to tell us when these roots have negative real parts. It would also be advantageous to have this method tell us something about relative stability or the size of the negative real parts of these roots. Two such methods will now be discussed.

### 6.21 ROUTH'S CRITERIA

In 1860, Dr. E. J. Routh developed a very elegant method of determining whether an equation of the form

$$P_0 s^n + P_1 s^{n-1} + P_2 s^{n-2} + \cdots + P_n = 0 \qquad (6.21\text{-}1)$$

has any roots with positive real parts. Unfortunately, there is no general method for finding these roots.

Let us first assume Eq. (6.21-1) has no pure imaginary roots. Routh's criteria, as this method is known today, can be developed as follows:

Let us form an array of numbers formed from the coefficients of (6.21-1) as follows:

$$\begin{array}{ccc} P_0 & P_2 & P_4 & \cdots \\ P_1 & P_3 & P_5 & \cdots \end{array} \qquad (6.21\text{-}2)$$

(It is immaterial whether the equation is of odd or even degree.) Form another row from these two rows by cross multiplying as follows:

$$\frac{P_1 P_2 - P_0 P_3}{P_1} \quad \frac{P_1 P_4 - P_0 P_5}{P_1} \quad \cdots \qquad (6.21\text{-}3)$$

Form a fourth row in the same manner. Proceeding thus, the number of terms in each row will approach zero and we stop when no term is left. The rows after the first two are called the *subsidiary functions* and the coefficients of the first column are called the *test functions*. This array of numbers will now be

$$
\begin{array}{cccc}
P_0 & P_2 & P_4 & P_6 \quad \cdots \\
P_1 & P_3 & P_5 & P_7 \quad \cdots \\
\dfrac{P_1P_2 - P_0P_3}{P_1} & \dfrac{P_1P_4 - P_0P_5}{P_1} & \dfrac{P_1P_6 - P_0P_7}{P_1} & \cdots \\
\dfrac{P_3\left[\dfrac{P_1P_2 - P_0P_3}{P_1}\right] - P_1\left[\dfrac{P_1P_4 - P_0P_5}{P_1}\right]}{\dfrac{P_1P_2 - P_0P_3}{P_1}} & \cdots
\end{array}
\tag{6.21-4}
$$

Note that the sum of the superscripts in each row is constant.

Routh's criteria may now be stated as follows:

In order that there be no roots whose real parts are positive, it is necessary and sufficient that the terms of the test functions (first column) should all be of the same sign. If this is not true, the number of variations of sign is equal to the number of roots with positive real parts.

As an example, consider the roots with positive real part of

$$
s^3 + 3s^2 + 3s + 3 = 0 \tag{6.21-5}
$$

To solve, first we form the array of numbers

$$
\begin{array}{cc}
1 & 3 \\
3 & 3 \\
2 & 0 \\
3 & 0
\end{array}
$$

Note that the test column will contain $n$ elements. Since the test column contains no sign changes, this equation contains no roots with positive real parts.

Consider now the general cubic equation

$$
bs^3 + cs^2 + ds + e = 0 \tag{6.21-6}
$$

Forming the array of numbers, we have

$$
\begin{array}{cc}
b & d \\
c & e \\
\dfrac{cd - be}{c} & 0 \\
e &
\end{array}
$$

For no roots with positive real parts, this states that

$$b, c, e > 0 \quad \text{and} \quad cd > be$$

Suppose now that the equation contains pure imaginary roots. This will cause a complete subsidiary function to be zero.

For instance, consider the equation

$$(s^2 + 2)(s + 1) = s^3 + s^2 + 2s + 2 = 0 \qquad (6.21\text{-}7)$$

We form the array and obtain

$$\begin{array}{cc} 1 & 2 \\ 1 & 2 \\ 0 & 0 \end{array}$$

Suppose now one term in the test function vanishes. This can be treated by considering this term as being $\epsilon$ and proceeding as usual. Consider the equation

$$s^4 + s^3 + s^2 + s + 2 = 0 \qquad (6.21\text{-}8)$$

We form the array

$$\begin{array}{ccc} 1 & 1 & 2 \\ 1 & 1 & 0 \\ 0 & 1 & 0 \end{array}$$

However, instead of 0 in the last test function, let us use $\epsilon$ (a very small number) and we obtain the array

$$\begin{array}{ccc} 1 & 1 & 2 \\ 1 & 1 & 0 \\ \epsilon & 2 & \\ \dfrac{\epsilon - 2}{\epsilon} & 0 & \\ 2 & & \end{array}$$

Since there are two sign changes in the test function, this indicates two roots with positive real parts (note that choosing $\epsilon$ negative would not change this answer).

It was shown that a complete subsidiary function vanished when the equation contained complex roots. However, consider the polynomial

$$(s + 1)(s - 1)(s + 2) = s^3 + 2s^2 - s - 2 = 0 \qquad (6.21\text{-}9)$$

Forming the array of numbers,

$$\begin{array}{cc} 1 & -1 \\ 2 & -2 \\ 0 & 0 \end{array}$$

It is seen that this has a subsidiary function that vanishes. (Actually Routh showed that whenever the function has equal and opposite roots a complete subsidiary function will vanish.) This can be treated as follows:

When a subsidiary function vanishes, return to the last function that does not vanish. (The $k$th row in our array is a polynomial in $s$ with the first term of the order $n + 1 - k$ and its coefficient is the number in the array. The order of this polynomial decreases by two for each column in this row.) Write the polynomial described by this subsidiary function. Take the derivative of this polynomial and replace the vanishing function with these coefficients.

Returning to Eq. (6.21-9) the last subsidiary function has the polynomial

$$2s^2 - 2 = 0 \qquad\qquad (6.21\text{-}10)$$

Solving this, it is seen that $s = \pm 1$ is an "equal and opposite" root. Taking the derivative, we obtain $4s$. The array now becomes

$$
\begin{array}{rr}
1 & -1 \\
2 & -2 \\
4 & \\
-8 &
\end{array}
$$

There is one sign change and hence one root with a positive real part.

Two important facts follow from these criteria. They are

1. If any power in $s$ is missing there is a root with a positive real part.
2. If there are any sign changes in the equation, there are roots with positive real parts. For instance, the two equations

$$s^3 - s^2 + s + 2 = 0 \qquad\qquad (6.21\text{-}11)$$

and $$s^3 + s + 2 = 0 \qquad\qquad (6.21\text{-}12)$$

have roots with positive real parts by this reasoning.

Let us now examine the system in Fig. 6.10-2 where the open loop response is

$$KG(s) = \frac{K}{s(0.1s + 1)(0.2s + 1)} \qquad\qquad (6.21\text{-}13)$$

The closed loop response becomes

$$\frac{C}{R}(s) = \frac{K}{s(0.1s + 1)(0.2s + 1) + K} \qquad\qquad (6.21\text{-}14)$$

Thus the problem is to choose $K$ as high as possible but not allow the roots of

$$0.02s^3 + 0.3s^2 + s + K = 0 \qquad (6.21\text{-}15)$$

to have positive real parts. From Eq. (6.21-6) the gain $K$ must satisfy the inequality

$$\frac{0.3}{0.02} > K \qquad (6.21\text{-}16)$$

Now if a unit velocity input is applied to the system of Eq. (6.21-13), the steady-state error will become

$$E_{\text{s.s.}} \approx 0.067 \text{ radians} \qquad (6.21\text{-}17)$$

This shows the disadvantage of Routh's criteria in that nothing is said concerning the transient response or relative stability of the system. This procedure also becomes quite complicated as the order of the characteristic equation increases.

### 6.22 NYQUIST CRITERION

The Nyquist criterion can be stated in its most general form by considering a function $f(s)$ which is analytic in a domain $D$, except for $P$ poles of multiplicity $m_1$, and the domain is bounded by a contour $C$ which in turn does not include any zeros of the analytical function. Under these conditions the Nyquist criterion states

$$\frac{1}{2\pi j} \oint \frac{f'(s)}{f(s)}\, ds = Z - P = N \qquad (6.22\text{-}1)$$

where $Z$ = number of zeros in the domain $D$,

$P$ = number of poles in the domain $D$,

$N$ = number of encirclements of the origin as the contour $C$ of the domain $D$ is transversed in the counterclockwise direction.

To use this theorem we must remember that the location of the zeros of the characteristic equation

$$1 + KG(s) \qquad (6.22\text{-}2)$$

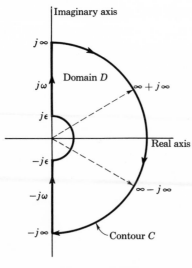

**Figure 6.22-1**

determine the stability of a closed loop system, for if the zeros have positive
real parts the system is unstable. Now let us define the right half portion
of the $s$ plane as the domain $D$ and take the contour $C$ as that shown in
Fig. 6.22-1.

The Nyquist criterion tells us that the number of poles and zeros of
$1 + KG(s)$ in this domain is related to the number of times that the
vector $1 + KG(s)$ encircles the origin as $s$ varies along the contour $C$. Since
there can be no zeros in this domain for a system to be stable, the stability
requirement becomes

$$N = -P \qquad\qquad (6.22\text{-}3)$$

The poles of $1 + KG(s)$ are the same as the poles of the open loop response
$KG(s)$. (These poles can be obtained by Routh's criteria or a similar
algebraic method.)

It is usual to plot the function $KG(s)$ instead of $1 + KG(s)$ and count
the encirclements around the $-1 + j0$ point.

Now for an example choose the system of Fig. 6.10-2 whose open loop
response is of the form

$$KG(s) = \frac{K}{s(\tau_1 s + 1)(\tau_2 s + 1)} \qquad\qquad (6.22\text{-}4)$$

This function has no poles in the domain of Fig. 6.22-1 and hence $P = 0$.
Thus to be stable a plot of (6.22-4) as $s$ varies along the contour $C$ cannot
encircle the $-1 + j0$ point.

A plot of Eq. (6.22-4) as $s$ varies from $s = j\omega = j\epsilon$ to $s = j\omega = j\infty$ is
the frequency response of the system. A plot of Eq. (6.22-4) as $s$ varies
along the negative imaginary axis will be the mirror image of the positive
imaginary axis. It can be confusing sometimes to ascertain the direction
of $KG(s)$ as $s$ varies along the infinite or infinitesimal semicircles. This
can be accomplished by first substituting

$$s = \Delta + j\Delta \qquad (\Delta \text{ very large})$$

into the open loop response. For Eq. (6.22-4) this procedure gives

$$KG(s)]_{s=j\Delta} = \frac{K}{\Delta\underline{/135°}} \approx 0^+\underline{/-135°}$$

The contour along the small semicircle can now be obtained by substitut-
ing $s = \epsilon + j\epsilon$ ($\epsilon$ very small). For Eq. (6.22-4) this procedure gives

$$KG(s)]_{s=\epsilon+j\epsilon} = \frac{K}{\epsilon\underline{/45°}} \approx \infty\underline{/-45°}$$

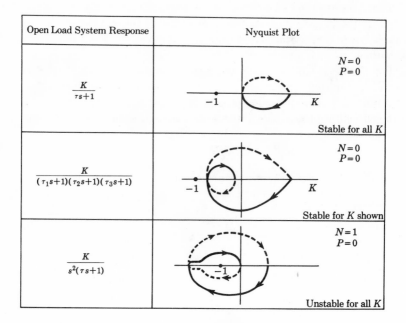

| Open Load System Response | Nyquist Plot |
|---|---|
| $\dfrac{K}{\tau s+1}$ | $N=0$ $P=0$ <br> **Stable for all $K$** |
| $\dfrac{K}{(\tau_1 s+1)(\tau_2 s+1)(\tau_3 s+1)}$ | $N=0$ $P=0$ <br> **Stable for $K$ shown** |
| $\dfrac{K}{s^2(\tau s+1)}$ | $N=1$ $P=0$ <br> **Unstable for all $K$** |

**Table 6.22-1**

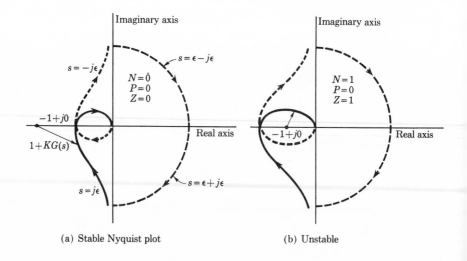

**Fig. 6.22-2** Nyquist plot for a Type 1 system.

The Nyquist plot is now shown in Fig. 6.22-2(a) and (b) for both a stable value of gain and an unstable value. Table 6.22-1 shows several systems with their open loop response and Nyquist plot. The frequency response at small frequencies is indicative of the type of system.

For systems with a simple feedback loop and an open loop response with no poles in the right half plane a simple rule of thumb is often used for stability: if the $-1 + j0$ point is to one's left as the response is traversed in the direction of increasing frequency then the system is stable.

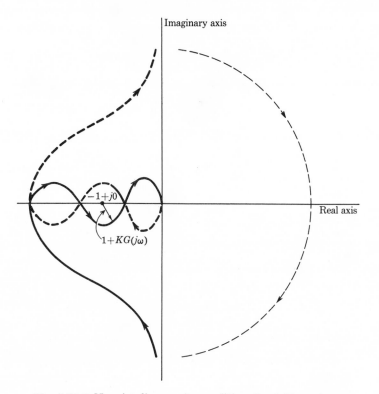

**Fig. 6.22-3** Nyquist diagram for conditionally stable system.

One final system should be discussed; it is called a *conditionally stable* system. Such a system, shown in Fig. 6.22-3, can be stable for very small and very large values of gain. This type of response is characteristic of missile systems. As the vector $1 + KG(s)$ traverses its route for the value of gain shown in Fig. 6.22-3 it will encircle the $-1 + j0$ point twice but each encirclement is in an opposing direction. Hence $N = P = 0$ and the Nyquist plot shows a stable system.

## 6.30 RELATIVE STABILITY

In Sec. 6.22 it was pointed out that the response of $KG(s)$ to the $s$ contour of $s = j\epsilon$ to $s = j\infty$ constitutes the open loop frequency response of the system. This portion of the contour can then be physically simulated by driving the open loop system with a sine wave generator and measuring the difference in amplitude between input and output and also the difference in phase after a steady-state output has been reached. Since this portion of a Nyquist plot can be obtained by direct measurement (it is not necessary to know the mathematical relation of the variables in this system) a closed loop control system is quite often designed by constraining its open loop frequency response to fall within certain values.

Consider now the vectors as shown in Fig. 6.30-1. Thus the closed loop response of this system is vector $A$ divided by vector $B$, and the closed loop response is obtained knowing the open loop response. The response of Fig. 6.30-1 is for one value of the open loop system gain $K$.

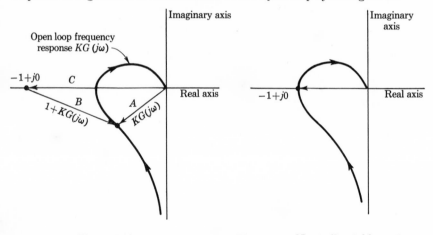

Figure 6.30-1                              Fig. 6.30-2 Neutrally stable system.

Now suppose the open loop response has a value of gain such that it passes through the $-1 + j0$ point as in Fig. 6.30-2. This response shows that the vector $1 + KG(j\omega) = 0$ and thus that the value of $j\omega$ for which this response passes through the $-1 + j0$ point is a pole of the closed loop system. It then seems reasonable to consider the gain of the open loop system at which the phase shift is 180 degrees and also the phase shift of the open loop system at which the gain is unity to be figures of merit for the relative stability of the system. Thus these two items have been defined as follows:

1. *Gain margin* is the distance from the intersection of the open loop frequency response and the negative real axis to the $-1 + j0$ point. If

this intersection is closer to the origin than the $-1 + j0$ point the gain margin is positive. Thus for systems with no poles in the domain $D$, a stable system has a positive gain margin.

2. *Phase margin* is the angular difference between the phase of the open loop frequency response when its magnitude is unity and the negative real axis. These concepts are illustrated in Fig. 6.30-3.

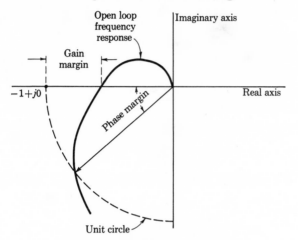

**Fig. 6.30-3** Gain and phase margin.

One other figure of merit exists for designing a closed loop system and that is the maximum magnitude of the closed loop frequency response $M_p$. In Chap. 2 it was shown that for a second-order system the maximum overshoot was related to the damping $\delta$ and hence the transient response by the equation

$$\omega_n^2 M_p = \frac{1}{2\delta \sqrt{1 - \delta^2}} \tag{6.30-1}$$

Let us now derive a method for determining the maximum overshoot of the closed loop system from the Nyquist plot. First, the open loop response can be expressed as a vector with a real and imaginary part:

$$KG(j\omega) = x(\omega) + jy(\omega) \tag{6.30-2}$$

Now the closed loop response becomes

$$\frac{C}{R}(j\omega) = \frac{x + jy}{1 + x + jy} \tag{6.30-3}$$

The magnitude of Eq. (6.30-3) is

$$M = \left|\frac{C}{R}\right| = \frac{\sqrt{x^2 + y^2}}{\sqrt{(1 + x)^2 + y^2}} \tag{6.30-4}$$

Squaring both sides of Eq. (6.30-4),

$$M^2 = \frac{x^2 + y^2}{(1 + x)^2 + y^2} \tag{6.30-5}$$

Rearranging Eq. (6.30-5),

$$M^2(1 + 2x + x^2) + M^2 y^2 = x^2 + y^2 \tag{6.30-6}$$

and

$$x^2[M^2 - 1] + 2M^2 x + y^2[M^2 - 1] = -M^2 \tag{6.30-7}$$

Completing the square of the $x$ terms in Eq. (6.30-7),

$$\left(x + \frac{M^2}{M^2 - 1}\right)^2 + y^2 = \frac{M^2}{(M^2 - 1)^2} \tag{6.30-8}$$

Thus from Eq. (6.30-8), the locus for constant $M$ is a circle with the parameters

$$\text{radius} = \frac{M}{M^2 - 1}$$

$$\text{center} = \begin{cases} x = -\dfrac{M^2}{M^2 - 1} \\ y = 0 \end{cases} \tag{6.30-9}$$

The same procedure can be used to find the locus of constant closed loop phase shift $N$. The relationship for $N$ in terms of the open loop response becomes

$$N = \tan^{-1}\frac{y}{x} - \tan^{-1}\frac{y}{1 + x} \tag{6.30-10}$$

Equation (6.30-10) can be put into the parametric form of a circle with the parameters

$$\text{radius} = \frac{1}{2}\sqrt{1 + \left(\frac{1}{\tan N}\right)^2}$$

and    (6.30-11)

$$\text{center} = \begin{cases} x = -\dfrac{1}{2} \\ y = \dfrac{1}{2 \tan N} \end{cases}$$

In Fig. 6.30-4 is shown a Nyquist plot of the open loop frequency response of a Type I system for some value of gain. Superimposed on this plot are the constant $M$ circles. The open loop response is tangent to the circle corresponding to a closed loop magnitude of $M = 2$. This tangency determines then the maximum overshoot of the closed loop system. The gain of the open loop system could be changed to have the response tangent to any $M$ circle and hence by adjusting the open loop gain any $M_p$ can be chosen for the closed loop system.

In Fig. 2.60-4 and Fig. 2.80-2(a) is shown the relation between frequency response, damping ratio, and transient response. It is usual to adjust a system to have a closed loop $M_p$ of between 1.2 to 1.5, which for a second-order system means the transient overshoot will be between 18% and 30%. It should be emphasized that the value of $M_p$ chosen is really based on the experience of the designer and not on any precise mathematical formula. The frequency at which the open loop response is tangent to the maximum $M$ circle is termed the *resonant frequency* $\omega_R$.

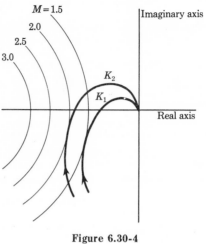

Figure 6.30-4

The frequency at which the closed loop response is 0.707 times the zero frequency is usually termed the *bandwidth* $\omega_B$ of the system. Thus in general the higher $\omega_R$ the higher $\omega_B$.

In general no use is made of the constant $N$ circles. It can be seen in Fig. 2.80-2(b) that for a simple second-order system the specification of $M_p$ serves to determine the $N$ and damping of the system. Hence when an engineer designs a control system for a specific $M_p$ he is assuming that the closed loop system has a pair of complex poles which completely overshadow any others.

### 6.31 GAIN ADJUSTMENT FOR A SPECIFIED $M_p$

Constructing a Nyquist diagram as in Fig. 6.30-4 and choosing a gain to produce a desired $M_p$ can be done numerically by trial and error. However, there exists a simple geometric procedure to adjust this gain.* Consider now the system in Fig. 6.31-1. A line tangent to any $M$ circle passes through the origin at an angle $\psi = \sin^{-1} 1/M$ with the negative real axis. The gain necessary to realize a desired $M_p$ can now be obtained by a simple procedure. The steps are as follows:

1. Construct the frequency response for unity gain, i.e. $G(j\omega)$.
2. Draw a line passing through the origin at an angle $\psi = \sin^{-1} 1/M$.

---

* Gordon S. Brown and Donald P. Campbell, *Principles of Servomechanisms* (New York: John Wiley & Sons, 1948).

3. By trial and error construct a circle whose center is on the negative axis and tangent to both the straight line and the $G(j\omega)$ locus.
4. Bring a perpendicular from the point of tangency of the $M$ circle and the $\psi$ line to the negative real axis. The desired gain is the reciprocal of the length from this point to the origin.

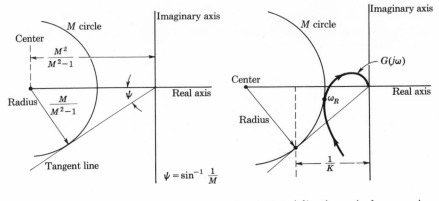

Figure 6.31-1

Fig. 6.31-2 Adjusting gain for a specified $M_p$.

These facts are illustrated in Fig. 6.31-2. The proof is simple and is left as a problem.

## 6.32 BODE PLOTS

The Nyquist plot is drawn on polar graph paper as shown in the preceding sections and hence shows simultaneously the phase and magnitude of the open loop response. It is sometimes convenient to graph this information to a logarithmic scale where the phase in degrees and magnitude in decibels are plotted separately vs. the log of the frequency. Such plots are called *Bode plots*. One great advantage of this method lies in the approximation of transfer functions by their asymptotes. To illustrate this technique consider the Type I system of Eq. (6.21-13):

$$KG(s) = \frac{K}{s(0.1s + 1)(0.2s + 1)} \tag{6.32-1}$$

Since we wish to plot the magnitude and phase of this transfer function,

$$|KG(j\omega)| = \frac{K}{\omega \sqrt{1 + (0.1\omega)^2} \sqrt{1 + (0.2\omega)^2}} \tag{6.32-2}$$

and

$$\underline{/KG(j\omega)} = -\frac{\pi}{2} - \tan^{-1}(0.1\omega) - \tan^{-1}(0.2\omega) \tag{6.32-3}$$

Equation 6.32-2 can be converted to decibels as $20 \log |KG(j\omega)|$. Hence

$$20 \log |KG(j\omega)| = 20 \log K - 20 \log \omega - 20 \log \sqrt{1 + (0.1\omega)^2}$$
$$- 20 \log \sqrt{1 + (0.2\omega)^2} \qquad (6.32\text{-}4)$$

Let us now examine the term $20 \log \sqrt{1 + (0.1\omega)^2}$. For small frequencies this term becomes approximately $20 \log \sqrt{1}$ or zero. For large frequencies it becomes approximately $20 \log \sqrt{(0.1\omega)^2}$. In Table 6.32-1 this term is

**TABLE 6.32-1**

| $\omega$ (rad/sec) | $20 \log \sqrt{(0.1\omega)^2}$ |
|:---:|:---:|
| 100 | 20 |
| 200 | 26 |
| 400 | 32 |
| 800 | 38 |
| 1000 | 40 |

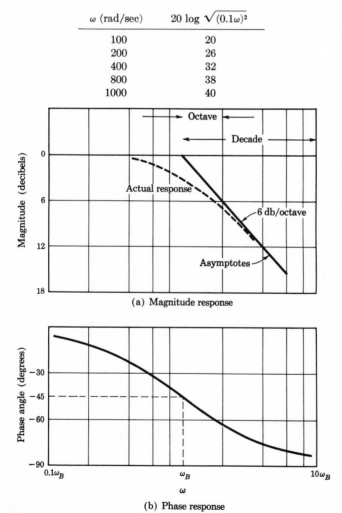

(a) Magnitude response

(b) Phase response

**Fig. 6.32-1** Bode plot for a first order term.

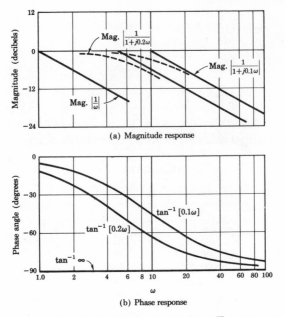

(a) Magnitude response

(b) Phase response

**Fig. 6.32-2** Developing the Bode plot for a Type 1 system.

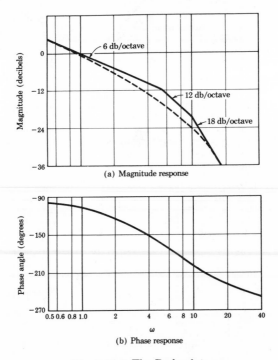

(a) Magnitude response

(b) Phase response

**Fig. 6.32-3** The Bode plot.

tabulated for large frequencies. Notice that the magnitude of this term decreases by 6 db every time the frequency is doubled. On semi-log paper this distance is termed an *octave*. Hence we say the high-frequency asymptote has a slope of 6 db/octave or, since a decade on semi-log paper is a factor of 10, 20 db/decade. At the break frequency $\omega_B = 10$, the magnitude of this term is approximately 3 db. At twice the break frequency the magnitude is approximately 7 db and at one-half the break frequency the magnitude is 1 db. There is no such approximation for the angle vs. log $\omega$ plot but at the break frequency the phase shift is $-45°$. Hence any first-order term can be represented by a plot as shown in Fig. 6.32-1.

Now the total response of Eq. (6.32-4) can be obtained by adding the response of the three first-order terms as in Fig. 6.32-2 and 6.32-3. The gain constant $K$ is not shown as this is to be determined. The Bode plot is often shown with both the magnitude and phase on the same graph as in Fig. 6.32-4.

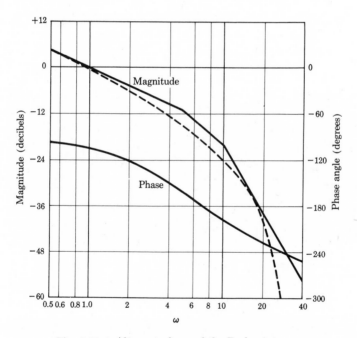

**Fig. 6.32-4** Alternate form of the Bode plot.

To adjust the gain for a specified $M_p$ the $M$-$N$ circles for the Nyquist plot are redrawn to a log scale and appear as shown in Fig. 6.32-5. This type of chart is often called the *Nichols chart*. The log magnitude (log-mag.) vs. phase relationship obtained from the Bode plot can now be

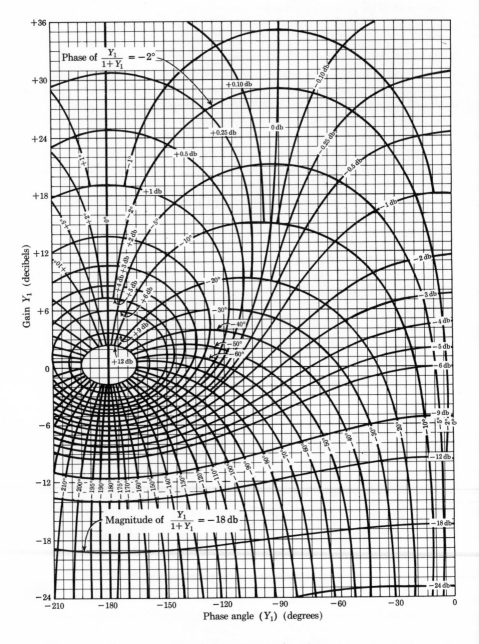

**Fig. 6.32-5** The Nichols chart.

plotted on this chart. Note that we chose $1.2 \leq M_p \leq 1.5$ for the Nyquist plot and hence for the Nichols chart we wish $1.6 \leq M_p \leq 3.52$ db. Now, since we are working with logs, increasing the gain of the system is the same as adding a constant amount to the system response. It is common to have a Nichols chart made up on an overlay and slide it up and down to determine the necessary gain for the desired $M_p$.

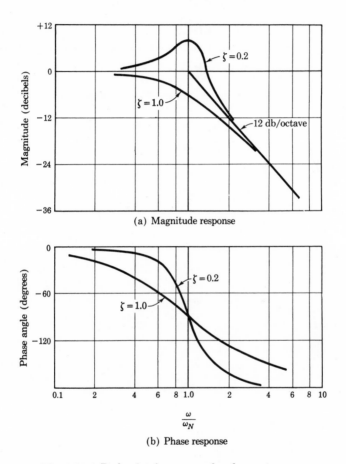

(a) Magnitude response

(b) Phase response

**Fig. 6.32-6** Bode plot for a second order system.

Although we will not develop a second-order system with complex roots it should be clear that its response will be as shown in Fig. 6.32-6 with the high-frequency asymptote falling off at $-12$ db/octave. This response can be obtained from Fig. 2.80-2 which shows the absolute magnitude of the response.

### 6.33 COMPENSATION

Since the gain of a system is limited by allowable maximum over-shoot, some means must be devised to alter the open loop response so as to allow an increase in gain and resonant frequency. This correction or compensating technique consists in adding a separate box to the block diagram of the system as shown in Fig. 6.33-1. Such series networks are called by several names such as *filters, equalizers,* or *compensating networks.* There is no step-by-step method for deriving a unique compensating network; rather this technique is based on the ingenuity of the engineer.

Some basic series compensating networks are shown in Table 6.33-1 with their asymptotes of the Bode plots. It is usually more convenient to use Bode plots than Nyquist plots to obtain the correct compensating

**TABLE 6.33-1** SOME SERIES COMPENSATING NETWORKS

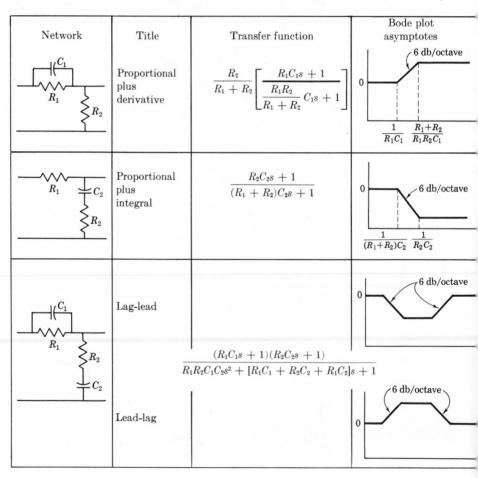

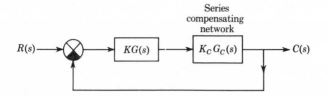

**Figure 6.33-1**

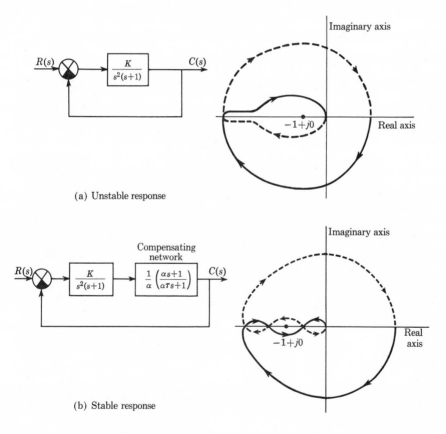

(a) Unstable response

(b) Stable response

**Fig. 6.33-2** Effect of series compensation.

network. The reason is the ease with which the plot of the compensating network can be added to that of the uncompensated system.

For example, the system with the open loop transfer function

$$KG(s) = \frac{K}{s^2(s+1)} \qquad (6.33\text{-}1)$$

is unstable for all values of gain. However, by adding proportional plus derivative compensation the system becomes stable for reasonable values of gain. This is illustrated in Fig. 6.33-2 by means of a Nyquist plot.

Networks can also be added in parallel to improve the relative stability of a system. This scheme is often used to improve the response of a particular element of a system.

### 6.34 ELEMENTS IN THE FEEDBACK PATH

If the system has dynamic elements in the feedback path as in Fig. 6.34-1, some additional steps must be taken to make use of the Nichols chart. The block diagram of Fig. 6.34-1 can be rewritten by using the rules developed in Chap. 5 to be as in Fig. 6.34-2. Thus the system is first considered to have the open loop transfer function,

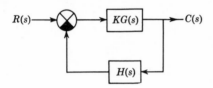

**Fig. 6.34-1** System with elements in the feedback path.

$$\frac{C'}{E}(s) = KG(s)H(s) \qquad (6.34\text{-}1)$$

and is adjusted on the Nichols chart for a given $M_p$. This response must then be multiplied by the reciprocal of the feedback transfer function. Thus

$$\frac{C}{R}(s) = \frac{KG(s)H(s)}{1 + KG(s)H(s)} \times \frac{1}{H(s)} \qquad (6.34\text{-}2)$$

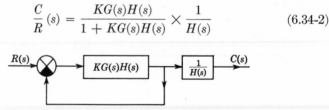

**Fig. 6.34-2** Reduction to a system with unity feedback.

### 6.35 A SHORT CUT

If the system under study has a transfer function with no zeros in the right half plane and no transportation lag (no terms of $\epsilon^{-as}$), then a quick approximation to the closed loop response may be obtained from the Bode plot. The procedure is shown in Fig. 6.35-1. A perpendicular is extended from the point at which the phase is $-135°$ (45° phase margin) to the magnitude response. The value of the magnitude response is the amount of gain that can be added to the system (if this value is positive the gain must be lowered.

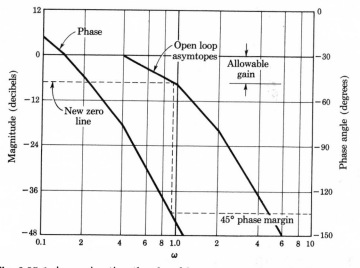

**Fig. 6.35-1** Approximating the closed loop response from the Bode plot.

The closed loop can be approximated by using a horizontal asymptote to this point and then using the open loop asymptotes to the right of this point. This procedure will usually approximate the actual response to within 10%.

## 6.36 DEAD TIME

In Chap. 2 it was shown that

$$\mathcal{L}[\epsilon^{-as}F(s)] = f(t - a)u_{-1}(t - a) \qquad (6.36\text{-}1)$$

Hence if a physical process has transport lag or dead time (the two are the same) its transfer function will have $\epsilon^{-as}$ appearing. Thus it is of interest to develop the frequency response of a term $\epsilon^{-as}$. This may be done as follows:

$$\epsilon^{-aj\omega} = \cos a\omega + j \sin a\omega \qquad (6.36\text{-}2)$$

and

$$|\epsilon^{-aj\omega}| = 1 \qquad (6.36\text{-}3)$$

$$\underline{/\epsilon^{-aj\omega}} = \tan^{-1}[\tan a\omega] = a\omega \qquad (6.36\text{-}4)$$

Hence the frequency response of $\epsilon^{-aj\omega}$ has only a phase shift and no magnitude change with frequency. In Fig. 6.36-1 is shown a Bode plot for dead time.

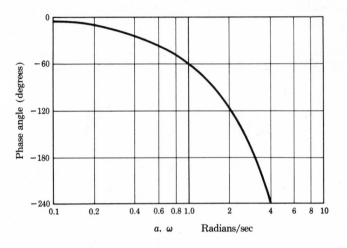

**Fig. 6.36-1** Bode plot for dead time.

## 6.40 THE ROOT-LOCUS METHOD

The frequency response method of designing or analyzing servomechanisms and regulators has the distinct advantage that the theoretical response of the system does not have to be known. An actual frequency response can be obtained from a system by measurement. However, when the theoretical response of a system is known and the open loop zeros and poles can be located, a system can be designed from a plot of the locus of the closed loop poles as the gain of the system is increased. These closed loop poles will tell us the nature of the transient response to any particular type of input. This procedure is called the *root-locus method* of design. As an example, consider first a simple second-order Type I system with the transfer function

$$KG(s) = \frac{K}{s(s + a)} \tag{6.40-1}$$

The closed loop response is

$$\frac{C}{R}(s) = \frac{\dfrac{K}{s(s + a)}}{1 + \dfrac{K}{s(s + a)}} \tag{6.40-2}$$

The closed loop poles must satisfy the two conditions

$$\left| \frac{K}{s(s + a)} \right| = 1 \tag{6.40-3}$$

$$\left/ \frac{K}{s(s + a)} \right. = 180° + n360° \tag{6.40-4}$$

Since this system is very simple it is quite simple to solve for the closed loop poles, which are roots of the characteristic equation

$$s^2 + as + K = 0 \tag{6.40-5}$$

Hence these poles become

$$s_1, s_2 = -\frac{a}{2} \pm \sqrt{\frac{a^2}{4} - K} \tag{6.40-6}$$

Since for zero gain the closed loop poles and zeros are the same as the open loop, the direction of the locus will be away from the open loop

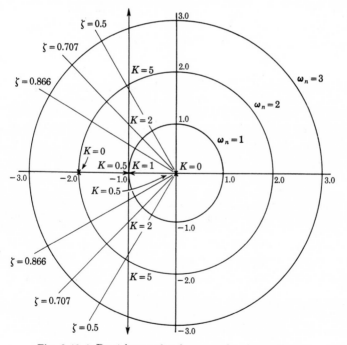

**Fig. 6.40-1** Root locus plot for second order system.

poles. The locus must start at a pole and end on a zero. In Fig. 6.40-1 is shown the root-locus plot of Eq. (6.40-2) for $a = 2$. Superimposed on this plot are the $\omega_n$ circles and $\zeta$ lines which were developed in Chap. 2. Thus

for a gain of $K = 5$, the closed loop system will have poles with a damping
ratio of about 0.5 and a natural frequency of $\omega_n = 2$ rad/sec. For a gain
$K \leq 1$ the two poles will lie on the negative real axis. The point at which
the root-locus moves off the negative real axis is termed the *breakaway
point*. The point at which the locus crosses the imaginary axis determines
the absolute stability limit of the system.

For higher-order systems the root-locus must be constructed from
Eqs. (6.40-3) and (6.40-4) rather than solving for the roots of the characteristic equation as a function of the gain. In Fig. 6.40-2 is shown the

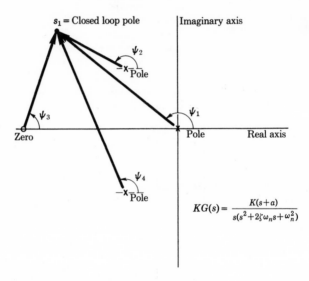

**Figure 6.40-2**

pole-zero location for a simple third-order system. The poles are indicated
by X's and the zeros by O's. If $s_1$ is a closed loop pole, Eq. (6.40-4) then
states that

$$\psi_1 + \psi_2 + \psi_4 - \psi_3 = 180° + 360n \qquad (6.40\text{-}7)$$

Thus the root-locus can be constructed by utilizing Eq. (6.40-4) to sketch
the shape of the locus and then utilizing Eq. (6.40-3) to set the scale of
the plot.

## 6.41 CONSTRUCTION OF THE ROOT-LOCUS

It is not necessary to find the locus by a random method; rather
there are several rules and techniques available for this method. These

rules can be summarized for the general system

$$KG(s) = K \left[ \frac{s^m + a_1 s^{m-1} + \cdots + 1}{s^n + b_1 s^{n-1} + \cdots + 1} \right] \qquad (6.41\text{-}1)$$

in Table 6.41-1. This table does not prove these rules but it is expected that the reader will do so. The rules are simply derived from Eq. (6.40-4).

### TABLE 6.41-1 RULES FOR CONSTRUCTING THE ROOT-LOCUS

1. The locus starts on a pole and ends on a zero.

2. For a locus to be on the real axis the number of poles and the number of zeros to the right of the point must be odd.

3. As the closed loop poles approach infinity they will have $(n - m)$ asymptotes at angles of

$$\pm \frac{180}{n - m}, \quad \pm \frac{540}{n - m}, \quad \pm \frac{900}{n - m} \cdots$$

4. These asymptotes will intersect the real axis at a point called the centroid $\bar{x}$ and obtained from

$$\bar{x} = \frac{\Sigma \text{ poles} - \Sigma \text{ zeros}}{\text{no. of finite poles} - \text{no. of finite zeros}}$$

(This can be a positive or negative number.)

5. The intersection with the imaginary axis can be obtained by Routh's array from the characteristic equation and by obtaining the gain for which a subsidiary function vanishes.

If the open loop system has no complex poles it is quite simple to find the breakaway point by using Eq. (6.40-4) and replacing the angles from the open loop poles and zeros to this point by their tangents. As an example a simple system is shown in Fig. 6.41-1.

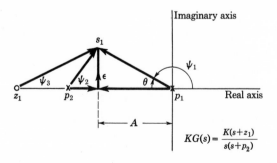

$$KG(s) = \frac{K(s+z_1)}{s(s+p_2)}$$

**Figure 6.41-1**

For $s_1$ to be on the loci,

$$\psi_1 + \psi_2 - \psi_3 = 180° \qquad (6.41\text{-}2)$$

But

$$\theta = 180 - \psi_1$$

$$\theta = \tan^{-1} \frac{\epsilon}{A}$$

$$\psi_2 = \tan^{-1} \frac{\epsilon}{p_2 - A} \qquad (6.41\text{-}3)$$

$$\psi_3 = \tan^{-1} \frac{\epsilon}{z_1 - A}$$

Since $\epsilon$ is an infinitesimal, Eq. (6.41-2) becomes

$$180 - \frac{\epsilon}{A} + \frac{\epsilon}{p_2 - A} - \frac{\epsilon}{z_1 - A} = 180° \qquad (6.41\text{-}4)$$

$$\frac{1}{p_2 - A} - \frac{1}{z_1 - A} - \frac{1}{A} = 0 \qquad (6.41\text{-}5)$$

The breakaway point $A$ is now obtained from Eq. (6.41-5).

The root-locus can be drawn to scale very quickly by means of a graphical aid called a *spirule** shown in Fig. 6.41-2 which consists of a

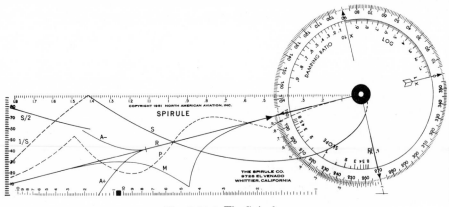

**Fig. 6.41-2** The Spirule.

disk and arm with a common pivot point. The disk has a protractor scale and the arm has a decimal scale on the radial edge.

To determine whether $s_1$ in Fig. 6.40-2 is a closed loop pole the pivot at the center of the disk is set on $s_1$ and held there. The arm can be rotated

---

* The Spirule Company, 9728 El Venado, Whittier, Cal.

with respect to the disk through each of the angles in succession to obtain their sum. The disk rotates with the arm at all other times owing to the clamping action of the standard eyelet which holds them together. The pivot is a special eyelet mounted inside the standard eyelet and rotates freely. If the sum of these angles is $180°$ then $s_1$ is a closed loop pole.

The gain associated with $s_1$ can be obtained from the spirule curve on the arm which gives the logarithm of a length as an angle. Addition of these angles adds logarithms, which corresponds to multiplying lengths.

TABLE 6.41-2 SOME TYPICAL ROOT-LOCI

| Transfer function | Root-locus |
|---|---|

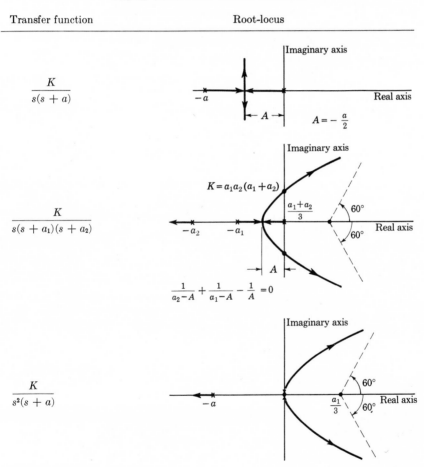

Table 6.41-2 shows sketches of root-loci for various functions. It should be evident that the stability requirement is that no loci cross the imaginary axis into the right half plane.

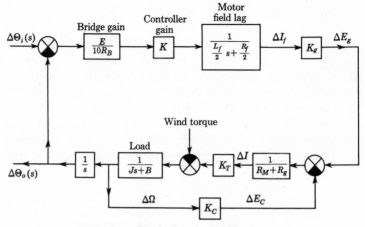

Fig. 6.50-1 Block diagram of Fig. 6.10-2.

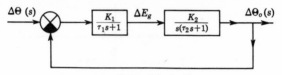

Fig. 6.50-2 Servo block diagram.

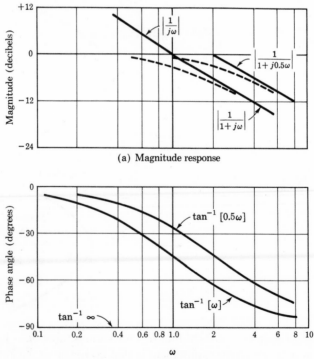

(a) Magnitude response

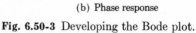

(b) Phase response

Fig. 6.50-3 Developing the Bode plot.

## 6.50  EXAMPLE

In Fig. 6.50-1 is shown a typical system which can serve as an example for the techniques we have developed in this chapter. This system can be considered a tracking radar which is used to follow the path of a missile. The load then consists of the antenna, and the disturbance is a wind gust against the antenna. The servo block diagram becomes that of Fig. 6.50-2, where

$$K' = K_1 K_2 = \frac{2EKK_g}{10R_f R_B} \times \frac{K_T}{B(R_m + R_g) + K_C K_T}$$

$$\tau_1 = \frac{L_f}{R_f} = 1.0$$

$$\tau_2 = \frac{(R_m + R_2)J}{B(R_m + R_g) + K_C K_T} = 0.5$$

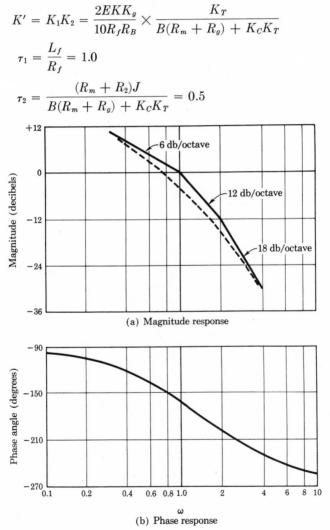

(a)  Magnitude response

(b)  Phase response

**Fig. 6.50-4**  Bode plot for

$$KG(s) = \frac{K}{s(s + 1)(0.5s + 1)}$$

Hence the servo open loop transfer function becomes

$$KG(s) = \frac{K'}{s(s + 1)(0.5s + 1)} \qquad (6.50\text{-}1)$$

The Bode plot for Eq. (6.50-1) is developed in Figs. 6.50-3 and 6.50-4. In Fig. 6.50-5 we see that for a phase margin of 45° the gain must be decreased 3.5 db or

$$K' = -3.5 \text{ db} = 0.666 \qquad (6.50\text{-}2)$$

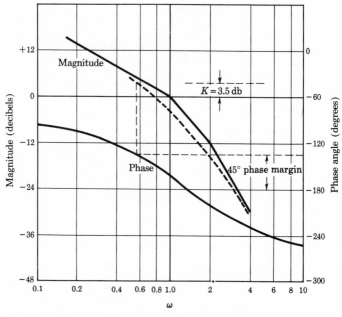

**Fig. 6.50-5** Alternate form of the Bode plot for

$$KG(s) = \frac{K}{s(s + 1)(0.5s + 1)}$$

In Fig. 6.50-6 the log magnitude vs. angle plot is shown. It is tangent to the $M_p = 2.3$ db locus and hence

$$K' = -3 \text{ db} = 0.707 \qquad (6.50\text{-}3)$$

This shows that adjusting the phase margin to 45° is quite close to adjusting the maximum overshoot to 2.3 db, a 30% overshoot. Figure 6.50-7 shows the Bode plot for the closed loop system with a gain of 0.707 or $-3.0$ db. This value of gain gives

$$K_v = 1.42$$

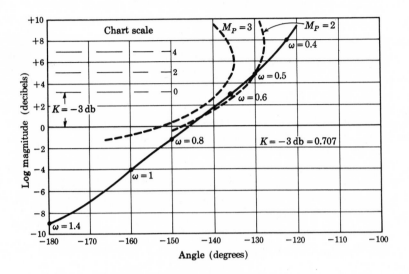

**Fig. 6.50-6** Log magnitude vs. angle plot.

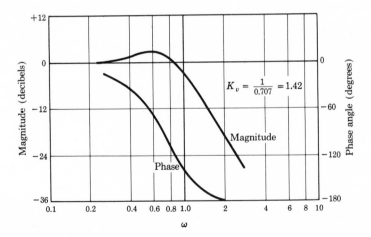

**Fig. 6.50-7** Closed loop servo response for uncompensated system.

As a comparison, the root-locus is shown in Fig. 6.50-8. Before developing the root-locus, the transfer function is written as

$$KG(s) = \frac{K'}{0.5} \frac{1}{s(s+1)(s+2)} \tag{6.50-4}$$

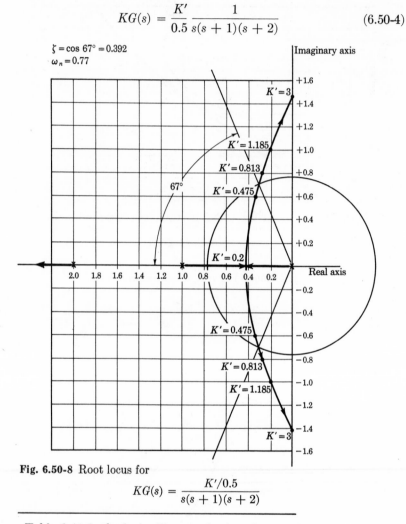

**Fig. 6.50-8** Root locus for
$$KG(s) = \frac{K'/0.5}{s(s+1)(s+2)}$$

From Table 6.41-2, the loci will cross the imaginary axis at

$$\frac{K'}{0.5} = 6 \quad \text{or} \quad K' = 3$$

The breakaway point will occur at a value of $A$ such that

$$\frac{1}{1-A} + \frac{1}{2-A} - \frac{1}{A} = 0 \tag{6.50-5}$$

or $A = 0.422$. The loci can now be sketched as shown in Fig. 6.50-8 in terms of $K'$. For comparison the two complex roots are shown for $K' \approx 0.7$. It is seen that the damping ratio is 0.392 and the frequency is 0.77. The closed loop system has a real pole also but it is much larger than 2 and hence is not shown.

Whereas the damping ratio and frequency response of the system might be acceptable, the value of $K_v$ seems somewhat high. Hence the next step is to add some type of series compensation to the system to decrease the $K_v$. The network of Fig. 6.50-9 is now added to Fig. 6.50-7 to obtain the

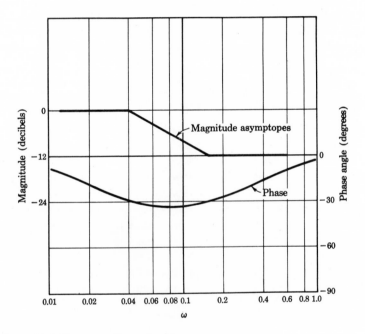

**Fig. 6.50-9** Compensating network.

$$KG(s) = \frac{(6.25s + 1)}{(25s + 1)}$$

compensated Bode plot of Fig. 6.50-10. Only the asymptotes are shown in this plot. A 40-deg phase margin has been chosen here and the gain can be increased to 1.985 with a $K_v = 0.505$. The compensating network used here could be more effective if the break frequencies were shifted to the left. If they were shifted any more to the right it would lose its effectiveness. In its present position the resonant frequency is at its highest value.

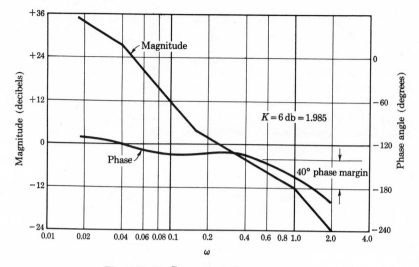

**Fig. 6.50-10** Compensated servo response.

## 6.60 SUMMARY

This example has served to emphasize the fact that there is no one unique method of designing a control system. For a quick answer the Bode plot is probably the best approach, but again this does not give the same insight into the transient response as the root-locus procedure. If the transfer function of a box is unknown, a frequency response can be obtained quite easily but nothing can be said in general about the poles and zeros.

The basic principles of control theory have been presented in this chapter, but specialized techniques are available which have not been covered.

## 6.70 PROBLEMS

1. Sketch the Nyquist plots for the following transfer functions:

(a) $\dfrac{K(s+2)}{s(s-1)(s+5)(s+6)}$  (b) $\dfrac{K}{s^2(s^2+s+1)}$

(c) $\dfrac{K(s+4)}{s(s+6)(s+3)(s+0.1)}$  (d) $\dfrac{K}{s^3(s+1)(s+2)}$

2. Sketch the root-loci for the transfer functions in prob. 1.

3. Determine the regulator response for the example in Sec. 6.50 with series compensation.

4. Adjust the gain for $M_p = 1.3$ of the system with the transfer function

$$KG(s) = \frac{K(s+1)}{s(0.5s+1)(0.1s+1)(0.25s+1)}$$

5. Adjust the system with the block diagram of Fig. 6.70-1 to have an $M_p = 1.3$. It is permissible to add a compensating network.

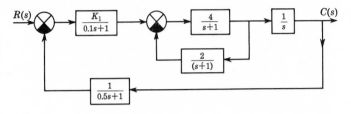

**Figure 6.70-1**

6. In some cases it is more convenient to plot the inverse of the transfer function, i.e. $1/KG(s)$. In this case

$$\frac{R}{C}(s) = \frac{1}{KG(s)} + 1$$

For the inverse system show that:

(a) If the $-1 + j0$ point is not enclosed the system is stable.

(b) The loci of constant $1/M$ are circles with a common center at $-1 + j0$ and the loci of constant angles are straight lines radiating from $-1 + j0$.

7. For the system of Eq. (6.70-1) plot the damping ratio $\zeta$ as

$$\frac{C}{R}(s) = \frac{\omega_n^2}{s^2 + 2\zeta\omega_n s + \omega_n^2} \qquad (6.70\text{-}1)$$

a function of the phase margin.

8. In Fig. 6.70-2 is shown a block diagram of a simple motor-generator set with tachometric feedback. Design a simple $R$-$C$ network as shown in

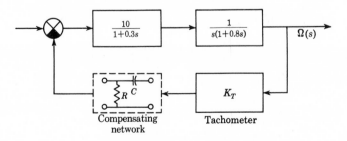

**Figure 6.70-2**

the dotted block to improve the response. The tach gain can be varied also. Compare this response to that obtained with only tachometric feedback.

9. Apply Routh's criteria to determine the stability of the following transfer functions:

(a) $\dfrac{K}{s(4s+1)(s+1)}$

(b) $\dfrac{K}{s^5 + s^4 + s^3 + 2s^2 + 3s + 1}$

(c) $\dfrac{K(s+4)}{s(s^3 + 2s^2 + 6s + 1)}$

(d) $\dfrac{K(s+1)}{s^2(0.5s+1)(0.1s+1)}$

10. Devise an expression for the breakaway point when a system has a pair of complex poles.

11. Compare the closed loop response approximated from the Bode plot and the actual closed loop response for the transfer function

$$KG(s) = \frac{K}{s(0.1s+1)(0.8s+1)}$$

# CHAPTER SEVEN

# LINEARIZATION

## 7.00 INTRODUCTION

In the preceding chapters we have discussed systems that can be characterized by linear differential equations with constant coefficients. The question is now raised as to what we can do if the system is not linear. It has been pointed out in Chap. 2 that there is no general method of solving nonlinear differential equations. Hence our transform theory will not help us to any extent. As a first approach, a "ball park" type answer, we can "linearize" the equation, i.e. characterize it by a linear equation. It is surprising how much information can be obtained in this manner. This chapter will be concerned with techniques whereby we can linearize the characterizing equation of a system.

## 7.10 SMALL-SCALE LINEARIZATION

To motivate our discussion of this topic let us consider a system consisting of a mass and a nonlinear dashpot similar to that shown in Fig. 7.10-1 but such that the restraining force is proportional to the square of the velocity. The equations of motion can be expressed as

$$m \frac{dv}{dt} + Rv^2 = f \qquad (7.10\text{-}1)$$

where $v$ = velocity of body,

$\quad f$ = force on body,

$\quad m$ = mass of body,

$\quad R$ = friction coefficient of dashpot.

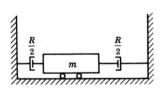

**Figure 7.10-1**

The dashpot is nonlinear and has the relationship

$$f_d = Rv^2$$

Now Eq. (7.10-1) is nonlinear and we are not assured of knowing its solution. However, suppose we consider the system for only small changes about some operating point. From the calculus we know that if $y = f(x)$, then

$$\Delta y = \frac{\partial f}{\partial x} \Delta x$$

Applying this same principle to our problem,

$$\Delta f_d = 2Rv \, \Delta v$$

We can now assume $\Delta v$ is an incremental change about an operating point and designate this point as $V_0$.

Equation (7.10-1) now becomes

$$m \frac{d}{dt} (\Delta v) + 2RV_0 \, \Delta v = \Delta f \qquad (7.10\text{-}2)$$

where we have the initial condition that at $t = 0$, $v = 0$. For a step input of $\Delta f$ the solution to Eq. (7.10-2) is

$$\Delta v(t) = \frac{\Delta f}{2RV_0} [1 - \epsilon^{(-2RV_0/m)t}] \qquad (7.10\text{-}3)$$

The actual linearized solution would be

$$v(t) = V_0 + \frac{\Delta f}{2RV_0} [1 - \epsilon^{(-2RV_0/m)t}]$$

The obvious question now is, how good an approximation is this? To illustrate, let us choose some values and in particular let $R$ and $m = 1$ and choose $\Delta f = 0.01$. Now consider the system operating about $v = 1$ ft/sec. Equation (7.10-3) becomes

$$\Delta v(t) = 0.005[1 - \epsilon^{-2t}] \qquad (7.10\text{-}4)$$

Equation (7.10-1) can now be expressed as

$$\frac{dv}{dt} + v^2 = 1.01$$

with the initial condition $t = 0$, $v = 1$. The solution can be obtained by separation of variables and is

$$v(t) = 1.005 \left[ \frac{401\epsilon^{1.005t} - \epsilon^{-1.005t}}{401\epsilon^{1.005t} + \epsilon^{-1.005t}} \right] \qquad (7.10\text{-}5)$$

To compare Eq. (7.10-5) to (7.10-4) let us write it as

$$\Delta v = 1.005 \left[ \frac{401\epsilon^{1.005t} - \epsilon^{-1.005t}}{401\epsilon^{1.005t} + \epsilon^{-1.005t}} \right] - 1$$

Shown below is a table comparing the two results.

| $t$ | $\Delta v$ linear | $\Delta v$ non-linear |
|-----|-----|-----|
| 0.2 | 0.00165 | 0.00165 |
| 0.4 | 0.00275 | 0.00276 |
| 0.6 | 0.00349 | 0.00350 |
| 0.8 | 0.00399 | 0.00400 |
| 1.0 | 0.00433 | 0.00433 |
| 2.0 | 0.00491 | 0.00491 |
| 4.0 | 0.004998 | 0.00500 |

Thus, for a signal of this size, the linearized equation gives an almost exact solution. It is not expected that larger inputs would correspond this closely. Now it is true that this signal is exceedingly small, but one obtains a very good idea of the system operation by employing such a technique. In addition, many systems act as regulators and by their nature tend to maintain their output at some constant level.

In our examples we will use the nomenclature where the delta indicates our incremental variable and the subscript zero indicates an operating point

## 7.20 ELECTRONIC DEVICES

Since the analysis of a vacuum tube amplifier is a familiar problem to electrical engineers, it serves as a good starting point in our illustrations of linearization techniques.

A typical circuit is shown in Fig. 7.20-1. Using Kirchhoff's laws, the equations of motion are

$$E_{bb} - I_b R_L = E_b \qquad (7.20\text{-}1)$$

and

$$I_b = f(E_c, E_b) \qquad (7.20\text{-}2)$$

where $E_{bb}$ is the supply voltage, $E_b$ is the plate voltage, and $E_c$ is the grid voltage. Equation (7.20-2) indicates that the plate current is some function

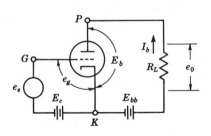

Fig. 7.20-1 Triode amplifier.

of the grid voltage and plate voltage. Although this function is not known in an analytical form, typical characteristic curves are shown in Fig. 7.20-2.

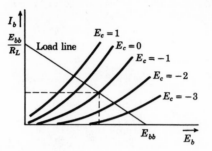

Fig. 7.20-2 Load line analysis of an amplifier.

We can now linearize Eq. (7.20-2) and obtain

$$\Delta I_b = \frac{\partial f}{\partial E_c} \Delta E_c + \frac{\partial f}{\partial E_b} \Delta E_b \qquad (7.20\text{-}3)$$

The partial derivatives as shown in Eq. (7.20-3) are slopes of the characteristic curves around the so-called load line. It is usual practice to express Eq. (7.20-3) with lower-case letters instead of delta as

$$i_p = g_m e_c - \frac{e_p}{r_p} \qquad (7.20\text{-}4)$$

where

$$\frac{\partial f}{\partial E_c}\bigg]_{E_b = \text{constant}} = g_m$$

$$\frac{\partial f}{\partial E_b}\bigg]_{E_c = \text{constant}} = -\frac{1}{r_p}$$

The equivalent circuit of Fig. 7.20-1 for small signals is shown in Fig. 7.20-3. The transfer function of the amplifier can be found as follows:

$$i_p = \frac{\mu e_g}{r_p + R_L} \qquad (\mu = g_m r_p)$$

$$e_0 = -i_p R_L$$

and

$$e_0 = -\frac{\mu e_g R_L}{r_p + R_L}$$

$$\frac{e_0}{e_g} = -\frac{\mu R_L}{r_p + R_L}$$

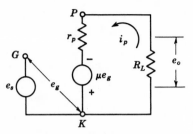

Fig. 7.20-3 Equivalent circuit of triode.

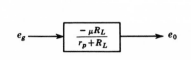

Figure 7.20-4

The block diagram becomes that of Fig. 7.20-4. This diagram is true for small signals about an equilibrium value or operating point. If $e_s$ changes 1 volt and $e_0$ changes 10 volts, the actual voltage across the resistor $R_L$ in Fig. 7.20-1 would be $I_p R_L - 10$. The parameters $\mu$, $r_p$, and $g_m$ are determined by the level of $I_b$, $E_{bb}$, and $E_{cc}$.

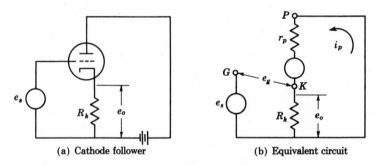

(a) Cathode follower                (b) Equivalent circuit

Fig. 7.20-5 Cathode follower.

For the cathode follower of Fig. 7.20-5, the equations are

$$e_g = e_s - e_0$$

$$i_p = \frac{\mu e_g}{r_p + R_k}$$

and

$$e_0 = R_k i_p$$

The block diagram becomes as shown in Fig. 7.20-6. The response is given by

$$\frac{e_0}{e_s} = \frac{\mu R_k}{r_p + R_k + \mu R_k}$$

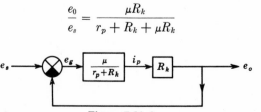

Figure 7.20-6

Rearranging,

$$\frac{e_0}{e_s} = \frac{1}{\dfrac{r_p}{\mu R_k} + \dfrac{1 + \mu}{\mu}}$$

Under the restrictions of $\mu R_k \gg r_p$ and $\mu \gg 1$ the response of the cathode follower approaches unity.

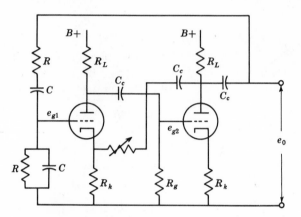

**Fig. 7.20-7** Wien bridge oscillator.

Electrical engineers make use of oscillators in many systems. An oscillator is a control system that is deliberately made unstable. As an example consider a simplified version of the Wien bridge oscillator as shown in Fig. 7.20-7. The two vacuum tubes, neglecting interelectrode capacitances, provide a gain and have the block diagram of Fig. 7.20-8. Since there are two tubes, the output $e_o$ is in phase with $e_{g_1}$. Let us now deter-

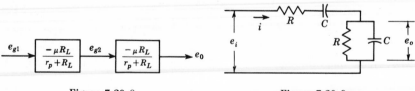

**Figure 7.20-8**                                    **Figure 7.20-9**

mine the transfer function of the Wien bridge as shown in Fig. 7.20-9, where

$$Z(s) = R + \frac{1}{Cs} + \frac{R/Cs}{R + 1/Cs}$$

Rearranging

$$Z(s) = \frac{(RCs + 1)^2 + RCs}{Cs(RCs + 1)}$$

Now

$$E_0(s) = \frac{R/Cs}{R + 1/Cs} I(s)$$

and hence,

$$\frac{E_0}{E_i}(s) = \frac{R}{RCs + 1} \times \frac{1}{Z(s)}$$

The transfer function of the Wien bridge can now be expressed as

$$\frac{E_0}{E_i}(s) = \frac{RCs}{(RCs)^2 + 3RCs + 1}$$

The block diagram becomes that of Fig. 7.20-10. The frequency response becomes

$$\frac{E_0}{E_i}(s) = \frac{ARCs/(RCs)^2 + 3RCs + 1}{1 - \frac{ARCs}{(RCs)^2 + 3RCs + 1}}$$

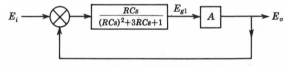

**Figure 7.20-10**

For this system to be neutrally unstable, the roots of the characteristic equation must be pure imaginary. This requires

$$ARCs = (RCs)^2 + 3RCs + 1$$

or

$$(RCs)^2 + (3 - A)RCs + 1 = 0$$

For pure imaginary roots, $A = 3$, and hence, the roots occur at $s_1, s_2 = \pm i(1/RC)$. This tells us that if we adjust the gain to a value of 3, the system will oscillate at a frequency of $1/RC$ radians per second.


## 7.30 ELECTROMECHANICAL SYSTEMS

Many missile systems obtain electrical power at the launch site from electromechanical power supplies. In Fig. 7.30-1 is shown an electrical generator supplying power to an electrical motor. This motor can be thought of as a hydraulic pump motor for the vane actuators. In this example the prime mover is not considered, although its dynamics would have to be included for a complete system study.

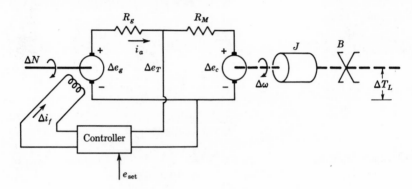

**Fig. 7.30-1** Electromechanical power supply.

The purpose of the controller is to maintain a constant terminal voltage. The motor is a separately excited d-c motor. The following assumptions are made:

1. The resistances of the brushes, armature, and compensating windings are constant.
2. The torque-current relationship is linear over the control region.
3. The inductance of the windings may be neglected.

The following definitions are necessary to write the equations of motion:

$e_g$ = generated voltage,

$N$ = rpm of the prime mover,

$i_f$ = field current,

$e_T$ = terminal voltage,

$R_g$ = generator resistance,

$R_M$ = motor resistance,

$i_a$ = armature current,

$e_c$ = back emf of motor,

$\omega_M$ = speed of motor in rad/sec,

$T_e$ = electrical torque in ft-lb,

$T_M$ = motor torque in ft-lb,

$T_L$ = load torque in ft-lb,

$J$ = polar moment of inertia of motor in lb-ft-sec$^2$,

$B$ = viscous friction constant in lb-ft/sec.

The equations of motion can now be written for this system. Since the generated voltage is a function of both the speed and field current, we will for the present indicate this as

$$e_g = f(N, i_f) \tag{7.30-1}$$

By Kirchhoff's laws

$$e_T = e_g - i_a R_g \tag{7.30-2}$$

By the same process

$$e_c = e_T - i_a R_M \tag{7.30-3}$$

Since the motor is separately excited, the back emf is a linear function of the speed, or

$$e_c = K_c \omega_M, \qquad (K_c \text{ in volt/rad/sec}) \tag{7.30-4}$$

Summing the torques,

$$T_e - T_L = T_M \tag{7.30-5}$$

But

$$T_e = K_T i_a \qquad (K_T \text{ in ft-lb/amp}) \tag{7.30-6}$$

and

$$T_M = J \frac{d\omega_M}{dt} + B\omega_M \tag{7.30-7}$$

Hence,

$$K_T i_a - T_L = J \frac{d\omega_M}{dt} + B\omega_M \tag{7.30-8}$$

It is now necessary to obtain an explicit linear form of Eq. (7.30-1). We will follow the same procedure as in the case of the vacuum tube amplifier (see Eq. (7.20-2) and (7.20-3)). Thus, the differential of Eq. (7.30-1) is

$$\Delta e_g = \frac{\partial f}{\partial N}\bigg]_{i_f = \text{constant}} \Delta N + \frac{\partial f}{\partial i_f}\bigg]_{N = \text{constant}} \Delta i_f \tag{7.30-9}$$

The operating point of the system must now be established. To simplify our calculations we will consider the motor and generator as the same type of machine. However, in actual practice the motor might be a different type of machine.

The prime mover is operating at 6000 rpm and the controller is adjusted to maintain 22.5 volts at the terminals of the generator. At rated load the motor draws 135 amperes and its field current is adjusted to 10 amperes.

The rated speed is 1645 rpm and the armature resistance is 0.075 ohms. From Fig. 7.30-2 it is seen that the back emf of the motor is

$$e_c = \frac{1645}{5700} \times 43 = 12.4 \text{ volts}$$

Hence,

$$K_c =$$

$$\frac{12.4}{\dfrac{1645 \times 2\pi}{60}} = 0.072 \text{ volts/rad/sec}$$

The generated voltage is $22.5 + (135)(0.075) = 32.6$ volts. From Fig. 7.30-3 this generated voltage is developed at 6000 rpm with a field current of $i_f = 3.75$ amperes. For small changes about this operating point,

$$\left.\frac{\partial f}{\partial N}\right]_{i_f=3.75} = \frac{35.5 - 30}{6500 - 5500}$$

$$= 0.0055 \text{ volts/rpm.}$$

**Fig. 7.30-2** Saturation curve for General Electric machine 2CM85D1. (Courtesy General Electric Company)

However, we cannot calculate $\partial f/\partial i_f]_{N=\text{constant}}$ in this manner owing to the time lag in the field of the generator and control amplifier. This lag can be obtained by making an actual frequency response test of the controller and field of the generator. In Fig. 7.30-4 is shown the frequency

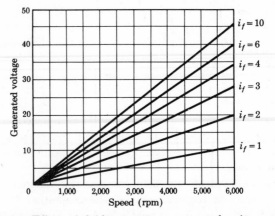

**Fig. 7.30-3** Effect of field current on generated voltage of General Electric 2CM85E1 machine. (Courtesy General Electric Company)

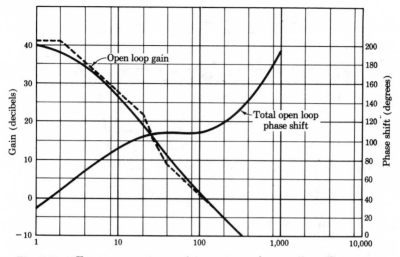

**Fig. 7.30-4** Frequency response of generator and controller. (Courtesy General Electric Company)

response of the generated voltage for small signal inputs to the controller. This response is given by

$$\frac{E_g}{(E_{\text{set}} - E_T)}(s) = \left[\frac{100\epsilon^{-0.002s}}{\left(\dfrac{s}{2} + 1\right)\left(\dfrac{s}{20} + 1\right)}\right]\left(\frac{s}{40} + 1\right)$$

The following items are obtained by measurements:

$R_g = R_M = 0.075$ ohms

$J = 0.0014$ ft-lb sec$^2$

$B = 0.005675$ ft-lb/rad/sec

(The elastance of the motor shaft has been neglected.) From Fig. 7.30-5 we obtain the value

torque $= 6.1$ ft-lb.

Hence

$$K_T = \frac{6.1}{135} = 0.0543 \text{ ft-lb/amp.}$$

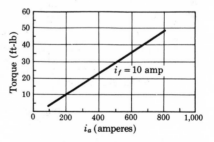

**Fig. 7.30-5** Torque-current relationship for General Electric 2CM85E1 machine. (Courtesy General Electric Company)

The block diagram of the motor-generator set can now be developed and is shown in Fig. 7.30-6. All variables have been written with a delta to emphasize they are deviations from some operating point.

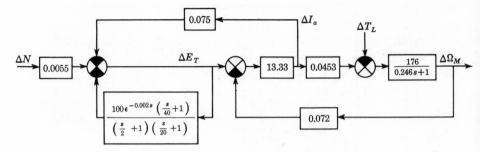

**Fig. 7.30-6** Linearized block diagram of electromechanical power supply.

## 7.40 A-C POWER SUPPLY

The preceding example concerned a d-c electromechanical power supply. If, however, the d-c machines are replaced by an a-c generator and an induction motor, the problem becomes more complicated owing to the phase relationships between current and voltage in an a-c system. Before defining the example to be discussed in this section, let us examine an a-c generator and an induction motor to obtain some understanding of their operation.

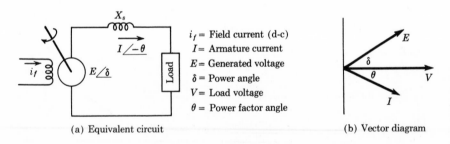

$i_f$ = Field current (d-c)
$I$ = Armature current
$E$ = Generated voltage
$\delta$ = Power angle
$V$ = Load voltage
$\theta$ = Power factor angle

(a) Equivalent circuit                              (b) Vector diagram

**Fig. 7.40-1** A-C generator.

In Fig. 7.40-1 is shown an a-c generator with a load. The equivalent circuit is quite similar to that of a d-c motor. However, whereas in a d-c generator the output voltage is obtained by subtracting the $IR$ drop due to the resistance from the generated voltage (inductance is usually neglected), the a-c output must be obtained by *vectorially* subtracting the $IZ_s$ drop from the generated voltage. The impedance $Z_s$ of the windings, commonly called *synchronous impedance*, is not the impedance of the windings but is a fictitious value which accounts for armature reaction.

In practice $R_s$ is small compared with $Z_s$ and thus $Z_s$ is generally considered an inductance $X_s$. The vector diagram is shown in Fig. 7.40-1 where $\theta$ is the angle between load voltage and load current (the power factor angle). It is common practice to consider the load voltage $V$ as the reference where the angle between $V$ and $E$ is the power angle $\delta$.

For a constant field current $i_f$, the magnitude of the generated voltage $E$ is directly proportional to the generator speed $N_s$. The power angle $\delta$ is determined by the power requirements of the load. The vector relationships are

$$E\underline{/\delta} + IX_s\underline{/90 - \theta} = V\underline{/0}$$

$$\frac{EV}{x_s} \sin \delta = EI \cos \theta$$

$$|E| = K_s N_s$$

The approximate equivalent circuit of an induction motor on a per phase basis is shown in Fig. 7.40-2. $V$ is the applied voltage and $R$ is a fictitious resistance which accounts for the power output of the machine.

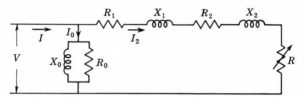

**Fig. 7.40-2** Approximate equivalent circuit for an induction motor.

$R_0$ and $X_0$ account for its no-load loss. $R_0$ and $X_0$ can be obtained by measuring the power input to the machine at no load. $R_1$ and $R_2$ account for stator and rotor losses. These values may be obtained by measuring the input to the machine when the rotor is blocked. $R_2$ and $X_2$ are the rotor values referred to the stator side of the machine. The steady-state relationships can be summarized as:

$f$ = frequency in cycles per sec,

$P$ = no. of poles,

$N_s$ = $120(f/P)$ rpm,

$N$ = motor speed in rps = $(1 - p)N_s$,

$I\underline{\ \theta} = I_0\underline{/\theta_0} + I_2\underline{/\theta_2}$,

$R = R_2\left(\dfrac{1 - p}{p}\right)$

$p$ = slip in decimal values,

$I_2^2 R$ = power developed by machine.

The operation of the induction motor for various values of slip is best shown by a circle diagram as in Fig. 7.40-3. $I_0$ is the no-load current and this determines the location of the point $P$ on the diagram. The line $\overline{PK}$ is then drawn. It is not necessary to know the length $\overline{PK}$. The line $\overline{OH}$ is then drawn which is the vector value of blocked rotor current at rated voltage. This establishes two points of the circle, i.e. $P$ and $H$. The line $\overline{PH}$ is then drawn. $\overline{PH}$ is bisected and the perpendicular $\overline{M'M}$ is drawn. $M$ is the center of the circle $PHK$. $\overline{PK}$ is the diameter of this semicircle and has the value

$$\overline{PK} = \frac{V}{X_1 + X_2}$$

A perpendicular $\overline{HJ}$ is drawn to $\overline{PK}$. This line is divided at $G$ such that $HG/GF = R_2/R_1$. The line $\overline{PG}$ is then drawn. The point $\overline{OE}$ now represents a value of current at some slip $p$. The following values can be read from the circle diagram:

output power $= \overline{DE} \times V$ per phase,

efficiency $= \overline{DE}/\overline{AE}$,

torque $= \dfrac{7.04 \times V \times \overline{CE}}{N_s}$ lb-ft/phase,

slip $= \overline{CD}/\overline{CE}$,

power factor $= \overline{EA}/I$.

Torque per phase can be calculated from the equivalent circuit as follows:

$$\text{power} = I_2^2 R_2 \left( \frac{1-p}{p} \right)$$

but

$$I_2 = \frac{V}{\sqrt{(R_1 + R_2/p)^2 + (X_1 + X_2)^2}}$$

and hence

$$\text{power} = \frac{V^2}{(R_1 + R_2/p)^2 + (X_1 + X_2)^2} \times \frac{R_2(1-p)}{p}$$

Since

$$\text{power} = \frac{746 \times 2\pi}{33,000} NT \tag{7.40-1}$$

$$T = V^2 \times R_2 \frac{(1-p)}{p} \times \frac{33,000}{2\pi(746)N} \times \frac{1}{(R_1 + R_2/p)^2 + (X_1 + X_2)^2}$$

With $N = (1-p)N_s$, Eq. (7.40-1) becomes

$$T = \frac{33,000}{2\pi(746)} \times \frac{R_2}{N_s} \times \frac{V^2}{p} \times \frac{1}{(R_1 + R_2/p)^2 + (X_1 + X_2)^2} \tag{7.40-2}$$

With these facts in mind, let us examine an a-c power supply with an induction motor as the load. The induction motor can be the erection motor for a missile, in which case the mechanical load is pure inertia. The terminal voltage of the generator is maintained constant by regulating the field current of the generator.

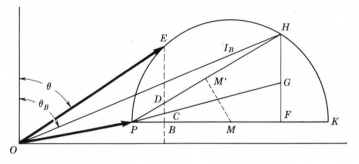

**Fig. 7.40-3** Circle diagram for an induction motor.

The no-load and blocked-rotor tests give the following results:

(a) No-load test:

$I_{NL} = 9.94$ amps,
$P_{NL} = 9.40$ watts,
$V_{NL} = 200$ volts line-to-line.

(b) Blocked-rotor test:

$I_{BR} = 164$ amps,
$P_{BR} = 25,880$ watts,
$V_{BR} = 201$ volts line-to-line.

From these tests,

$$R_1 + R_2 = \frac{25,880}{3(164)^2} = 0.3215\Omega/\text{phase}$$

$$Z = \frac{201}{\sqrt{3}\,164} = 0.705\Omega/\text{phase}$$

$$X_1 + Y_2 = \sqrt{0.496 - 0.1065} = 0.625\Omega/\text{phase}$$

The circle diagram can now be constructed as shown in Fig. 7.40-3. However, the presence of $X_0$ and $R_0$ as in Fig. 7.40-4 will complicate the block diagram which we wish to develop. Instead of drawing the circle diagram, which would be offset from the origin, let us construct a circle diagram that does not have no-load losses but will have essentially the same torque-speed characteristics as the actual machine. To accomplish this, first examine the circle diagram. Torque can be obtained by

$$T = \frac{7.04 V \overline{CE}}{N_s}$$

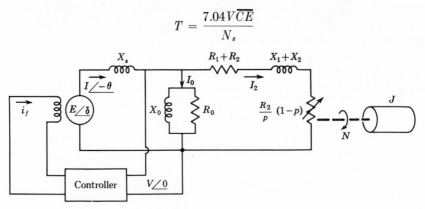

**Fig. 7.40-4** A-C power supply.

$\overline{CE}$ can be adjusted by changing the ratio $\overline{HG}/\overline{GF}$, which is equivalent to adjusting the ratio $R_2/R_1$. After "trial and error" the torque-speed characteristic shown in Fig. 7.40-5 is obtained for $\overline{HG}/\overline{GF} = 40/30$. This gives a close check to the measured value.

The equations can now be written as follows:

Let $T_e$ = electrical torque,

$\quad T_L$ = load torque,

$\quad N$ = speed of motor in rps,

$\quad N_s$ = synchronous speed,

$\quad p$ = slip,

$\quad J$ = load inertia.

Now

$$T_e - T_L = \frac{J}{2\pi} \frac{dN}{dt} \tag{7.40-3}$$

$$T_e = \frac{33,000}{2\pi(746)N_s} \frac{3V^2}{R_2} \frac{1}{p[(R_1 + R_2/p)^2 + X^2]} \tag{7.40-4}$$

Equation (7.40-4) is of the form $T_e = f(p, V)$, and as in the case of the vacuum tube we can now linearize about some operating point:

$$\Delta T_e = \frac{\partial f}{\partial p} \Delta p + \frac{\partial f}{\partial V} \Delta V \tag{7.40-5}$$

If the load is disconnected from the generator and a sinusoidal signal of varying frequency is applied to the regulator, the Bode plot as shown

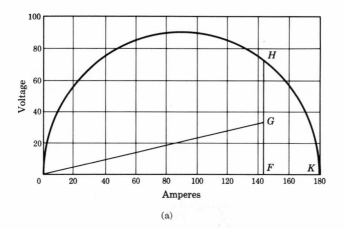

(a)

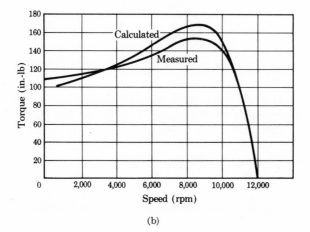

(b)

**Fig. 7.40-5** (a) Equivalent circle diagram; (b) Comparison of actual and equivalent responses.

in Fig. 7.40-6 is obtained. The transfer function of the regulator and generated voltage is

$$\frac{\Delta E}{\Delta V}(s) = \frac{40\left(\dfrac{s}{55} + 1\right)\epsilon^{-0.002s}}{\left(\dfrac{s}{20} + 1\right)\left(\dfrac{s}{40} + 1\right)\left(\dfrac{s}{80} + 1\right)} \qquad (7.40\text{-}6)$$

Let us consider the speed of the generator as constant and also as the synchronous speed of the motor. The circuit shown in Fig. 7.40-1 will serve as the equivalent circuit if $R_0$ and $X_0$ are removed. (This makes $I = I_2$.)

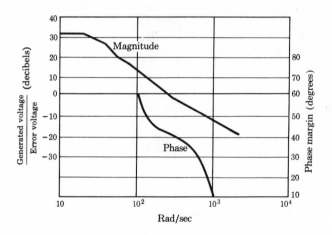

**Fig. 7.40-6** A-C regulator bode plot. (Courtesy General Electric Company)

There are two operating conditions that should be examined to determine the stability of this system, i.e. low-slip or normal running conditions and high-slip or starting conditions. To examine these conditions it will be considered that the mechanical load determines the transient conditions. This means that at any instant of time the currents and voltages may be calculated from the equivalent circuit if we know the speed. In this example we will develop the block diagram for only the low-slip case.

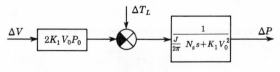

**Figure 7.40-7**

Returning to Eq. (7.40-4), we can simplify as

$$\lim_{p \to 0} T_e \approx K_1 V^2 p$$

where

$$K_1 = \frac{33{,}000 \times 3}{(2\pi)(746)N_s R_2^3}$$

Equation (7.40-4) now becomes

$$\Delta T_e = K_1 V_0^2 \, \Delta p + 2K_1 p_0 V_0 \, \Delta V \tag{7.40-7}$$

As in Sec. 7.10, the subscript zero denotes an operating point and the delta an incremental change around this operating point. Unlike the vacuum tube, an explicit functional relationship between the variables exists.

Equation (7.40-3) becomes

$$K_1 V_0^2 \, \Delta p + 2K_1 V_0 P_0 \, \Delta V - \Delta T_L = \frac{J}{2\pi} \frac{d}{dt}(\Delta N)$$

but

$$N = N_s(1 - p) \quad \text{and} \quad \Delta N = -N_s \, \Delta p$$

Hence

$$K_1 V_0^2 \, \Delta p + 2K_1 V_0 P_0 \, \Delta V - \Delta T_L = -\frac{J}{2\pi} N_s \frac{d}{dt}(\Delta p)$$

Rearranging,

$$\Delta T_L - \left(K_1 V_0^2 + \frac{J}{2\pi} N_s s\right) \Delta P = 2K_1 V_0 P_0 \, \Delta V \tag{7.40-8}$$

where $s$ is the Laplace operator.

The block diagram for Eq. (7.40-8) becomes that of Fig. 7.40-7. The block diagram for Eq. (7.40-6) becomes that of Fig. 7.40-8. The negative

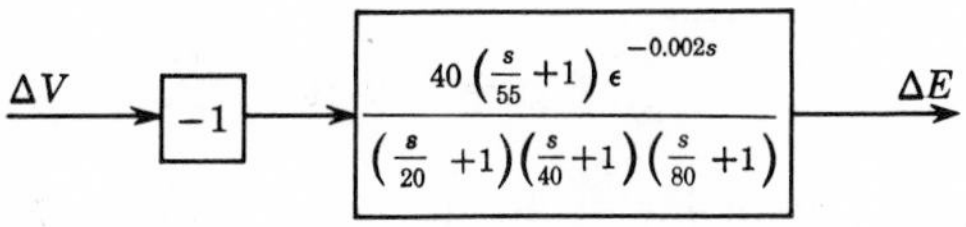

$$\Delta V \quad \boxed{-1} \quad \longrightarrow \quad \boxed{\frac{40\left(\frac{s}{55}+1\right)\epsilon^{-0.002s}}{\left(\frac{s}{20}+1\right)\left(\frac{s}{40}+1\right)\left(\frac{s}{80}+1\right)}} \quad \Delta E$$

**Figure 7.40-8**

sign takes care of the controller action; if the voltage is too high, $E$ must decrease.

From Fig. 7.40-2 the impedance angle of the motor is

$$\tan \theta = \frac{X}{R_1 + R_2/p} = \frac{pX}{R_1 p + R_2}$$

Hence, for small values of slip,

$$\tan \theta = p \frac{X}{R_2} \quad \text{or} \quad \theta = \tan^{-1} p \frac{X}{R_2}$$

Thus $$\Delta\theta = K_2 \, \Delta p$$

where $$K_2 = \frac{X}{R_2(1 + P_0^2 X^2/R_2^2)}$$

The impedance angle block diagram becomes that of Fig. 7.40-9. The terminal voltage $V$ and the current $I$ are related to the generated voltage $E$ by

$$E\underline{/\delta} - jX_s I \underline{/-\theta} = V \quad 0°$$

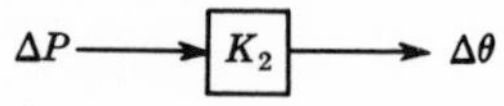

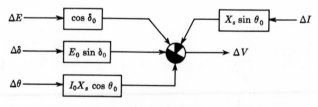

$\Delta P \longrightarrow \boxed{K_2} \longrightarrow \Delta\theta$

**Figure 7.40-9**

Equating real and imaginary components:

$$E \cos \delta - IX_s \sin \theta = V \qquad (7.40\text{-}9)$$

$$E \sin \delta = IX_s \cos \theta \qquad (7.40\text{-}10)$$

Linearizing Eq. (7.40-9),

$$\Delta E \cos \delta_0 - E_0 \sin \delta_0 \, \Delta\delta - (IX_s \cos \theta)_0 \, \Delta\theta - (X_s \sin \theta)_0 \, \Delta I = \Delta V$$

Linearizing Eq. (7.40-10),

$$\Delta E \sin \delta_0 + E_0 \cos \delta_0 \, \Delta\delta = (X_s \cos \theta)_0 \, \Delta I - (IX_s \sin \theta)_0 \, \Delta\theta$$

From the linearization of Eq. (7.40-9), Fig. 7.40-10 is obtained.

$\Delta E \longrightarrow \boxed{\cos \delta_0}$ $\qquad$ $\boxed{X_s \sin \theta_0} \longleftarrow \Delta I$

$\Delta\delta \longrightarrow \boxed{E_0 \sin \delta_0}$ $\qquad \longrightarrow \Delta V$

$\Delta\theta \longrightarrow \boxed{I_0 X_s \cos \theta_0}$

**Figure 7.40-10**

From the linearization of Eq. (7.40-10) we obtain Fig. 7.40-11. The power angle $\delta$ can be found from the relationship

$$\frac{EV}{X_s} \sin \delta = VI \cos \theta \qquad (7.40\text{-}11)$$

Linearizing Eq. (7.40-11),

$$\Delta E \sin \delta_0 + E_0 \cos \delta_0 \, \Delta\delta = -(IX_s \sin \theta)_0 \, \Delta\theta + X_s \cos \theta_0 \, \Delta I$$

The block diagram becomes that of Fig. 7.40-12. The system block diagram can now be formed and is shown in Fig. 7.40-13.

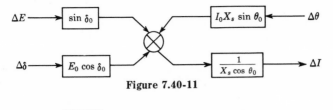

**Figure 7.40-11**

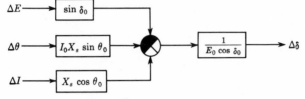

**Figure 7.40-12**

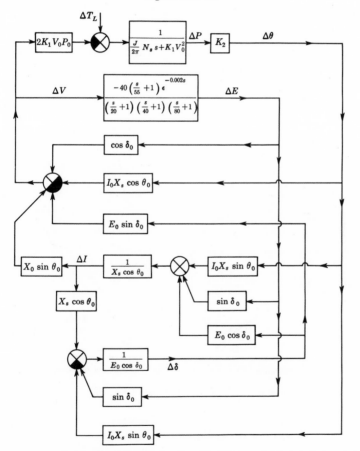

**Fig. 7.40-13** Block diagram for linearized a-c motor generator set. (Low slip)

257

## 7.50 TWO-PHASE SERVO MOTORS

In Fig. 7.50-1 is shown a schematic of a two-phase servo motor. Such a motor is ordinarily a two-phase induction motor constructed with a high-resistance rotor and low-inertia rotating members. A constant volt-age is applied to one field and a varying volt-age 90° out of phase with the fixed voltage to the other field. The steady-state responses of these motors are usually shown in graphical form as in Fig. 7.50-2. These motors are used for instrument servos requiring torque outputs of a few inch-ounces.

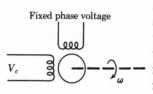

Fixed phase voltage

$V_c$    $\omega$

**Fig. 7.50-1** Two-phase servo motor.

For a load consisting of inertia and viscous friction, Eq. (7.40-4) can be used to develop the transfer function of this motor as follows:

$$\Delta T_e = K_c \, \Delta V_c - K_N \, \Delta N$$

For a positional servo with the angular position in radians denoted by $\Theta$,

$$\frac{\Delta \Theta}{\Delta V_c}(s) = \frac{K}{s(\tau s + 1)}$$

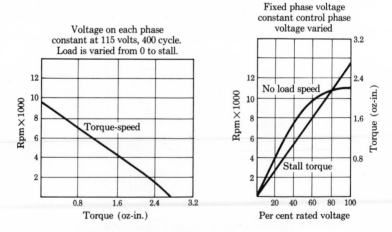

**Fig. 7.50-2** Characteristics of Kearfott R112 two-phase servo motor. (Courtesy Kearfott Division, General Precision, Inc.)

The viscous motor friction is computed by assuming that the stalled torque $T_s$ is developed at the rotor for all speeds, but as the speed is allowed to increase by reducing the external load, the internal losses due to bearing friction, windage, and electrical damping limit the speed to the measured value. This assumption is good for a speed range not much in excess of one-half synchronous. The equation for the total motor friction is

$$B + K_N = \frac{T_s - T_V}{N}$$

where $T_V$ is delivered torque at the shaft velocity $N$. Hence

$$B + K_N = \frac{\text{stall torque}}{\text{no-load speed}}$$

The mechanical time constant $\tau$ is

$$\tau = \frac{\text{rotor inertia} \times \text{no-load speed}}{\text{stall torque}}$$

The gain $K$ of the system is taken as the slope of the no-load speed vs. per cent rated voltage curve in Fig. 7.50-2. For the Kearfott R112-2, $-5$ motor this value is 174 rpm/volt. Since the rotor inertia is 4.0 gm-cm$^2$,

$$J = \frac{2\pi}{60}\left[\frac{6000}{0.8}\right]\frac{4}{7.06 \times 10^4} = 0.0444 \text{ sec}$$

and the transfer function for small deviations around zero speed (positional servo) is

$$\frac{\Delta\Theta}{\Delta V_c}(s) = \frac{174 \times 2\pi/60}{0.0444s + 1}$$

## 7.60   ELECTROHYDRAULIC SYSTEMS

For the reader who is unfamiliar with fluid power systems, we will first enumerate some of the features that make the use of hydraulic systems particularly attractive to control engineers. These features are:

1. size
2. weight
3. power level
4. torque to inertia ratio
5. reliability
6. cost
7. ease of control.

Items 1 and 2 are of prime importance for power devices in the aircraft and missile field. Items 3 and 4 are advantages of hydraulic motors in certain ranges. A typical hydraulic motor has a torque to inertia ratio of 410,000 rad/sec² and weighs 1.75 lb. The d-c machine discussed in the preceding section has a torque to inertia ratio of 4357 rad/sec².

Since hydraulic control valves are built to very tight tolerances their costs are quite high, but they still compare to other types of control devices. The mechanical nature of their construction, however, leads to a very high degree of reliability.

### 7.61  HYDRAULIC GENERATOR

Hydraulic power is delivered to a motor in the form of a volumetric flow rate of the fluid which operates against some load-induced pressure. A very simple reciprocating pump is shown in Fig. 7.61-1. The piston is

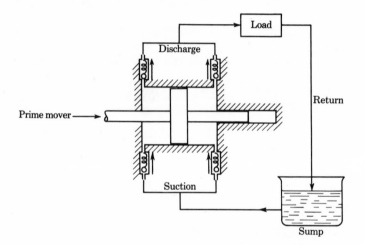

Fig. 7.61-1 Simple hydraulic generator.

connected to suction and discharge ports by means of appropriate valving such that on the section part of the stroke the chamber formed by the piston and the bore in which it operates is completely filled with fluid taken from the suction line. During the discharge stroke this volume of fluid is delivered to the discharge line at a higher pressure. In actual practice a multiplicity of such pistons must be provided. In addition, the angular phasing of the pistons should be such that each piston performs its suction and discharge functions in a fixed phase relationship to the piston that follows it. (Note the similarity with the commutator on a d-c machine.)

## 7.62 HYDRAULIC MOTOR AND SPOOL VALVE

In Fig. 7.62-1 is shown, as a typical application of a valve-controlled hydraulic servomotor, a vane actuator for an aircraft or missile. The supply pressure $p_s$ in psi is supplied by a pump as shown in Fig. 7.61-1.

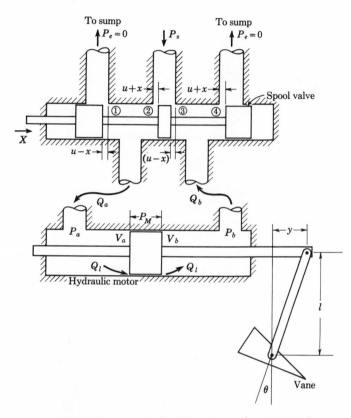

**Fig. 7.62-1** Four-way hydraulic motor and vane actuator.

The servo valve is a four-way valve and the motor is a ram-type motor which drives the vane. A change in the spool valve position changes the orifice openings which changes the rate at which the ram piston moves.

The derivation of the block diagram for the spool valve and ram with an inertia load has been developed in great detail by others.* We will not show the development in its entirety here but we will emphasize the salient points.

---

* See Bibliography, Chap. 7.

The development starts with the fundamental equation for the volume rate of flow through orifice 1 in Fig. 7.62-1 which is

$$q_1 = C_d A_1 \sqrt{\frac{2}{\rho} [p_{\text{up}} - p_{\text{down}}]} \qquad (7.62\text{-}1)$$

where $q_1$ = volume rate of flow in in.³/sec,

$\quad C_d$ = discharge coefficient (dimensionless),

$\quad A_1$ = orifice area in in.²,

$\quad p_{\text{up}}$ = upstream pressure in lb/in.²,

$\quad p_{\text{down}}$ = downstream pressure in lb/in.²,

$\quad \rho$ = fluid mass density in lb-sec²/in.⁴

Equation (7.62-1) is a nonlinear equation of the form

$$q_1 = f(p_{\text{differential}}, A_1)$$

Instead of treating this equation as in Sec. 7.20, Eq. (7.20-1), let us first take the logarithm of each side to obtain

$$\log q_1 = \frac{1}{2} \log \frac{p_{\text{up}} - p_{\text{down}}}{\rho} + \log C_d A_1 \qquad (7.62\text{-}2)$$

Note that $A_1$ is a variable which is proportional to the displacement $x$. Taking the derivative of Eq. (7.62-2),

$$\frac{dq_1}{q_1} = \frac{1}{2} \frac{d(p_{\text{up}} - p_{\text{down}})}{(p_{\text{up}} - p_{\text{down}})} + \frac{dA_1}{A_1}$$

and thus,

$$\frac{\Delta q_1}{Q_{1_0}} = \frac{1}{2} \frac{\Delta(p_{\text{up}} - p_{\text{down}})}{(P_{\text{up}} - P_{\text{down}})_0} + \frac{\Delta A_1}{A_{1_0}}$$

where the delta and subscript zero have our usual meaning. Now since $p_{\text{up}}$ is our supply pressure $p_s$ and is considered constant,

$$\frac{\Delta q_1}{Q_{1_0}} = \frac{1}{2} \frac{\Delta p_a}{P_{a_0}} + \frac{\Delta A_1}{A_{1_0}}$$

But

$$\Delta A_1 = - \frac{\Delta x}{u - x_0}$$

and hence

$$\frac{\Delta q_1}{Q_{1_0}} = \frac{1}{2} \frac{\Delta p_a}{P_{a_0}} - \frac{\Delta x}{u - x_0}$$

It is evident that four such equations can be written, one for each orifice.

When the motion of the ram is restricted to small values, i.e. $v_a \approx v_b$, the linearized transfer function between ram velocity $dy/dt$, spool position $x$, and leakage flow $q_l$ is

$$A \, \Delta \dot{Y}(s) = k_1 \, \Delta X(s) - C_1 \, \Delta P_m(s) - \Delta Q_l(s) - \frac{1}{2}\left(k_e + \frac{V_0}{\beta}\right) s \, \Delta P_m(s)$$

where $A$ = ram area,

$$k_1 = \frac{\partial q_m}{\partial x}\bigg]_{p_m = \text{constant}}$$

$$C_1 = \frac{\partial q_m}{\partial p_m}\bigg]_{x = \text{constant}}$$

$k_e$ = elasticity of the lines,

$\beta$ = bulk modulus of the fluid.

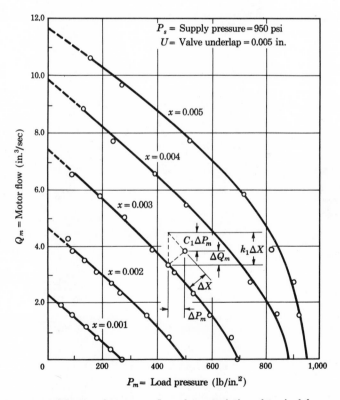

Fig. 7.62-2 Measured pressure-flow characteristics of typical four-way control valve: port width $u \approx 1$ in. (Reprinted from " Dynamic Characteristics of Valve-Controlled Hydraulic Servo Motors" by J. L. Shearer. *Trans. ASME*, August, 1954, pp. 895–903.)

For laminar leakage flow $q_l$ past the ram

$$\Delta q_l = C_2 \, \Delta p_m$$

$k_1$ and $C_1$ are obtained from curves as shown in Fig. 7.62-2.

Now by defining

$$k_2 = C_1 + C_2 \quad \text{and} \quad k_3 = \tfrac{1}{2}(k_e + V_0/\beta)$$

we obtain

$$A \, \Delta \dot{Y} = k_1 \, \Delta X - k_2 \, \Delta P_m - k_3 s \, \Delta P_m \tag{7.62-3}$$

To obtain the angular rotation of the vane, we note that

$$\text{valve force} = A \, \Delta P_m$$

and

$$\text{vane torque} = I_v s^2 \, \Delta \Theta \qquad \text{(neglecting aerodynamic damping)}$$

where $I_v$ = polar moment of vane inertia

$\Delta \Theta$ = angular position of vane

Hence

$$A \, \Delta P_m = I_v s^2 \, \Delta \Theta + \Delta T_L$$

where $\Delta T_L$ = torque due to wind. Equation (7.62-3) becomes

$$A \, \Delta \dot{Y} = k_1 \, \Delta X - (k_2 + k_3 s) \frac{I_v s^2 \, \Delta \Theta + \Delta T_L}{l_A}$$

The block diagram of this system is shown in Fig. 7.62-3.

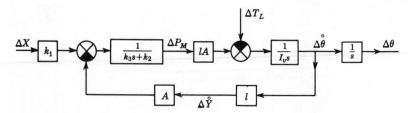

**Fig. 7.62-3** Block diagram for four-way servo-valve and vane actuator.

## 7.70 BALLISTIC MISSILE CONTROL SYSTEMS

The linearization techniques as developed in this chapter are used quite extensively in the design of missile control systems. In general, a missile system is designed to impact a warhead (either nuclear or con-

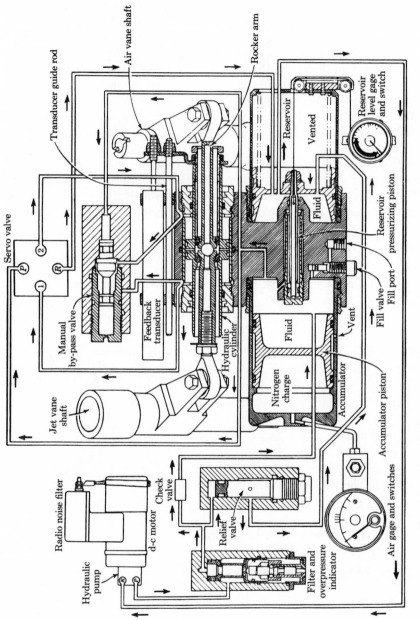

**Fig. 7.62-4** A typical vane actuating servo. (Courtesy Martin Marietta Corp.)

ventional) upon a selected target within a certain accuracy. In a typical surface-to-surface missile system, it is necessary to provide the missile with a control system to stabilize it in flight and guide it along a pre-selected trajectory. The input to the control system can be in the form of a contour on a cam or in the form of bits on magnetic tape. The winds aloft act as the disturbance, and the thrust of the burning propellant deflected by control vanes supplies the power to put the missile back on the trajectory. To illustrate this technique, we shall choose an extremely simple example of a missile that has both air vanes and jet vanes. The actuator for such a set of vanes is shown in Fig. 7.62-4. We will first write the equations of motion for the systems in the pitch plane only and will consider the wind as acting in a horizontal direction. We will also consider that the missile is a rigid body. Our linearization techniques will then be applied to these equations and a pitch block diagram for the system will be developed.

## 7.71 KINEMATIC DIAGRAM AND NOMENCLATURE

$x, z$ Reference axes, with $z$ directed vertically upward, $x$ forward.

$x_m, z_m$ Missile body axes, originating at the center of mass, with $x_m$ forward through the nose, $z_m$ at right angles downward in the pitch plane.

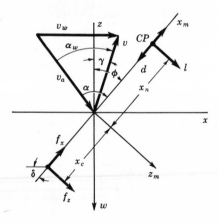

Fig. 7.71-1 Kinematic diagram and nomenclature.

$v$ Velocity of the missile with respect to the reference axes.

$v_a$ The airflow velocity, or velocity of the air relative to vehicle.

$v_w$ Velocity of the atmosphere, or wind velocity, with respect to the reference axes.

$\gamma$ Flight path angle. The inclination of the velocity vector to the reference vertical, positive in the forward direction.

$\alpha$ Angle of attack. The angle between the $x_m$ axis and the airflow vector, measured as shown in the kinematic diagram.

$\alpha_w$ Relative wind angle. The angle between airflow and missile velocity vectors, measured as shown in the kinematic diagram.

$\phi$ Pitch angle. The angular position of the $x_m$ axis relative to the reference vertical, measured clockwise.

$x_c$ Control moment arm.

$x_n$ Center of pressure moment arm. Positive when the C.P. is forward of the C.G.

$\delta$ Control vane angle.

$f$ Thrust, $f_x$ is the forward component, $f_z$ is the perpendicular component arising from control action.

$I$ Pitch moment of inertia.

$l$ Retarding force of the atmosphere normal to $x_m$ axis.

$d$ Retarding force of the atmosphere along $x_m$ axis.

$w$ Missile weight.

$m$ Missile mass.

## 7.72 PITCH PLANE EQUATIONS OF MOTION

Angular rotation in the plane formed by the $x$ and $y$ axis is called pitch and we can write our equations of motion in this plane by utilizing two basic laws of nature, i.e.,

$$\Sigma \text{ Forces} = \text{Rate of Change of Momentum} \qquad (7.72\text{-}1)$$

$$\Sigma \text{ Moments} = \text{Rate of Change of Angular Momentum} \qquad (7.72\text{-}2)$$

There are two basic aerodynamic forces, the normal force denoted here as $l$ and the axial force denoted as $d$. Both of these forces are functions of the configuration and are calculated from semi-empirical formulas. There are two basic components of force due to the thrust of the propellant and they are determined by the control vane angle $\delta$. Hence, utilizing equation 7.72-1, two equations are obtained.

$$m\ddot{x} = l \cos \phi - d \sin \phi + f_x \sin \phi + f_z \cos \phi \qquad (7.72\text{-}3)$$

$$m\ddot{z} = -l \sin \phi - d \cos \phi + f_x \cos \phi - f_z \sin \phi - w \qquad (7.72\text{-}4)$$

Equation 7.72-2 can be rewritten in the form

$$I\ddot{\phi} = M_a + M_f \qquad (7.72\text{-}5)$$

where

$$M_a = \text{aerodynamic moment}$$

$$M_f = \text{thrust moment}$$

From the kinematic diagram it is seen that there are eight basic variables in the system, $v_w$ and $\delta$ being the independent variables. Thus, five more equations are needed to completely define our system. These equations can be obtained from the geometry of the kinematic diagram and are

$$\alpha = \phi - \gamma + \alpha_w \tag{7.72-6}$$

$$v_a^2 = v_w^2 + v^2 - 2vv_w \sin \gamma \tag{7.72-7}$$

$$v_w \cos \gamma = (v - v_w \sin \gamma) \tan \alpha_w \tag{7.72-8}$$

$$\left. \begin{aligned} \dot{x} &= v \sin \gamma \\ \dot{z} &= v \cos \gamma \end{aligned} \right\} \tag{7.72-9}$$

$$v^2 = \dot{x}^2 + \dot{z}^2 \tag{7.72-10}$$

## 7.73 INITIAL CONDITIONS

The initial conditions for the set of non-linear differential equations developed in Sec. 7.73 are usually obtained by considering the missile as flying with the total thrust $F$ directed along the $x$ axis. For zero wind velocity and angle of attack, the initial conditions are given as

$$t = 0$$

$$\alpha = v_w = \delta = l = f_z = 0$$

$$f_x = F$$

$$d = D = \text{drag at zero angle of attack}$$

Thus the set of equations in section 7.72 becomes

$$m\ddot{x} = (F - D) \sin \phi \tag{7.73-1}$$

$$m\ddot{z} = (F - D) \cos \phi - w \tag{7.73-2}$$

$$\ddot{\phi} = 0 \tag{7.73-3}$$

$$\phi = \gamma \tag{7.73-4}$$

$$v = v_a \tag{7.73-5}$$

$$\left. \begin{aligned} v \sin \gamma &= \dot{x} \\ v \cos \gamma &= \dot{z} \end{aligned} \right\} \tag{7.73-6}$$

$$v^2 = \dot{x}^2 + \dot{z}^2 \tag{7.73-7}$$

Note that equation 7.72-6 does not appear here and thus we only have seven equations.

## 7.74 THE LINEARIZED EQUATIONS OF MOTION

The linearization technique can now be applied to the set of non-linear differential equations in Sec. 7.72. To do this we will consider the system as fixed at some point in a standard trajectory. Thus at each point of this trajectory there will exist a linearized transient or frequency response. The weight and mass of the missile as well as the moment arms are then considered constant at each point although they vary along the trajectory. With the upper case letter and subscript zero denoting an operating point, the linearized equations of motion become

$$m\Delta\ddot{x} = (-L_0 \sin \phi_0 - D_0 \cos \phi_0 + F_{x0} \cos \phi_0 - F_{z0} \sin \phi_0) \, \Delta\phi$$
$$+ \cos \phi_0 \, \Delta l - \sin \phi_0 \, \Delta d + \sin \phi_0 \, \Delta f_x + \cos \phi_0 \, \Delta f_z \qquad (7.74\text{-}1)$$

$$m \, \Delta \ddot{z} = (-L_0 \cos \phi_0 + D_0 \sin \phi_0 - F_{z_0} \sin \phi_0 - F_{z_0} \cos \phi_0) \, \Delta\phi$$
$$- \sin \phi_0 \, \Delta l - \cos \phi_0 \, \Delta d + \cos \phi_0 \, \Delta f_x - \sin \phi_0 \, \Delta f_z \qquad (7.74\text{-}2)$$

$$I \, \Delta\ddot{\phi} = \Delta M_a + \Delta M_f \qquad (7.74\text{-}3)$$

$$\Delta\alpha = \Delta\phi - \Delta\gamma + \Delta\alpha_w \qquad (7.74\text{-}4)$$

$$V_{a_0} \, \Delta v_a = (V_{w_0} - V_0 \sin \gamma_0) \, \Delta v_w + (V_0 - V_{w_0} \sin \gamma_0) \, \Delta v$$
$$- V_0 V_{w_0} \cos \gamma_0 \, \Delta\gamma \qquad (7.74\text{-}5)$$

$$-V_{w_0} \sin \gamma_0 \, \Delta\gamma + \cos \gamma_0 \, \Delta v_w = (V_0 \sec^2 \alpha_{w_0} - \sin \gamma_0 \sec^2 \gamma_{w_0}) \, \Delta\alpha_w$$
$$+ (\tan \gamma_{w_0} - \sin \gamma_0 \tan \gamma_{w_0}) \, \Delta v$$
$$- (V_{w_0} \cos \gamma_0 \tan \alpha_{w_0}) \, \Delta\gamma \qquad (7.74\text{-}6)$$

$$\Delta\dot{x} = V_0 \cos \gamma_0 \, \Delta\gamma + \sin \gamma_0 \, \Delta v$$
$$\Delta\dot{z} = V_0 \sin \gamma_0 \, \Delta\gamma + \cos \gamma_0 \, \Delta v \qquad (7.74\text{-}7)$$

$$V_0 \, \Delta v = \dot{X}_0 \, \Delta\dot{x} + \dot{Z}_0 \, \Delta\dot{z} \qquad (7.74\text{-}8)$$

## 7.75  AERODYNAMIC DIFFERENTIALS

The next step is to apply our linearization technique to the aerodynamic differentials $l$, $d$ and $M_a$. The normal or lift force $l$ can be linearized by assuming it consists of two components one of which is $l_\alpha$, a function of angle of attack and the other, $l_\delta$, a function of control vane deflection. Thus

$$l_\alpha = f_1(\alpha) \qquad (7.75\text{-}1)$$

and

$$l_\delta = f_2(\delta) \qquad (7.75\text{-}2)$$

Utilizing our usual notation where an upper case letter indicates an operating point and the delta a linearized variable,

$$\Delta l_\alpha = \frac{\partial f_1}{\partial \alpha} \Delta\alpha = L_\alpha \, \Delta\alpha \qquad (7.75\text{-}3)$$

and

$$\Delta l_\delta = \frac{\partial f_2}{\partial \delta} \Delta\delta = L_\delta \, \Delta\delta \qquad (7.75\text{-}4)$$

The axial or drag force $d$ can be linearized by assuming it is a function of air flow velocity $v_a$ for small angles of attack $\alpha$ and control vane deflection $\delta$. Thus, since

$$d = \tfrac{1}{2}\rho v_a^2 A C_L \tag{7.75-5}$$

where                     $\rho$ = air density

$A$ = reference area of the missile

$C_L$ = drag coefficient

then the linearized variable becomes

$$\Delta d = \frac{2D}{V_{a_0}} \Delta V \tag{7.75-6}$$

For a given configuration the aerodynamic moment is a function of the angle of attack, pitch rate and control vane deflection. Thus

$$\Delta M_a = L_\alpha x_n \, \Delta\alpha - L_\delta x_c \, \Delta\delta - M_{\dot\phi} \, \Delta\dot\phi \tag{7.75-7}$$

## 7.76 THRUST MOMENT DIFFERENTIALS

The thrust moment $M_f$ can be linearized by assuming that it is unaffected by forward component of thrust $f_x$. Hence

$$\Delta f_x = 0 \tag{7.76-1}$$

Now we define a dimensionless factor $C_{F\delta}$ which for small angles is equivalent to the ratio of effective thrust deflection to jet vane deflection. This constant is defined as

$$C_{F\delta} = \frac{1}{F} \frac{\partial f_z}{\partial \delta} \tag{7.76-2}$$

Proceeding with linearizing the thrust moment and differentials, $\Delta f_z$ is obtained as

$$\Delta f_z = \frac{\partial f_z}{\partial \delta} \Delta\delta = F C_{F\delta} \, \Delta\delta \tag{7.76-3}$$

and            $$\Delta M_f = \frac{\partial M_f}{\partial \delta} \Delta\delta = -F x_c C_{F\delta} \, \Delta\delta \tag{7.76-4}$$

## 7.77 TRANSFORMED EQUATIONS

The constants of Sec. 7.74 have now been determined and are

$$V_{w_0} = \alpha_{w_0} = L_0 = F_{z_0} = 0$$

$$F_{x_0} = F; \qquad \gamma_0 = \phi_0$$

$$F' = F C_{F\delta} + L_\delta; \qquad V_{a_0} = V_0$$

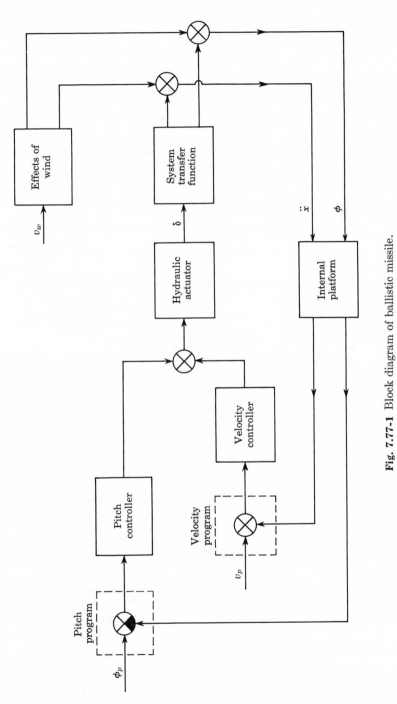

**Fig. 7.77-1** Block diagram of ballistic missile.

The remainder of the constants are determined by the particular point of the trajectory. The Laplace transform of the linearized equations of motion now become (the Greek letters are left lower case in Sec. 7.77, 7.78, and 7.79 to avoid confusion)

$$ms^2 \, \Delta X = (L_\alpha \cos \phi_0) \, \Delta\alpha + [(F - D) \cos \phi_0] \, \Delta\phi$$
$$- \left(\frac{2D}{V_{a_0}} \sin \phi_0 \right) \Delta V_a + (F' \cos \phi_0) \, \Delta\delta \qquad (7.77\text{-}1)$$

$$ms^2 \, \Delta Z = -(L_\alpha \sin \phi_0) \, \Delta\alpha - [(F - D) \sin \phi_0] \, \Delta\phi$$
$$- \left(\frac{2D}{V_{a_0}} \cos \phi_0 \right) \Delta V_a - (F' \sin \phi_0) \, \Delta\delta \qquad (7.77\text{-}2)$$

$$Is^2 \, \Delta\phi = L_\alpha x_n \, \Delta\alpha - M_{\dot\phi} s \, \Delta\phi - F' x_c \, \Delta\delta \qquad (7.77\text{-}3)$$

$$\Delta\alpha = \Delta\phi - \Delta\gamma + \Delta\alpha_w \qquad (7.77\text{-}4)$$

$$\Delta V_a = \Delta V - \sin (\phi_0) \, \Delta V_w \qquad (7.77\text{-}5)$$

$$\cos \phi_0 \, \Delta V_w = V_0 \, \Delta\alpha_w \qquad (7.77\text{-}6)$$

$$s \, \Delta X = V_0 \cos \phi_0 \, \Delta\gamma + \sin \phi_0 \, \Delta V \qquad (7.77\text{-}7)$$

$$\Delta V = \sin \phi_0 s \, \Delta X - \cos \phi_0 s \, \Delta Z \qquad (7.77\text{-}8)$$

## 7.78 THE OPEN LOOP BLOCK DIAGRAM

The eight equations of Section 7.77 are somewhat unwieldy and can be reduced to a set of four dependent variables $\Delta\alpha$, $\Delta\phi$, $\Delta X$ and $\Delta Z$ and the two independent variables $\Delta V_w$ and $\Delta\delta$. By substituting Eq. (7.77-8) into Eq. (7.77-5) we obtain

$$\Delta V_a = \sin \phi_0 s \, \Delta X + \cos \phi_0 s \, \Delta Z - \sin \phi_0 \, \Delta V_w \qquad (7.78\text{-}1)$$

Substituting Eq.(7.77-8) into Eq. (7.77-7) we obtain

$$\Delta\gamma = \frac{1}{V_0 \cos \phi_0} [s \, \Delta X - \sin^2 \phi_0 s \, \Delta X + \sin \phi_0 s \, \Delta Z] \qquad (7.78\text{-}2)$$

From Eq. (7.77-6) we have

$$\Delta\alpha_w = \frac{\cos \phi_0}{V_0} \Delta V_w \qquad (7.78\text{-}3)$$

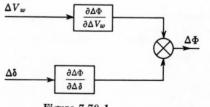

**Figure 7.78-1**

Now by substituting Eq. (7.78-3), (7.78-2) and (7.78-1) into the first four equations in Sec. 7.77 we obtain the set of equations which can be written in matrix form as

$$
\begin{bmatrix}
-L_\alpha \cos \phi_0 & -(F-D)\cos\phi_0 & \dfrac{2D}{V_{a_0}}\sin^2\phi_0 s + ms^2 & \dfrac{2D}{V_{a_0}}\cos\phi_0\sin\phi_0 s \\[2mm]
L_\alpha \sin \phi_0 & (F-D)\sin\phi_0 & \dfrac{2D}{V_{a_0}}\cos\phi_0\sin\phi_0 s & \dfrac{2D}{V_{a_0}}\cos^2\phi_0 s + ms \\[2mm]
-L_\alpha x_m & M_{\dot\phi}s + Is^2 & 0 & 0 \\[2mm]
-V_0 & V_0 & -\cos\phi_0 s & \sin\phi_0 s
\end{bmatrix}
$$

$$
\times
\begin{bmatrix}
\Delta\alpha \\[2mm]
\Delta\phi \\[2mm]
\Delta X \\[2mm]
\Delta Z
\end{bmatrix}
=
\begin{bmatrix}
(F'\cos\phi_0)\Delta\delta & \left(\dfrac{2D}{V_{a_0}}\sin^2\phi_0\right)\Delta V_w \\[2mm]
-(F'\sin\phi_0)\Delta\delta & \left(\dfrac{2D}{V_{a_0}}\cos\phi_0\sin\phi_0\right)\Delta V_w \\[2mm]
-F'X_c\,\Delta\delta & 0 \\[2mm]
0 & -\cos\phi_0\,\Delta V_w
\end{bmatrix}
$$

The determinant of this matrix is

$$
\Delta = s^2\left\{\left[\frac{2D}{V_{a_0}}(F-D)L_\alpha x_n\right] + L_\alpha\left[(F-3D)mx_n + \frac{2D}{V_{a_0}}M_{\dot\phi}\right]s\right.
$$

$$
+\left[(L_\alpha + 2D)mM_{\dot\phi} + \frac{2D}{V_{a_0}}IL_\alpha - m^2V_{a_0}L_\alpha x_n\right]s^2
$$

$$
\left. + m\left[(L_\alpha + 2D)I + mV_{a_0}M_{\dot\phi}\right]s^3 + m^2V_{a_0}Is^4\right\}
$$

Since the matrix indicates two independent variables we must indicate our transfer functions as partial derivatives with respect to $\Delta V_w$ or $\Delta\delta$. As an example

$$
\Delta\frac{\partial\Delta\phi}{\partial\Delta V_w} = mL_\alpha x_n \cos\phi_0 s^3\left[\frac{2D}{V_{a_0}} + ms\right]
$$

and

$$
\Delta\frac{\partial\Delta\phi}{\partial\Delta\delta} = -F's^2\left\{\left[\frac{2D}{V_{a_0}}L_\alpha(x_c + x_n)\right] + [mL_\alpha(x_c + x_n) + 2mDx_c]s\right.
$$

$$
\left. + m^2V_{a_0}x_c s^2\right\}
$$

Thus for the response to a simultaneous wind and control vane deflection, we would add these two transfer functions. The open loop block diagram for pitch can be shown as in Fig. 7.78-1.

**7.79** ADVANTAGES OF RATE FEEDBACK.

The air loads on a missile frame are dependent in general upon three factors, namely, the rate of change of flight path angle $\Delta\dot\gamma$, angle of attack $\Delta\alpha$, and acceleration $\Delta A$. In order to keep these loads at a reasonable figure, it would be advantageous to measure the three variables as listed above and use this information to control these magnitudes. The acceleration can of course be measured by means of a body-mounted accelerometer. However, some difficulty would be experienced in trying to measure the angle of attack, although there are angle of attack transducers. Rather than measure these variables, it is more advantageous to measure the rate of change of pitch as shown in Fig. 7.79-1. The linearized equations of motion can be solved to obtain the transfer functions

$$\frac{\Delta\alpha}{\Delta\dot\phi}, \frac{\Delta\dot\gamma}{\Delta\dot\phi} \quad \text{and} \quad \frac{\Delta A}{\Delta\dot\phi}$$

These transfer functions, $G_1(s)$, $G_2(s)$ and $G_3(s)$ express time lags between pitch rate and the various variables.

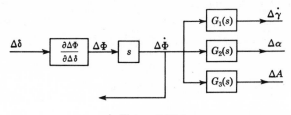

**Figure 7.79-1**

Thus we obtain a clue to the reason for rate feedback. That is, rate feedback can anticipate changes in $\Delta\alpha$, $\Delta\dot\gamma$ and $\Delta A$. Note that if either pure angle of attack or acceleration feedback were used, the time lags in the system would effectively decrease the system damping. Thus, for instance, to make $\alpha$ feedback effective, a lead type compensation circuit would be necessary for a control improvement to result.

**7.80 PNEUMATIC SYSTEMS**

Pneumatic controls are extensively used in industrial processes and in aircraft and missile applications. In industrial applications such as chemical and petroleum processes the reasons are the safety, reliability, and economy of operation. In missiles and aircraft the reasons are the availability of compressed air and the fact that as in air cycle refrigeration pressurization and heating this is the most practical method of performing such functions.

The basic unit of an industrial pneumatic controller is the flapper-nozzle amplifier as shown in Fig. 7.80.1. A constant pressure $p_s$ is supplied to the amplifier through a supply restriction. This produces an air flow $q_s$ in cubic feet/sec. Owing to the supply restriction,

$$q_s = C_d A_s \sqrt{\frac{2}{\rho} (p_s - p_N)}$$

where $C_d$ = supply restriction orifice constant,

$A_s$ = area of supply restriction orifice in in.[2],

$p_s$ = supply pressure in psi,

$p_N$ = nozzle pressure in psi,

$\rho$ = mass density of air in lb-sec²/in.[4]

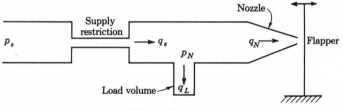

**Figure 7.80-1**

Now, by the same technique as in Sec. 7.62,

$$\frac{\Delta Q_s}{Q_{s_0}} = \frac{1}{2} \frac{\Delta (P_s - P_N)}{(P_s - P_N)_0} + \frac{\Delta A_s}{A_{s_0}}$$

Since $P_s$ and $A_s$ are constant

$$\frac{\Delta Q_s}{Q_{s_0}} = -\frac{1}{2} \frac{\Delta P_N}{P_{N_0}}$$

and

$$\Delta Q_s = -\frac{\Delta P_N}{R_s} \tag{7.80-1}$$

where $R_s = 2(P_{N_0}/Q_{s_0})$. By continuity of flow,

$$\Delta Q_s = \Delta Q_v + \Delta Q_N \tag{7.80-2}$$

But

$$\Delta Q_v = C_N s \, \Delta P_N \tag{7.80-3}$$

where $C_N$ = pneumatic capacitance of volume in in.$^5$/lb. The flapper acts to vary the nozzle orifice area $A_f$ as $x_f$ is displaced from its center position.

Hence
$$q_N = C_d A_f \sqrt{\frac{2}{\rho}} (p_N)$$

and
$$\frac{\Delta Q_N}{Q_{N_0}} = \frac{1}{2} \frac{\Delta P_N}{P_{N_0}} + \frac{\Delta A_f}{A_{f_0}}$$

But
$$\frac{\Delta A_f}{A_{f_0}} = - \frac{\Delta X_f}{X_{f_0}}$$

where $\Delta X_f$ is in inches, and thus

$$\frac{\Delta Q_f}{Q_{f_0}} = \frac{1}{2} \frac{\Delta P_N}{P_{N_0}} - \frac{\Delta X_f}{X_{f_0}} \tag{7.80-4}$$

Now by defining $\quad R_f = \dfrac{2P_{N_0}}{Q_{f_0}} \quad$ and $\quad k_f = \dfrac{P_{N_0}}{X_{f_0}}$

the block diagram of the flapper-nozzle amplifier becomes that shown in Fig. 7.80-2.

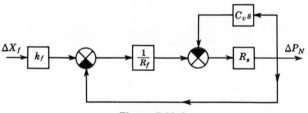

Figure 7.80-2

A typical example of a pneumatic controller is shown in Fig. 7.80-3. This is a Foxboro Model 40 proportional controller which positions a control valve. The valve is controlling a process flow and recording the flow rate by means of the pen. The measuring element is a Bourdon tube which moves the flapper to cover the nozzle orifice.

If the amplifier were connected directly to the large volume of the valve the time constant $R_s C_v$ would be large. Hence the control relay is inserted between the amplifier and valve, much like a pneumatic cathode follower. To derive the linearized equations for the control relay of Fig. 7.80-3 we must write our orifice equation of the relay output to the valve. Defining

$p_n$ = pressure developed by flapper-nozzle in psi,

$x_{CR}$ = displacement of diaphragm in inches,

$k_{CR}$ = spring constant of relay spring in lb/in.,

$A_{CR}$ = area of relay diaphragm in in.²

$A_B$ = orifice area due to ball in in.²

$A_C$ = orifice area due to cone in in.²,

$p_L$ = valve pressure in psi,

$q_L$ = valve flow in in.³/sec,

$q_s$ = supply flow in in.³/sec,

$q_a$ = flow to atmosphere in in.³/sec,

$C_L$ = valve capacitance in in.⁵/lb,

we can obtain

$$\frac{\Delta Q_s}{Q_{s_0}} = -\frac{1}{2}\frac{\Delta P_L}{P_{L_0}} + \frac{\Delta A_B}{A_{B_0}}$$

$$\frac{\Delta Q_a}{Q_{a_0}} = \frac{1}{2}\frac{\Delta P_L}{P_{L_0}} + \frac{\Delta A_C}{A_{C_0}}$$

$$\Delta Q_L = \Delta Q_s - \Delta Q_a = C_L s\,\Delta P_L$$

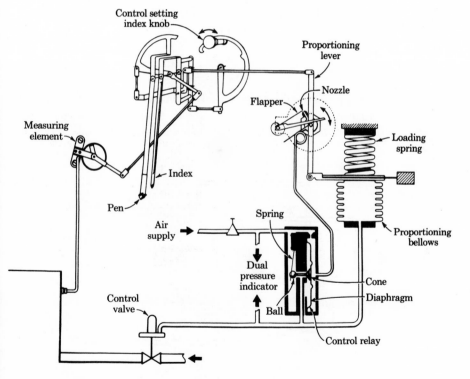

**Fig. 7.80-3** A Foxboro model 40 proportional controller. (Courtesy Foxboro Company, Foxboro, Mass.)

Assuming the cone and ball have equal area changes (the ball and cone can be designed for other relations) and neglecting the dynamics of the diaphragm and spring,

$$\frac{\Delta A_B}{A_{B_0}} = \frac{\Delta X_{CR}}{X_{CR_0}}$$

$$\frac{\Delta A_C}{A_{C_0}} = -\frac{\Delta X_{CR}}{X_{CR_0}}$$

$$k_{CR}\,\Delta X_{CR} = A_{CR}\,\Delta P_N$$

The transfer function of the control relay becomes

$$\frac{\Delta P_L}{\Delta P_N} = \left(\frac{2P_{L_0}}{X_{CR_0}}\right)\left(\frac{A_{CR}}{k_{CR}}\right)\frac{1}{\left[\left(\frac{2C_L P_{L_0}}{Q_{s_0} + Q_{a_0}}\right)s + 1\right]}$$

## 7.90 CONTROL VALVES

In previous sections the relationship among flow, pressure drop across the orifice, and orifice area has been presented and is

$$q = C_d A \sqrt{\frac{2(p_{\text{up}} - p_{\text{down}})}{\rho}}$$

Note that if the upstream pressure and downstream pressure are maintained at a constant value, the flow is directly proportional to the orifice area. Although these pressures do not necessarily remain constant, con-

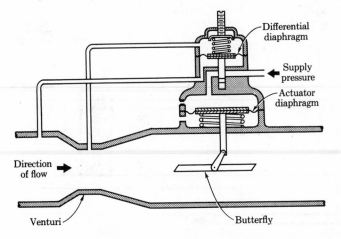

**Fig. 7.90-1** A typical fluid regulator utilizing a butterfly valve. (Courtesy Garrett Corp., AiResearch Manufacturing Division, Phoenix, Arizona)

trolling orifice area is a standard way of controlling flow. Devices that accomplish this are referred to as *control valves*.

In general there are two types of process control valves as shown in Figs. 7.90-1 and 7.90-2. Fig. 7.90-1 shows a typical fluid flow regulator where a venturi measures the flow and a butterfly valve controls the flow. A movement of the actuator diaphragm causes a rotation of the butterfly plate which in turn changes the orifice area. The block diagram can be developed as follows:

Let $k_d$ = spring constant of differential diaphragm in lb/in.,

$A_d$ = area of differential diaphragm in in.$^2$,

$x_d$ = movement of differential stem in in.,

$p_d$ = venturi pressure differential applied to differential diaphragm in lb/in.

For the purposes of this problem we will neglect the volume of the differential actuator and the actuator mass. Hence

$$k_d \, \Delta X_d = \Delta P \qquad (7.90\text{-}1)$$

and

$$\Delta P = k_1 \, \Delta Q_f \qquad (7.90\text{-}2)$$

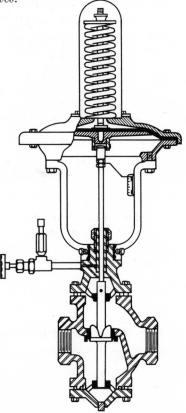

**Fig. 7.90-2** A single seat, air-to-open pneumatically operated control valve. (Courtesy Foxboro Company, Foxboro, Mass.)

where $q_f$ is the mass flow in lb/sec and $k_1$ is obtained from Fig. 7.90-3. The movement of the differential spring controls the supply orifice area and allows pressure to build up on the actuator diaphragm. Hence, neglecting actuator volume and utilizing the technique of Sec. 7.60,

$$q_a = C_d A_a \sqrt{\frac{2}{\rho} (p_s - p_a)} \qquad (7.90\text{-}3)$$

where $q_a$ = actuator flow in in.$^3$/sec,

$p_s$ = supply pressure in psi,

$p_a$ = actuator pressure in psi,

$C_d$ = orifice constant

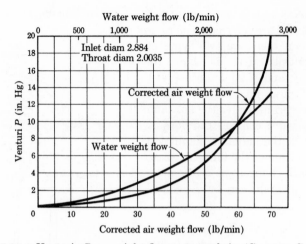

**Fig. 7.90-3** Venturi $\Delta P$ vs. weight flow water and air. (Courtesy Garrett Corp., AiResearch Manufacturing Division, Phoenix, Arizona)

Linearizing Eq. (7.90-3) we obtain

$$\frac{\Delta Q_a}{Q_{a_0}} = -\frac{1}{2}\frac{\Delta P_a}{P_{a_0}} + \frac{\Delta X_d}{X_{d_0}}$$

When the actuator diaphragm moves, its volume will change. If, however, we neglect this change,

$$\Delta Q_a = C_a s\, \Delta P_a \qquad\qquad (7.90\text{-}4)$$

and

$$k_a\, \Delta X_a = \Delta P_a \qquad\qquad (7.90\text{-}5)$$

where $k_a$ = actuator spring constant in lb/in.,

$x_a$ = actuator movement in in.

$C_a$ = actuator capacitance in in.$^5$/lb.

The effective area of the butterfly valve can be related to the actuator movement from a curve as shown in Fig. 7.90-4. If the slope of this curve is defined as $k_2$ and the effective area of the valve as $A_b$, then

$$q_f = C_d A_b \sqrt{\frac{2(p_{\text{up}} - p_{\text{down}})}{\rho}}$$

$$\frac{\Delta Q_f}{Q_{f_0}} = \frac{1}{2}\frac{\Delta(P_{\text{up}} - P_{\text{down}})}{(P_{\text{up}} - P_{\text{down}})} - k_2\, \Delta X_a$$

The block diagram is shown in Fig. 7.90-5.

The valve shown in Fig. 7.90-2 changes the area of the orifice as the stem moves a valve plug off a seat. In general there are three types of

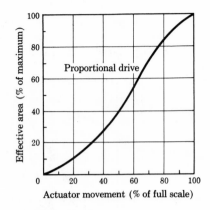

**Fig. 7.90-4** Proportional butterfly drive. (Courtesy Garrett Corp., AiResearch Manufacturing Division, Phoenix, Arizona)

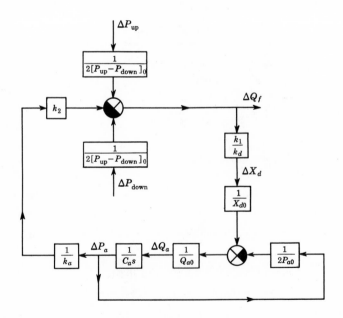

**Fig. 7.90-5** Block diagram of Fig. 7.90-1.

valve plugs, which for constant upstream pressure give flow characteristics
referred to as

   (a)  equal percentage
   (b)  parabolic
   (c)  linear.

A plot of these three operating characteristics is shown in Fig. 7.90-6.

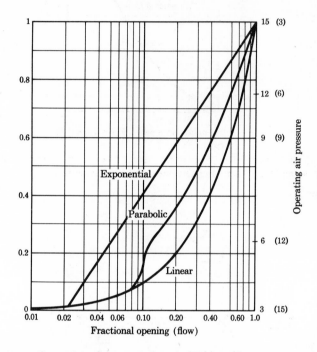

**Fig. 7.90-6** Operating characteristics of a Foxboro pneumatic control
valve. (Courtesy Foxboro Company, Foxboro, Mass.)

The block diagram can be derived by the same method as in the case
of the butterfly valve.

Let $R$ = viscous friction coefficient of valve stem in lb-sec/in.,

$\quad k_v$ = spring constant of valve spring in lb/in.,

$\quad p_1$ = pressure on valve diaphragm in lb/in.$^2$,

$\quad A_d$ = area of valve diaphragm in in.$^2$,

$\quad A$ = orifice area of valve in in.$^2$,

$\quad x$ = displacement of valve stem in in.,

$\quad q_f$ = process flow in in.$^3$/sec,

$\quad m$ = mass of valve stem in lb-sec$^2$/in.

Then

$$q_f = C_d A \sqrt{\frac{2}{\rho}(p_{up} - p_{down})} \qquad (7.90\text{-}6)$$

Hence

$$\frac{\Delta Q_f}{Q_{f_0}} = \frac{1}{2}\frac{\Delta(P_{up} - P_{down})}{(P_{up} - P_{down})_0} - \frac{\Delta A_f}{A_{f_0}}$$

From Fig. 7.90-5,

$$\frac{\Delta A_f}{A_{f_0}} = k_1 \, \Delta X$$

where $k_1$ is the slope of the fractional stroke vs. fractional opening curve. Summing the forces on the valve diaphragm,

$$A_d p_i = m\frac{d^2 x}{dt^2} + R\frac{dx}{dt} + k_v x$$

(We have assumed here that any friction is viscous.)

The block diagram now becomes that shown in Fig. 7.90-7.

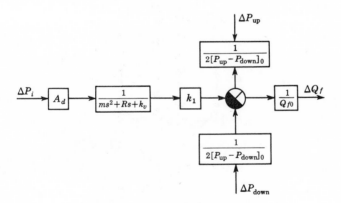

Figure 7.90-7

## 7.100  PROBLEMS

1. A missile chamber is supplied with conditioned air through a 50-ft duct which can be considered lossless. Heat is supplied to the chamber through electronic devices. A thermistor is inserted in the chamber to measure the temperature. If the thermal time constant of the chamber is 0.5 sec and the air velocity to the chamber is 500 ft/sec, derive the linearized block diagram of the system.

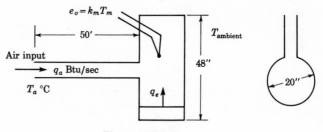

**Figure 7.100-1**

2. Derive the block diagram for the a-c power supply of Fig. 7.40-4 with the induction motor operating at the high-slip condition.

3. Derive the linearized block diagram of the flyball governor shown in Fig. 7.100-2.

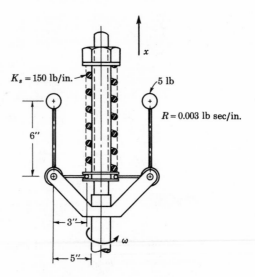

**Fig.7.100-2** A flyball governor.

4. In Fig. 7.100-3 is shown a schematic diagram of a Foxboro D/P cell which is used to measure differential pressure across a calibrated orifice and hence flow. If the load consists of a volume $C_v$, derive the linearized block diagram with a flow change as the input.

5. Derive the linearized block diagram for a tuned-grid, tuned-plate electronic oscillator.

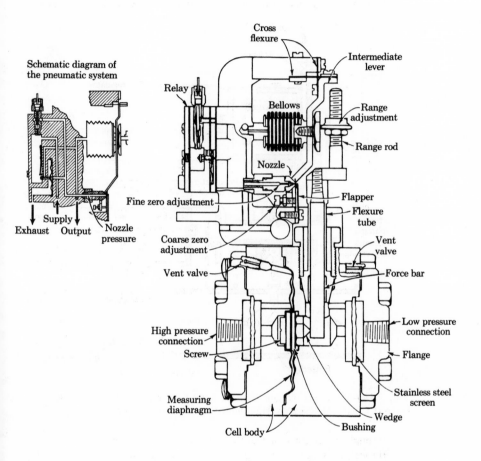

Schematic diagram of the pneumatic system

Exhaust Supply Output Nozzle pressure

Cross flexure

Intermediate lever

Relay

Bellows

Range adjustment

Range rod

Nozzle

Fine zero adjustment

Flapper

Flexure tube

Coarse zero adjustment

Vent valve

Vent valve

Force bar

High pressure connection

Low pressure connection

Screw

Flange

Stainless steel screen

Measuring diaphragm

Wedge

Cell body

Bushing

**Fig. 7.100-3** Foxboro D/P Cell. (Courtesy Foxboro Company, Foxboro, Mass.)

6. Figure 7.100-4 is a schematic representation of an AiResearch pneumatically actuated, liquid flow control of the venturi type. The liquid
flow rate is ultimately controlled by modulating the position of a butterfly in the exit nozzle of the control. Liquid entering the inlet port passes

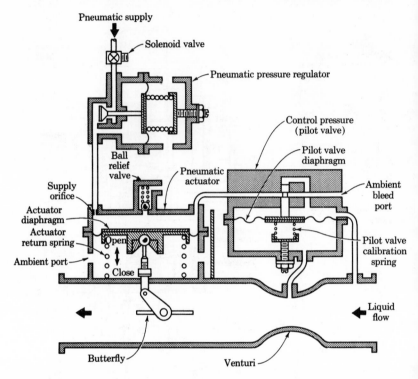

**Fig. 7.100-4** Liquid oxygen Venturi type flow regulator. (Courtesy
Garrett Corp., AiResearch Manufacturing Division, Phoenix, Arizona)

through the venturi inlet to the throat. These pressures are transmitted
through sensing ports to a pilot valve diaphragm which is spring-loaded
toward the high-pressure side. This pilot diaphragm operates a small
pilot valve, the downstream side of which is ported to ambient and the
upstream side of which is ported to the unit actuator. This actuator
consists of a diaphragm to which a shaft is connected which operates a
lever arm on the butterfly shaft, thereby permitting the butterfly to be
rotated in the valve bore by the actuator. The actuator diaphragm is
spring-loaded to hold the butterfly in the full-open position. Pneumatic
supply pressure is regulated to a constant value by means of a small
pressure regulator and is supplied through an orifice to the actuator.
Without flow through the valve, the pilot valve is in the normally open
position. This permits the pneumatic supply to be bled off from the
actuator at a rate sufficiently high to cause a pressure drop across the

supply orifice great enough to prevent the pressure on the actuator diaphragm from reaching a value which will compress the actuator spring. Derive the block diagram of the regulator. For this problem assume that as liquid flows through the venturi, the pressure differential generated from inlet to throat is proportional to the weight flow through the venturi. As the weight flow increases, the pressure differential increases until a value is reached which will overcome the pilot valve spring force. At this point, the pilot valve moves toward the closed position, reducing the pressure drop across the supply orifice, and allows actuator pressure to build up sufficiently to overcome the actuator spring force and move the butterfly toward the closed position. A ball relief valve is provided in the actuator chamber to preclude the remote possibility of a malfunctioning pressure regulator's permitting actuator pressure to increase high enough to rupture the diaphragm, and also to permit operation, even though out of limits, should the pressure regulator malfunction.

# CHAPTER EIGHT

# FOURIER'S SERIES

## 8.00 INTRODUCTION

The input and output variables of many systems are not truly sinusoidal in nature but do have some fundamental frequency associated with them—for example, the output of a multistage compressor. In many cases the system itself acts as a low-pass filter allowing only the lower frequencies to appear in the output. In this case the Fourier's series is a valuable tool for the engineer. This chapter will serve to develop this tool first in an analytic form and then as a graphical technique for the determination of the coefficients of the series. The second portion of the chapter is devoted to the development of describing functions by means of Fourier's series and to their application to automatic control theory.

## 8.10 ANALYTICAL FORM OF FOURIER'S SERIES

If a function $f(x)$ is periodic, single-valued, and has only a finite number of discontinuities, it may be expanded into the infinite trigonometric series

$$f(x) = a_0 + a_1 \cos x + a_2 \cos 2x + \cdots$$
$$+ b_1 \sin x + b_2 \sin 2x + \cdots \qquad (8.10\text{-}1)$$

Equation (8.10-1) can be put into a more compact form as

$$f(x) = a_0 + \sum_{n=1}^{\infty} [a_n \cos nx + b_n \sin nx] \qquad (8.10\text{-}2)$$

The coefficients of Eq. (8.10-2) can now be determined by first multiplying both sides of this equation by $dx$ and integrating between 0 and $2\pi$. Thus

$$\int_0^{2\pi} f(x)\, dx = \int_0^{2\pi} a_0\, dx + \int_0^{2\pi} \left( \sum_{n=1}^{\infty} [a_n \cos nx + b_n \sin nx] \right) dx \qquad (8.10\text{-}3)$$

But

$$\int_0^{2\pi} a_n \cos nx = 0$$

$$\int_0^{2\pi} b_n \sin nx = 0$$

and Eq. (8.10-3) becomes

$$\int_0^{2\pi} f(x)\, dx = \int_0^{2\pi} a_0\, dx \qquad (8.10\text{-}4)$$

From Eq. (8.10-4) is obtained the relationship

$$a_0 = \frac{1}{2\pi} \int_0^{2\pi} f(x)\, dx \qquad (8.10\text{-}5)$$

To find $b_k$ we multiply both sides of Eq. (8.10-2) by $\sin kx\, dx$ and again integrate between 0 and $2\pi$. Thus

$$\int_0^{2\pi} f(x) \sin kx\, dx = \int_0^{2\pi} a_0 \sin kx\, dx$$

$$+ \int_0^{2\pi} \left( \sum_{n=1}^{\infty} [a_n \cos nx + b_n \sin nx] \right) \sin kx\, dx \qquad (8.10\text{-}6)$$

But

$$\int_0^{2\pi} a_0 \sin kx\, dx \qquad = 0$$

$$\int_0^{2\pi} a_n \cos nx \sin kx\, dx = 0$$

$$\int_0^{2\pi} b_n \sin nx \sin kx\, dx = \pi \qquad (k = n)$$

$$\int_0^{2\pi} b_n \sin nx \sin kx\, dx = 0 \qquad (k \neq n)$$

Thus, Eq. (8.10-6) becomes

$$\int_0^{2\pi} f(x) \sin kx\, dx = \pi b_k \qquad (8.10\text{-}7)$$

and the general formula for the $k$th sine coefficient is

$$b_k = \frac{1}{\pi} \int_0^{2\pi} f(x) \sin kx \, dx \tag{8.10-8}$$

The $a_k$ coefficients are found by multiplying both sides of Eq. (8.10-2) by $\cos kx \, dx$ and integrating between 0 and $2\pi$. Knowing the relationships

$$\int_0^{2\pi} a_n \cos nx \cos kx \, dx = 0 \qquad (k \neq n)$$

and

$$\int_0^{2\pi} a_n \cos nx \cos kx \, dx = \pi \qquad (k = n)$$

we obtain

$$a_k = \frac{1}{\pi} \int_0^{2\pi} f(x) \cos kx \, dx \tag{8.10-9}$$

The infinite series as expressed by either Eq. (8.10-1) or (8.10-2) is called *Fourier's series* and the coefficients as expressed by Eq. (8.10-5), (8.10-8), and (8.10-9) are called *Fourier coefficients.*

Actually it is not necessary for the function $f(x)$ to have the period $2\pi$ as long as it is periodic in some region, say $-L$ to $L$. In this case, Eq. (8.10-2) becomes

$$f\left(\frac{\pi}{L} x\right) = a_0 + \sum_{n=1}^{\infty} \left[ a_n \cos \frac{2\pi n}{L} x + b_n \sin \frac{2\pi n}{L} x \right] \tag{8.10-10}$$

The Fourier coefficients then are given by the relationships

$$a_0 = \frac{1}{2L} \int_{-L}^{L} f\left(\frac{\pi x}{L}\right) d\left(\frac{\pi x}{L}\right) \tag{8.10-11}$$

$$a_k = \frac{1}{L} \int_{-L}^{L} f\left(\frac{\pi x}{L}\right) \cos \frac{2\pi k x}{L} d\left(\frac{\pi x}{L}\right) \tag{8.10-12}$$

and

$$b_k = \frac{1}{L} \int_{-L}^{L} f\left(\frac{\pi x}{L}\right) \sin \frac{2\pi k x}{L} d\left(\frac{\pi x}{L}\right) \tag{8.10-13}$$

The electrical engineer often refers to $a_0$ as the d-c or average value of the function. The $k$th sine and cosine terms are called the $k$th harmonic with $\sin x$ and $\cos x$ being the fundamental terms.

The following facts are helpful in developing the Fourier's series.

1. If the average value of the function is zero then the term $a_0$ is zero.
2. If the function has odd symmetry, i.e., $f(x) = -f(x)$, $a_0$ and all cosine terms are zero.

3. If the function has even symmetry, i.e., $f(x) = f(-x)$, all sine terms are zero.

4. If the function has half-wave symmetry, i.e., $f(x) = -f(x + \pi)$, $a_0$ and all even harmonics are zero.

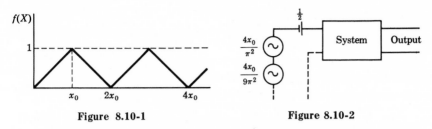

Figure  8.10-1                                        Figure 8.10-2

Consider now the Fourier's series for the function shown in Fig. 8.10-1. To facilitate the integration process, let us define a new variable $\lambda = \dfrac{\pi x}{x_0}$. The new function $f(\lambda)$ can now be expressed as

$$f(\lambda) = \frac{\lambda}{\pi} \qquad (0 \le \lambda \le \pi)$$

$$f(\lambda) = -\frac{\lambda}{\pi} + 2 \qquad (\pi \le \lambda \le 2\pi)$$

The Fourier coefficients become

$$a_0 = \frac{1}{2\pi} \int_0^{2\pi} f(\lambda)\, d\lambda$$

$$a_0 = \frac{1}{2\pi} \int_0^{\pi} \frac{\lambda}{\pi}\, d\lambda + \frac{1}{2\pi} \int_{\pi}^{2\pi} \left( -\frac{\lambda}{\pi} + 2 \right) d\lambda$$

and thus

$$a_0 = \tfrac{1}{2} \tag{8.10-14}$$

The $k$th sine harmonic has the coefficient

$$b_k = \frac{1}{\pi} \int_0^{\pi} \frac{\lambda}{\pi} \sin k\lambda\, d\lambda + \frac{1}{\pi} \int_{\pi}^{2\pi} \left( -\frac{\lambda}{\pi} + 2 \right) \sin k\lambda\, d\lambda$$

Integrating, we obtain

$$b_k = \left[ \frac{\sin k\lambda - k\lambda \cos k\lambda}{k^2 \pi^2} \right]_0^{\pi} + \left[ \frac{-\sin k\lambda + \lambda \cos k\lambda}{k^2 \pi^2} - \frac{2 \cos k\lambda}{k\pi} \right]_{\pi}^{2\pi}$$

Substituting the limits,

$$b_k = 0 \qquad (k = 1, 2, 3, \cdots) \tag{8.10-15}$$

The $k$th cosine harmonic has the Fourier coefficient

$$a_k = \frac{1}{\pi} \int_0^{2\pi} f(\lambda) \cos k\lambda \, d\lambda$$

Hence

$$a_k = \left[ \frac{\cos k\lambda + k\lambda \sin k\lambda}{k^2 \pi^2} \right]_0^\pi + \left[ \frac{-\cos k\lambda - k\lambda \sin k\lambda}{k^2 \pi^2} + \frac{2 \sin k\lambda}{k\pi} \right]_\pi^{2\pi}$$

and

$$a_k = -\frac{4}{k^2 \pi^2} \qquad (k = 1, 3, 5, \cdots) \qquad (8.10\text{-}16)$$

$$a_k = 0 \qquad (k = 2, 4, 6, \cdots) \qquad (8.10\text{-}17)$$

The Fourier's series now becomes

$$f(\lambda) = \frac{1}{2} - \frac{4}{\pi^2} \cos \lambda - \frac{4}{9\pi^2} \cos 3\lambda - \cdots \qquad (8.10\text{-}18)$$

To return to a function whose variable is $x$ instead of $\lambda$, multiply the right-hand side of Eq. (8.10-10) by $x_0/\pi$ and substitute $\pi x/x_0$ for $\lambda$.

$$f\left(\frac{\pi x}{x_0}\right) = \frac{x_0}{\pi} \left[ \frac{1}{2} - \frac{4}{\pi^2} \cos \frac{\pi x}{x_0} - \frac{4}{9\pi^2} \cos \frac{3\pi x}{x_0} - \cdots \right] \qquad (8.10\text{-}19)$$

The value of an expansion such as Eq. (8.10-19) is twofold for the systems engineer. The first asset has to do with the theory of superposition as applied to a linear system. We can consider the function $f(x)$ of Eq. (8.10-19) as consisting of an infinite number of sine or cosine generators applied to the system as shown in Fig. 8.10-2. The output of the system is then the sum of the responses to each individual component of the input. The second asset arises when the system in itself acts as a low-pass filter which attenuates the higher frequencies. In this case a few terms of Eq. (8.10-19) will usually suffice to determine the output of the system.

As an example let us consider Eq. (8.10-19) as a voltage and to further this analog replace $x$ with $t$ and set $x_0 = \pi$. Now let us apply this voltage to the low-pass filter of Fig. 8.10-3. The filter has the transfer function

$$G(j\omega) = \frac{1}{1 + jRC\omega} \qquad (8.10\text{-}20)$$

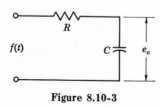

**Figure 8.10-3**

If the break frequency of the filter is $1/RC = 1$, the magnitude of the output voltage due to the fundamental is

$$E_{01} = \frac{4}{\sqrt{2}\,\pi^2} \qquad (8.10\text{-}21)$$

The magnitude of the output due to the third harmonic is

$$E_{03} = \frac{4}{9\pi^2 \sqrt{10}}$$    (8.10-22)

Thus the ratio of the third harmonic to the first is

$$\frac{E_{03}}{E_{01}} = \frac{1}{9 \sqrt{5}} = 0.04975$$    (8.10-23)

Since the magnitude of the third harmonic term is approximately 1/20 of the fundamental, the output of the filter is essentially

$$e_0 = \frac{1}{2} - \frac{4}{\sqrt{2}\,\pi^2} \cos\left(t - \frac{\pi}{4}\right)$$    (8.10-24)

## 8.11 GRAPHICAL TECHNIQUES

When an analytical expression cannot be developed for the desired function, a graphical technique must be utilized to determine the Fourier coefficients. Let us use the same function as shown in Fig. 8.10-1 with $x_0 = \pi$ to develop this technique. First divide the $x$ axis into $m$ equally spaced increments. Next erect ordinates at the middle of each increment as

$$y_k = f\left(km - \frac{m}{2}\right)    (k = 1, 2, 3)$$

From a study of the calculus, we visualize the integral of a function $y = f(x)$ as the area under the curve traced by a plot of this function. Now, since

$$a_0 = \frac{1}{2\pi} \int_0^{2\pi} f(x)\, dx$$

the approximation is

$$a_0 = \frac{1}{m}(y_1 + y_2 + y_3 + \cdots + y_m)$$    (8.11-1)

The sine and cosine harmonics are approximated by

$$b_n = \frac{2}{m} \sum_{k=1}^{k=m} y_k \sin\left[\left(k - \frac{1}{2}\right)\frac{2\pi n}{m}\right]$$    (8.11-2)

and

$$a_n = \frac{2}{m} \sum_{k=1}^{k=m} y_k \cos\left[\left(k - \frac{1}{2}\right)\frac{2\pi n}{m}\right]$$    (8.11-3)

Generally the function can be adequately represented by the fundamental and two or three harmonics. The increment $m$ can be taken between 10 and 20 degrees.

**TABLE 8.11-1**

$$m = 18$$
$$x_{k+1} - x_k = 10°$$

(a) AVERAGE VALUE

| $k$ | $x_{k-(1/2)}$ | $f(x_{k-(1/2)})$ |
|---|---|---|
| 1 | 5 | 0.0276 |
| 2 | 15 | 0.0830 |
| 3 | 25 | 0.1386 |
| 4 | 35 | 0.1940 |
| 5 | 45 | 0.2500 |
| 6 | 55 | 0.3040 |
| 7 | 65 | 0.3600 |
| 8 | 75 | 0.4150 |
| 9 | 85 | 0.4700 |
| 10 | 95 | 0.5250 |
| 11 | 105 | 0.5775 |
| 12 | 115 | 0.6315 |
| 13 | 125 | 0.6875 |
| 14 | 135 | 0.7415 |
| 15 | 145 | 0.7975 |
| 16 | 155 | 0.8500 |
| 17 | 165 | 0.9050 |
| 18 | 175 | 0.9600 |
|  |  | 8.9177 |

(b) FUNDAMENTAL

| $k$ | $x_{k-(1/2)}$ | $f(x_{k-(1/2)})$ | $\cos x_{k-(1/2)}$ + | $\cos x_{k-(1/2)}$ − | $f(x_{k-(1/2)}) \cos x_{k-(1/2)}$ + | $f(x_{k-(1/2)}) \cos x_{k-(1/2)}$ − |
|---|---|---|---|---|---|---|
| 1 | 5 | 0.0276 | 0.996 |  | 0.027 |  |
| 2 | 15 | 0.0830 | 0.966 |  | 0.080 |  |
| 3 | 25 | 0.1386 | 0.906 |  | 0.126 |  |
| 4 | 35 | 0.1940 | 0.819 |  | 0.159 |  |
| 5 | 45 | 0.2500 | 0.707 |  | 0.177 |  |
| 6 | 55 | 0.3040 | 0.575 |  | 0.174 |  |
| 7 | 65 | 0.3600 | 0.422 |  | 0.152 |  |
| 8 | 75 | 0.4150 | 0.259 |  | 0.108 |  |
| 9 | 85 | 0.4700 | 0.087 |  | 0.041 |  |
| 10 | 95 | 0.5250 |  | 0.087 |  | 0.047 |
| 11 | 105 | 0.5775 |  | 0.259 |  | 0.150 |
| 12 | 115 | 0.6315 |  | 0.422 |  | 0.267 |
| 13 | 125 | 0.6875 |  | 0.574 |  | 0.394 |
| 14 | 135 | 0.7415 |  | 0.707 |  | 0.525 |
| 15 | 145 | 0.7975 |  | 0.819 |  | 0.650 |
| 16 | 155 | 0.8500 |  | 0.906 |  | 0.770 |
| 17 | 165 | 0.9050 |  | 0.966 |  | 0.880 |
| 18 | 175 | 0.9600 |  | 0.996 |  | 0.950 |
|  |  |  |  | 1.044 |  | 4.633 |

(c) THIRD HARMONIC

| $k$ | $3x_{k-(1/2)}$ | $f(x_{k-(1/2)})$ | cos $3x_{k-(1/2)}$ | | $f(x_{k-(1/2)})$ cos $3x_{k-(1/2)}$ | |
|---|---|---|---|---|---|---|
| | | | + | − | + | − |
| 1 | 15 | 0.0276 | 0.966 | | 0.0266 | |
| 2 | 45 | 0.0830 | 0.707 | | 0.0586 | |
| 3 | 75 | 0.1386 | 0.259 | | 0.0359 | |
| 4 | 105 | 0.1940 | | 0.259 | | 0.0503 |
| 5 | 135 | 0.2500 | | 0.707 | | 0.1770 |
| 6 | 165 | 0.3040 | | 0.966 | | 0.2940 |
| 7 | 195 | 0.3600 | | 0.966 | | 0.3500 |
| 8 | 225 | 0.4150 | | 0.707 | | 0.2940 |
| 9 | 255 | 0.4700 | | 0.259 | | 0.1220 |
| 10 | 285 | 0.5250 | 0.259 | | 0.1360 | |
| 11 | 315 | 0.5775 | 0.707 | | 0.4075 | |
| 12 | 345 | 0.6315 | 0.966 | | 0.6105 | |
| 13 | 375 | 0.6875 | 0.966 | | 0.6650 | |
| 14 | 405 | 0.7415 | 0.707 | | 0.5250 | |
| 15 | 435 | 0.7975 | 0.259 | | 0.2070 | |
| 16 | 465 | 0.8500 | | 0.259 | | 0.2510 |
| 17 | 495 | 0.9050 | | 0.707 | | 0.6400 |
| 18 | 525 | 0.9600 | | 0.966 | | 0.9700 |
| | | | | | 2.6721 | 3.1483 |

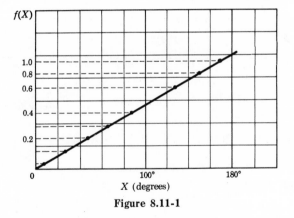

$f(X)$

1.0
0.8
0.6

0.4

0.2

0        100°        180°

$X$ (degrees)

**Figure 8.11-1**

To illustrate the technique and compare with analytical results, let us take the function of Fig. 8.11-1 whose Fourier's series was developed in Sec. 8.10 with $x_0 = \pi$. For purposes of calculation choose $m = 10$ degrees. Since $f(x) = f(-x)$, only the interval $0 \le x \le 180°$ is shown in Fig. 8.11-1.

The necessary computations can most conveniently be shown in tabular form as in Table 8.11-1. Since $m = 36$ in this case,

$$a_0 = \frac{2}{36} \sum_{k=1}^{k=9} f(x_{k-(1/2)}) = 0.496 \qquad (8.11\text{-}4)$$

To determine the cosine fundamental use Eq. (8.11-3); i.e.

$$a_1 = \tfrac{2}{36}\,[2(4.633 - 1.044)] = 0.3987 \tag{8.11-5}$$

and

$$a_3 = \tfrac{2}{36}\,[2(3.1483 - 2.6721)] = 0.0529 \tag{8.11-6}$$

The approximate expression for the function of Fig. 8.11-1 is now

$$f(x) = 0.496 - 0.3987 \cos x - 0.0529 \cos 3x + \cdots \tag{8.11-7}$$

In Fig. 8.11-2 is a comparison between the actual and calculated functions. For most engineering purposes this is an adequate approximation.

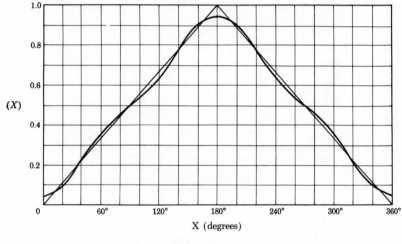

Figure 8.11-2

## 8.12 COMPLEX FORM OF FOURIER'S SERIES

In Sec. 8.10 the Fourier's series expansion for a function $f(x)$ periodic in the region $-L$ to $L$ was developed and is

$$f\left(\frac{\pi}{L}\,x\right) = a_0 + \sum_{n=1}^{\infty}\left(a_n \cos\frac{n\pi}{L}\,x + b_n \sin\frac{n\pi}{L}\,x\right) \tag{8.12-1}$$

We can express this equation somewhat differently by making use of Euler's equations, which are

$$\cos x = \frac{1}{2}\left(\epsilon^{ix} + \epsilon^{-ix}\right) \tag{8.12-2}$$

and

$$\sin x = \frac{1}{2j}\left(\epsilon^{ix} - \epsilon^{-ix}\right) \tag{8.12-3}$$

Substituting Eqs. (8.12-2) and (8.12-3) into (8.12-1),

$$f\left(\frac{\pi}{L}x\right) = a_0 + \sum_{n=1}^{\infty} \left[\frac{a_n}{2}\left(\epsilon^{j(n\pi/L)x} + \epsilon^{-j(n\pi/L)x}\right)\right.$$

$$\left. + \frac{b_n}{2j}\left(\epsilon^{j(n\pi/L)x} - \epsilon^{-j(n\pi/L)x}\right)\right] \qquad (8.12\text{-}4)$$

If a new variable $c_n$ is defined such that

$$c_n = \frac{a_n + jb_n}{2} \quad \text{and} \quad c_{-n} = \frac{a_n - jb_n}{2}$$

Eq. (8.12-4) becomes

$$f\left(\frac{\pi}{L}x\right) = \sum_{n=-\infty}^{\infty} c_n \epsilon^{j(n\pi/L)x} \qquad (8.12\text{-}5)$$

The complex Fourier coefficient becomes

$$c_n = \frac{1}{2L}\int_{-L}^{L} \epsilon^{-j(n\pi/L)x} f\left(\frac{\pi}{L}x\right) d\left(\frac{\pi x}{L}\right) \qquad (8.12\text{-}6)$$

For $\omega_0 = \pi/L$, which is the fundamental frequency of (8.12-5), Eq. (8.12-6) becomes

$$c_n = \frac{1}{2\pi\omega_0}\int_{-\pi}^{\pi} \epsilon^{-jn\omega_0 x} f(\omega_0 x)\, d(\omega_0 x) \qquad (8.12\text{-}7)$$

$c_n$ has a discrete value for integer values of $n$. Since it is complex, its absolute value is taken as a measure of the frequency spectrum of a function and is called a *line spectrum*. The spectrum for the triangular pulse of Eq. (8.10-19) can serve as an example. For this function the complex coefficients are

$$|c_0| = \frac{x_0}{2\pi}$$

$$|c_1| = \frac{4x_0}{\pi^3}$$

$$c_2 = c_4 = \cdots = 0$$

$$|c_3| = \frac{4x_0}{9\pi^3}$$

In Fig. 8.12-1 is shown the line spectrum for a triangular pulse. Since we are considering the absolute value of $c_n$ the curve is symmetrical about the $y$ axis.

If Eq. (8.12-7) is substituted into Eq. (8.12-5), we obtain

$$f(\omega_0 x) = \sum_{n=-\infty}^{\infty} \left[ \frac{1}{2\pi} \int_{-\pi}^{\pi} \epsilon^{-in\omega_0 x} f(\omega_0 x) \, d(\omega_0 x) \right] \epsilon^{-in\omega_0 x} \qquad (8.12\text{-}8)$$

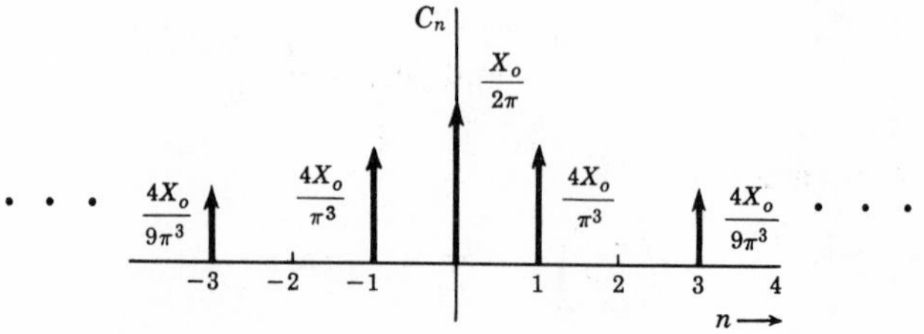

Fig. 8.12-1 Line spectrum for a triangular pulse.

Equation (8.12-8) can serve as the starting point for a heuristic development of the Fourier transform by finding its limit as the fundamental frequency $\omega_0$ approaches zero. This means that $f(x)$ becomes nonperiodic or aperiodic. In this limit, Eq. (8.12-8) becomes

$$f(x) = \int_{-\infty}^{\infty} \left[ \frac{1}{2\pi} \int_{-\infty}^{\infty} f(x) \epsilon^{-i\omega x} \, dx \right] \epsilon^{i\omega x} \, d\omega \qquad (8.12\text{-}9)$$

The Fourier transform is then defined as

$$F(\omega) = \frac{1}{2\pi} \int_{-\infty}^{\infty} f(x) \epsilon^{-i\omega x} \, dx \qquad (8.12\text{-}10)$$

Fourier transforms are of great value in examining systems in the presence of noise or statistical inputs. However these inputs are not discussed in this volume and we will use the Laplace transform in every case.

With these three sections developed, the rest of this chapter will now be devoted to the application of Fourier's series to system problems.

## 8.20 FLOW PULSATIONS

In Fig. 8.20-1 is shown a simplified process for the manufacture of polyethylene. In this process ethylene gas is pumped to a high pressure by means of a multistage compressor. It is then mixed with water which helps absorb the heat of polymerization. An initiator is added to start the chemical reaction by which the ethylene molecules band together to form the long chains constituting the plastic polyethylene. This reaction

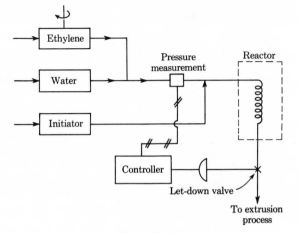

**Figure 8.20-1**

takes place in a tubular reactor which is maintained at a constant pressure by controlling the position of a "let down" valve. The valve is positioned on the basis of a pressure measurement at the reactor inlet.

Although there are two compressors (water and ethylene) supplying inputs to the system, only the flow variations of the ethylene compressor as shown in Fig. 8.20-2 are appreciable. These flow variations will give rise to pressure variations at the reactor inlet, and thus the pressure controller must be designed to operate in the same frequency range. The problem discussed in this section is the use of Fourier's series in choosing an adequate control system for the reactor pressure.

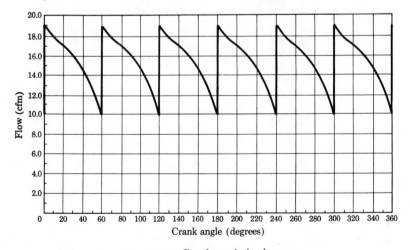

**Fig. 8.20-2** Crank angle in degrees.

## TABLE 8.20-1

### AVERAGE

| $k$ | $6x_{k-(1/2)}$ | $f(6x_{k-(1/2)})$ |
|---|---|---|
| 1 | 5 | 17.8 |
| 2 | 15 | 17.0 |
| 3 | 25 | 16.5 |
| 4 | 35 | 14.8 |
| 5 | 45 | 13.2 |
| 6 | 55 | 11.0 |
| | | 90.3 |

### FUNDAMENTAL

| $k$ | $6x_{k-(1/2)}$ | $\sin 6x_{k-(1/2)}$ + | − | $\cos 6x_{k-(1/2)}$ + | − | $f(6x_{k-(1/2)}) \sin 6x_{k-(1/2)}$ + | − | $f(6x_{k-(1/2)})$ |
|---|---|---|---|---|---|---|---|---|
| 1 | 30 | 0.500 | | 0.866 | | 8.90 | | 17.8 |
| 2 | 90 | 1.000 | | 0.000 | | 17.00 | | 17.0 |
| 3 | 150 | 0.500 | | | 0.866 | 8.25 | | 16.5 |
| 4 | 210 | | 0.500 | | 0.866 | | 7.4 | 14.8 |
| 5 | 270 | | 1.000 | 0.000 | | | 13.2 | 13.2 |
| 6 | 330 | | 0.500 | 0.866 | | | 5.5 | 11.0 |
| | | | | | | 34.15 | 26.1 | |

| $f(6x_{k-(1/2)}) \cos 6x_{k-(1/2)}$ + | − |
|---|---|
| 15.415 | |
| 0.0 | |
| | 14.289 |
| | 12.817 |
| | 0.0 |
| 9.526 | |
| 24.941 | 27.106 |

### SECOND HARMONIC

| $k$ | $12x_{k-(1/2)}$ | $f(6x_{k-(1/2)})$ | $\sin 12x_{k-(1/2)}$ + | − | $\cos 12x_{k-(1/2)}$ + | − | $f(6x_{k-(1/2)}) \sin 12x_{k-(1/2)}$ + | − |
|---|---|---|---|---|---|---|---|---|
| 1 | 60 | 17.8 | 0.866 | | 0.500 | | 15.415 | |
| 2 | 180 | 17.0 | 0.000 | | | 1.000 | 0.0 | |
| 3 | 300 | 16.5 | | 0.866 | 0.500 | | | 14.289 |
| 4 | 420 | 14.8 | 0.866 | | 0.500 | | 12.817 | |
| 5 | 540 | 13.2 | 0.000 | | | 1.000 | 0.0 | |
| 6 | 660 | 11.0 | | 0.866 | 0.500 | | | 9.526 |
| | | | | | | | 28.232 | 23.815 |

| $f(6x_{k-(1/2)})$ cos $12x_{k-(1/2)}$ | |
|:---:|:---:|
| + | − |
| 8.90 | |
| | 17.00 |
| 8.20 | |
| 7.40 | |
| | 13.20 |
| 5.50 | |
| 30.00 | 30.20 |

THIRD HARMONIC

| $k$ | $18x_{k-(1/2)}$ | $f(6x_{k-(1/2)})$ | sin $18x_{k-(1/2)}$ | | cos $18x_{k-(1/2)}$ | | $f(6x_{k-(1/2)})$ sin $18x_{k-(1/2)}$ | |
|:---:|:---:|:---:|:---:|:---:|:---:|:---:|:---:|:---:|
| | | | + | − | + | − | + | − |
| 1 | 90 | 17.8 | 1.000 | | 0 | | 17.80 | |
| 2 | 270 | 17.0 | | 1.000 | | 0 | | 17.00 |
| 3 | 450 | 16.5 | 1.000 | | 0 | | 16.50 | |
| 4 | 630 | 14.8 | | 1.000 | | 0 | | 14.80 |
| 5 | 810 | 13.2 | 1.000 | | 0 | | 13.20 | |
| 6 | 990 | 11.0 | | 1.000 | | 0 | | 11.00 |
| | | | | | | | 47.50 | 42.80 |

| $f(6x_{k-(1/2)})$ cos $18x_{k-(1/2)}$ | |
|:---:|:---:|
| + | − |
| 0.0 | |
| 0.0 | |
| 0.0 | |
| 0.0 | |
| 0.0 | |
| 0.0 | 0.0 |

The first step is to obtain a Fourier's series expansion for the flow rate by our graphical technique. From Fig. 8.20-2 if the compressor is rotating at $2\pi$ rad/sec (60 rpm), the flow output has a peak every $\pi/3$ radians. Hence the fundamental frequency is

$$\omega_0 = \frac{2\pi}{\pi/3} = 6 \text{ rad/sec}$$

To expedite our analysis the graphical procedure makes use of every 10° between 0 and 60°. In Table 8.20-1 the pertinent information is tabulated. From this table the Fourier's series for the first three harmonics becomes

$$q(6t) = 15.05 + 2.68 \sin 6t + 1.47 \sin 12t + \cdots$$
$$- 0.73 \cos 6t - 0.05 \cos 12t - \cdots \qquad (8.20\text{-}1)$$

Since we will make use of the frequency response technique, let us convert Eq. (8.20-1) into a sine series. Hence

$$q(6t) = 15.05 + 2.84 \sin (6t - 36°) + 1.5 \sin 12t$$
$$+ 1.56 \sin 18t + \cdots \qquad (8.20\text{-}2)$$

(The phase shift in the second harmonic has been neglected.) Equation (8.20-2) indicates the amplitudes and frequencies at which the control system must operate.

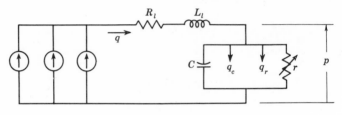

**Figure 8.20-3**

The next step is to obtain the block diagram and hence the transfer function of the system. To accomplish this an equivalent circuit of the process is derived.

The compressor is analogous to a current source with a load consisting of resistance, capacitance, and inductance. The capacity of the line to the reactor can be neglected. Let us also consider the resistance of the reactor as due entirely to the let down valve. The following terminology is now necessary:

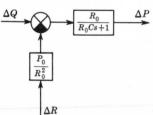

**Fig. 8.20-4** Process block diagram.

$R_l$ = hydraulic line resistance in lb-sec/ft⁵,

$L_l$ = process inertance in lb-sec²/ft⁵,

$C$ = reactor capacity in ft⁵/lb,

$r$ = valve resistance lb-sec/ft⁵,

$q$ = process flow in ft³/sec,

$p$ = reactor pressure in lb/ft².

Note that flow $q$, pressure $p$, and valve resistance $r$ are all written with lower case letters as they are the variables of the problem. The equivalent circuit is now shown in Fig. 8.20-3.

The equations for Fig. 8.20-3 can be obtained by summing flows at the parallel load as

$$q = C \frac{dp}{dt} + \frac{p}{r} \qquad (8.20\text{-}3)$$

Linearizing Eq. (8.20-3),

$$\Delta q = C \frac{d(\Delta p)}{dt} + \frac{\Delta p}{R_0} - \frac{P_0}{R_0^2} \Delta r \qquad (8.20\text{-}4)$$

The process block diagram becomes that shown in Fig. 8.20-4. The system block diagram is shown in Fig. 8.20-5. Note that the input to the summer from $\Delta R$ is negative. This is due to the control action, for if pressure increases, resistance must decrease.

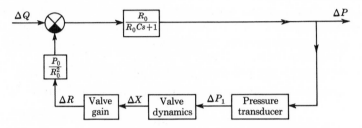

**Fig. 8.20-5** System block diagram.

Let us now define a constant $K$ as the combined steady-state gain of the ratio $\Delta R/\Delta P$. For a typical case

$R_0 = 8.5 \times 10^6$ lb-sec/ft$^5$

$C = 14 \times 10^{-7}$ ft$^5$/lb

$L_l = 1.0 \times 10^5$ lb-sec$^2$/ft$^5$

$R_l = 7.2 \times 10^5$ lb-sec/ft$^5$

$P_0 = 23.7 \times 10^5$ lb/ft$^2$

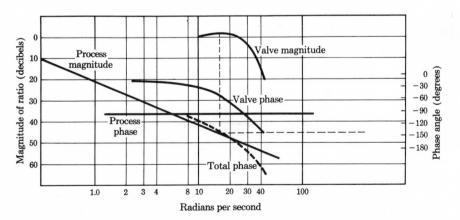

**Fig. 8.20-6** System transfer function.

In general the engineer who designs the control system is an employee of the chemical company and not a valve positioner manufacturer. Hence the problem here is to choose an adequate positioner which has a steady-state resistance as above and an adequate frequency response. In Fig. 8.20-6 is shown the frequency response of a valve positioner that might be used in this problem. With this response the adequacy of the system can now be determined.

It is not necessary to make an exact frequency response study as developed in our control chapter. In Fig. 8.20-6, the frequency response of the process and control system are shown. Since the break frequency of the process and control systems are so far apart only the 90° phase shift is shown for the process. If the phase margin is chosen as $-45°$ the gain can be 44.5 db. Note that the closed loop will be falling off at 52 db/octave. Since the control portion of the system is in the feedback path, the regulator closed loop gain can be obtained by using the fact that

$$\frac{KP_0}{R_0} = 44.5 \text{ db} = 168$$

The regulator gain is

$$\frac{\Delta P}{\Delta Q}\bigg]_{\text{s.s.}} = \frac{R_0}{1 + KP_0/R_0} = \frac{R_0}{1 + 168} = 5.04 \times 10^4 \qquad (8.20\text{-}5)$$

The frequency response of the regulator can be approximated as shown in Fig. 8.20-7. Hence for frequencies up to 15 rad/sec the gain of the regulator is $5.04 \times 10^4$. After 15 rad/sec, this gain decreases at the rate of 6 db/octave. Returning to Eq. (8.20-2), the necessary data can be tabulated as in Table 8.20-2.

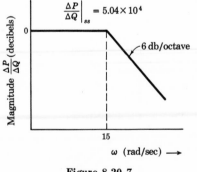

**Figure 8.20-7**

The kinematics of the chemical reaction will determine whether this response is adequate. If it is not equalizing circuits must be added to the control portion of the system. A word of caution is necessary here. If the response is considered marginal, care should be taken as portions of

**TABLE 8.20-2**

| Frequency rad/sec | Flow amplitude ft³/min | Pressure amplitude lb/ft² |
|---|---|---|
| 6 | 2.84 | $2.385 \times 10^4$ |
| 12 | 1.5 | $1.26 \times 10^4$ |
| 18 | 1.56 | $1.02 \times 10^4$ |

the system have been linearized. Hence the response shown in Table 8.20-2 must be more than adequate.

The calculations that have been made can also be used to determine the temperature fluctuations to be expected at the reactor inlet. This can be shown by a heat balance at the reactor inlet. With the definitions

$W$ = mass flow in lb/hr,

$\theta$ = temperature in °C,

$c$ = specific heat in Btu-hr/lb-°C,

the heat balance becomes

$$c_e W_e(\theta_i - \theta_r) + c_w W_w(\theta_i - \theta_r)$$
$$= c_w W_w(\theta_w - \theta_r) + c_e W_e(\theta_e - \theta_r) \qquad (8.20\text{-}6)$$

The subscripts $e$, $w$, $i$, and $r$ refer to ethylene, water, inlet, and reference respectively. Since $\theta_r$ is arbitrary choose it equal to $\theta_e$. Since $c_w = 1$ and $c_e = 0.7$, Eq. (8.20-6) becomes

$$\theta_i = \frac{W_w(\theta_w - \theta_e)}{W_w + 0.7 W_e} + \theta_e \qquad (8.20\text{-}7)$$

Equation (8.20-7) shows that the inlet temperature $\theta_i$ is a function of ethylene mass flow $W_e$. After linearizing this equation,

$$\Delta\theta_i = - \left[ \frac{W_{w_0}(\theta_{w_0} - \theta_{e_0})}{(W_{w_0} + 0.7 W_{e_0})^2} \right] \Delta W_e \qquad (8.20\text{-}8)$$

As in Chap. 7, the subscript zero indicates an operating point and the multiplication of Eq. (8.20-2) by the specific weight of ethylene will then give the amplitudes to be used for $\Delta W_e$.

## 8.30  DESCRIBING FUNCTIONS

In the chapter on control techniques it was emphasized that these techniques were only applicable to linear systems. Thus in Chap. 7 linearization techniques were developed to enable some analytical information to be obtained for nonlinear systems. However, there is another procedure available to us for certain nonlinearities. Extensive development based on the use of Fourier's series has been done by R. J. Kochenburger* for use in analyzing contactor servos.

To develop this technique let us use the control system shown in Fig. 8.30-1 where the box $n$ has a nonlinear element which is an amplifier with a gain $K$ that is subject to saturation. The gain of the amplifier is shown in Fig. 8.30-2(a) and (b). To simplify the development the gain curve of its amplifier has been idealized as in part (b) of this figure. At an amplitude $T$ of the input signal the output is saturated.

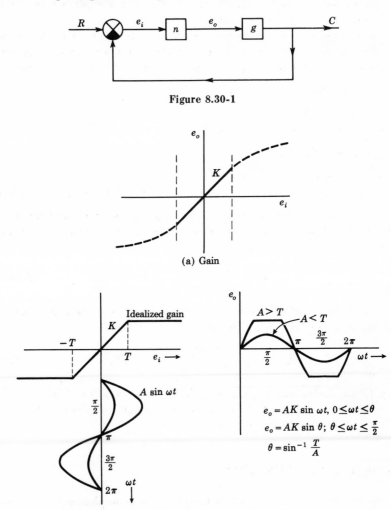

**Figure 8.30-1**

(a) Gain

$$e_o = AK \sin \omega t, \; 0 \le \omega t \le \theta$$

$$e_o = AK \sin \theta; \; \theta \le \omega t \le \frac{\pi}{2}$$

$$\theta = \sin^{-1} \frac{T}{A}$$

**Figure 8.30-2**

* See Bibliography.

Let us start our development by assuming the input to the amplifier is a sinusoid $e_{\text{in}} = A \sin \omega t$, and examine the output wave shape as it appears in Fig. 8.30-2(b). Since the output of the amplifier is nonsinusoidal but periodic it can be developed in a Fourier's series. However, as it is symmetrical, only the odd sine harmonics will appear. Proceeding with the series, the fundamental coefficient can be calculated as

$$b_1 = \frac{4}{\pi} \int_0^\theta AK \sin^2 \omega t \, d(\omega t) + \frac{4}{\pi} \int_\theta^{\pi/2} AK \sin \theta \sin \omega t \, d(\omega t)$$

$$b_1 = \frac{4AK}{\pi} \left[ \frac{\omega t}{2} - \frac{\sin 2\omega t}{4} \right]_0^\theta + \frac{4AK \sin \theta}{\pi} \left[ -\cos \omega t \right]_\theta^{\pi/2}$$

and thus

$$b_1 = \frac{AK}{\pi} [2\theta + \sin 2\theta]$$

The $k$th harmonic can be calculated as above and is

$$b_k = \frac{2AK}{k\pi} \left[ \frac{\sin (k-1)\theta}{(k-1)} + \frac{\sin (k+1)\theta}{(k+1)} \right] \tag{8.30-1}$$

From Eq. (8.30-1), the ratio of the first harmonic coefficient to the third is

$$\frac{b_3}{b_1} = \frac{1}{6} \left[ \frac{2 \sin 2\theta + \sin 4\theta}{2\theta + \sin 2\theta} \right] \tag{8.30-2}$$

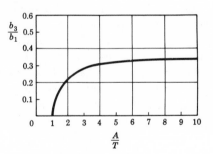

To plot Eq. (8.30-2) let us use the variable $A/T$ instead of $\theta$. For $A/T < 1$ the system is not saturated and for $A/T > 1$ saturation is present. A plot of Eq. (8.30-3) is shown in Fig. 8.30-3. From this figure we see that the third harmonic of the Fourier's series is never more than 30% of the first harmonic, and the higher harmonics will be of lesser consequence.

**Fig. 8.30-3** Ratio of third harmonic to first harmonic for saturation.

Suppose now that the box $g$ after the amplifier in Fig. 8.30-1 contains low-pass elements. This would mean that the higher harmonics of our Fourier's series would be attenuated even more in passing through the system. In this case it is possible to speak of an amplitude transfer function for the saturated amplifier as

$$N(A) = \frac{b_1}{A} = \frac{2K}{\pi} \left[ \theta + \frac{\sin 2\theta}{2} \right] \tag{8.30-3}$$

This transfer function is given the name *describing function*, and is the amplitude of the first harmonic coefficient to the ratio of the amplitude of the input signal. For the case of an amplifier with saturation this transfer function has only a magnitude but no phase shift. (Later on we will develop a describing function with magnitude and phase.)

Let us digress a moment at this point and make sure we are aware of the assumptions that have been made to develop this describing function. They can be listed as follows:

1. The input to the nonlinear device is a sinusoid.
2. The nonlinearity is not time variant.
3. Only the first harmonic will contribute to the output of the nonlinear device.

(Condition 2 does not exclude a nonlinearity that is frequency dependent.)

Now that the describing function has been developed, it can be used by a technique analogous to that of the Nyquist criteria as explained in Chap. 6. In that chapter, the stability of a system as in Fig. 8.30-1 was examined by determining whether the characteristic equation

$$1 + NG(s) = 0 \tag{8.30-4}$$

had roots with positive real parts. This was accomplished by making a frequency response plot, i.e. for $s = j\omega$, and counting the encirclements of the $-1 + j0$ point. In another sense we asked whether there was a frequency at which Eq. (8.30-4) had roots with positive real parts. If such a frequency existed there resulted an unstable system which had steady oscillations at this frequency. In this case the amplitudes of the input to the control system had no bearing on the frequency of oscillation.

For the nonlinear device discussed in this section, the analogous question must be asked as to the presence of an amplitude and frequency at which

$$1 + N(A)G(j\omega) = 0 \tag{8.30-5}$$

can have roots with positive real parts.   Equation (8.30-5) can be written as

$$G(j\omega) = \frac{-1}{N(A)} \tag{8.30-6}$$

Hence if the locus of the negative inverse describing function and the open loop frequency response intersect, an oscillation will occur at a frequency obtained from the frequency response and at an amplitude obtained from the describing function. This type of oscillation is termed a *limit cycle* and is, in general, a small amplitude oscillation. A system can be stable in the Nyquist sense but have a limit cycle.

To illustrate the use of describing functions let us consider the system as shown in Fig. 8.30-1 with the process block having the form

$$G(s) = \frac{1}{s(\tau_1 s + 1)(\tau_2 s + 1)} \qquad (8.30\text{-}7)$$

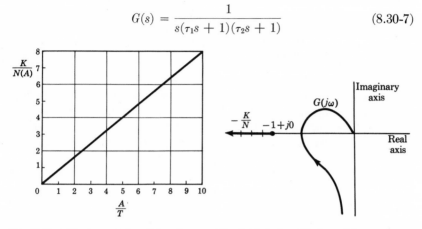

**Fig. 8.30-4** Reciprocal describing function for saturation.

**Fig. 8.30-5** Amplitude and frequency locus for a system with saturation.

In Fig. 8.30-4 is shown a plot of the reciprocal describing function vs. the ratio $A/T$. Since the gain $K$ of the amplifier is a variable in most applications the plot is nondimensionalized; i.e., we plot $N/K$ instead of $N$. This plot can be combined with Eq. (8.30-7) as in Fig. 8.30-5. Since these two loci do not intersect, no limit cycle is present. In fact for a system with saturation no limit cycle will occur unless the open loop frequency response intersects the negative real axis at a magnitude greater than 1. But in Chap. 6 we saw that systems with no right half plane poles in the open loop transfer function can not encircle the $-1 + j0$ point and be stable. Hence we arrive at this conclusion. A system with an open loop transfer function which has no poles in the right half plane and no zeros at all will not have a limit cycle in the presence of saturation. In Fig. 8.30-6 is shown the open loop transfer function of a system with zeros in the left half plane.

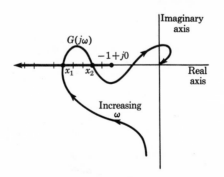

**Fig. 8.30-6** A conditionally stable system.

This is a conditionally stable system and intersects the negative real axis at two points. The question now arises at which frequency and amplitude the limit cycle will occur. Our analog with the Nyquist criteria will enable us to answer this question. If the point $X_2$ coincided with the $-1 + j0$ value we would expect the system to oscillate at that frequency. However, at that point, if the gain were increased slightly the oscillations would die out since the frequency locus would not then encircle the $-1 + j0$ point. Conversely if the gain were decreased the oscillations would diverge since the frequency locus encircles the $-1 + j0$ point. Hence this point $X_2$ is not a stable operating condition but $X_1$ is a stable operating point.

Now consider the $-1 + j0$ point as replaced by the value of $-1/N$. As the amplitude $A$ of the signal increases, this point moves to the left in Fig. 8.30-6. Suppose $-1/N$ intersected the $G(j\omega)$ locus at $X_2$. As oscillations built up, the amplitude of the input to the box containing the nonlinear gain would increase. The value of $-1/N$ would then move to the left until the point $X_1$ was reached. Now if the amplitude increased more, the oscillations would die out until $X_1$ again intersected the $G(j\omega)$ locus. Hence a stable limit cycle exists at $X_1$. Its frequency is determined from the $G(j\omega)$ locus and its amplitude from the $-1/N$ locus.

### 8.31 SATURATION AND DEAD ZONE

A more general type of nonlinearity is shown in Fig. 8.31-1. This is a device with both saturation and a dead zone. The output of this device is zero until the input signal amplitude is greater than $T_1$. The output is linear with a gain $K$ until the input signal amplitude is greater than $T_2$,

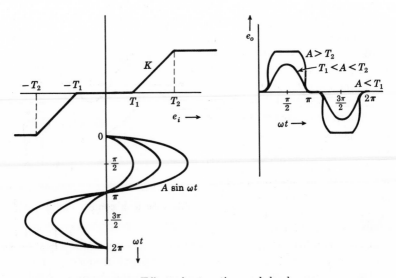

**Fig. 8.31-1** Effect of saturation and dead zone.

at which point the output is saturated. Following the same procedure as in Sec. 8.30 the describing function can be developed as follows:

$$\text{input} = A \sin \omega t$$

$$\text{output} = \begin{cases} 0 & (0 \leq \omega t \leq \theta_1) \\ AK[\sin \omega t - \sin \theta_1] & (\theta_1 \leq \omega t \leq \theta_2) \\ AK[\sin \theta_2 - \sin \theta_1] & (\theta_2 \leq \omega t \leq \pi/2) \end{cases}$$

where $\theta_1 = \sin^{-1} T_1/A$,

   $\theta_2 = \sin^{-1} T_2/A$.

The $k$th harmonic coefficient is

$$b_k = \frac{4}{\pi} \int_0^{\theta_1} (0) + \frac{4}{\pi} \int_{\theta_1}^{\theta_2} AK[\sin \omega t - \sin \theta_1] \sin k\omega t \, d\omega t$$

$$+ \frac{4}{\pi} \int_{\theta_2}^{\pi/2} AK[\sin \theta_2 - \sin \theta_1] \sin k\omega t \, d\omega t \qquad (8.31\text{-}1)$$

Hence

$$b_k = \frac{2K}{\pi} \left[ \frac{\sin (k-1)\theta_2 - \sin (k-1)\theta_1}{k-1} \right]$$

$$+ \frac{2K}{\pi} \left[ \frac{\sin (k+1)\theta_2 - \sin (k+1)\theta_1}{k+1} \right] \qquad (8.31\text{-}2)$$

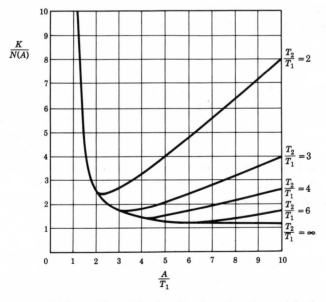

**Fig. 8.31-2** Reciprocal describing function for saturation and dead zone.

The ratio of third to first harmonic is

$$\frac{b_3}{b_1} = \frac{1}{6}\left[\frac{\sin 2\theta_2 - \sin 2\theta_1 + \frac{1}{2}(\sin 4\theta_2 - \sin 4\theta_1)}{\theta_2 - \theta_1 + \frac{1}{2}(\sin 2\theta_2 - \sin \theta_1)}\right] \qquad (8.31\text{-}3)$$

The describing function is

$$N = \frac{b_1}{A} = \frac{2K}{\pi}\left[\theta_2 - \theta_1 + \frac{1}{2}(\sin 2\theta_2 - \sin 2\theta_1)\right] \qquad (8.31\text{-}4)$$

A nondimensional plot of the reciprocal describing function is shown in Fig. 8.31-2. This function begins at minus infinity and for increasing amplitudes approaches the $-1 + j0$ point. At some value of $A/T_1$ depending on the ratio $\theta_2/\theta_1$ the curve will reverse and move along the negative real axis back to minus infinity. Again we see that if the open loop transfer function has no poles in the right half plane only a conditionally stable system will have a limit cycle.

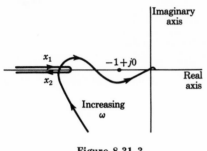

Figure 8.31-3

In Fig. 8.31-3 is shown the frequency locus for a conditionally stable system. Plotted on the same graph is shown the describing function for saturation and dead zone. In this system a stable limit cycle will occur at the frequency and amplitude at point $X_2$.

## 8.32 BACKLASH

In Fig. 8.32-1 is shown the input-output relation for a common non-linearity termed *backlash*. This type of nonlinearity is found most often in gear trains where the teeth do not mesh exactly or in control linkages that are not tight. The output curve can be separated into three distinct portions which are periodic. In portion 1, the output is a fixed quantity less than the input. During portion 2 the output is constant and during portion 3 it is larger than input by the same fixed quantity. Expressed mathematically

$$\text{input} = A \sin \omega t$$

$$\text{output} = \begin{cases} A \sin \omega t - b/2 & \theta \leq \omega t \leq \pi/2 \\ A - b/2 & \pi/2 \leq \omega t \leq \pi - \theta \\ A \sin \omega t + b/2 & \pi - \theta \leq \omega t \leq \pi \end{cases} \qquad (8.32\text{-}1)$$

To derive the describing function it is necessary to find the fundamental Fourier coefficient. But this output is not symmetrical as in the case of saturation, hence the fundamental will consist of both a sine and cosine term. Expressed mathematically Eq. (8.32-1) will become

$$\text{input} = A \sin \omega t$$
$$\text{output} = b_1 \sin \omega t + a_1 \cos \omega t + \cdots$$

(8.32-2)

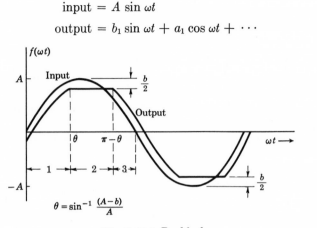

**Fig. 8.32-1** Backlash.

We can combine the sine and cosine terms of the output into a sine term which has a phase angle. Thus Eq. (8.32-2) becomes

$$\text{input} = A \sin \omega t$$
$$\text{output} = \sqrt{a_1^2 + b_1^2} \sin (\omega t + \psi) + \cdots$$

(8.32-3)

where $\psi = \tan^{-1} (a_1/b_1)$. Since the describing function $N(A)$ is the ratio of the fundamental coefficient to the input amplitude, we will have for backlash the vector

$$N(A) = \frac{1}{A} \sqrt{a_1^2 + b_1^2} \underline{/\psi}$$

(8.32-4)

We can now proceed to find the Fourier coefficients as follows:

$$b_1 = \frac{2}{\pi} \int_0^{\pi/2} \left( A \sin \omega t - \frac{b}{2} \right) \sin \omega t \, d\omega t + \frac{2}{\pi} \int_{\pi/2}^{\pi - \theta} \left( A - \frac{b}{2} \right) \sin \omega t \, d\omega t$$

$$+ \frac{2}{\pi} \int_{\pi - \theta}^{\pi} \left( A \sin \omega t + \frac{b}{2} \right) \sin \omega t \, d\omega t$$

(8.32-5)

Performing the integrations as indicated in Eq. (8.32-5),

$$b_1 = \frac{2}{\pi} \left[ \frac{A\pi}{4} - \frac{b}{2} \right] - \frac{2}{\pi} \left( A - \frac{b}{2} \right) [\cos (\pi - \theta)]$$

$$+ \frac{2}{\pi} \left[ \frac{A\pi}{2} + \frac{b}{2} - \frac{A}{2} (\pi - \theta) + \frac{A}{4} \sin 2(\pi - \theta) + \frac{b}{2} \cos (\pi - \theta) \right]$$

(8.32-6)

Let us next define a constant $R$ such that

$$R = \frac{b}{2A} \tag{8.32-7}$$

Hence,

$$\cos(\pi - \theta) = \sqrt{4R - 4R^2} \tag{8.32-8}$$

and

$$\sin 2(\pi - \theta) = \tfrac{1}{2}(1 - 2R)\sqrt{4R - 4R^2} \tag{8.32-9}$$

Substituting Eqs. (8.32-7), (8.32-8), (8.32-9) into Eq. (8.32-6),

$$b_1 = \frac{A}{\pi}\left[2(1 - 2R)\sqrt{R(1 - R)} + \frac{\pi}{2} + \theta\right] \tag{8.32-10}$$

The cosine Fourier coefficient is now found as

$$a_1 = \frac{2}{\pi}\int_0^{\pi/2}\left(A\sin\omega t - \frac{b}{2}\right)\cos\omega t\, d\omega t + \frac{2}{\pi}\int_{\pi/2}^{\pi-\theta}\left(A - \frac{b}{2}\right)\cos\omega t\, d\omega t$$
$$+ \frac{2}{\pi}\int_{\pi-\theta}^{\pi}\left(A\sin\omega t + \frac{b}{2}\right)\cos\omega t\, d\omega t \tag{8.32-11}$$

Performing the same procedure as for Eq. (8.32-6),

$$a_1 = \frac{4AR}{\pi}(R - 1) \tag{8.32-12}$$

The describing function for backlash is now obtained by substituting Eqs. (8.32-12) and (8.32-10) into Eq. (8.32-4), thus

$$N(A) = \frac{1}{\pi}\left\{\left(\frac{\pi}{2} + \theta\right)^2 + 4R(1 - R)\right.$$
$$\left. + \left[2R(1 - 2R)\sqrt{\frac{1 - R}{R}}\right](\pi + 2\theta)\right\}^{1/2}\underline{/\psi} \tag{8.32-13}$$

where

$$\underline{/\psi} = \tan^{-1}\left[\frac{4R(R - 1)}{\pi/2 + \theta + 2R(1 - 2R)\sqrt{(1 - R)/R}}\right]$$

We can alternately express Eq. (8.32-13) in the complex form

$$N(A) = \frac{1}{\pi}\left[2R(1 - 2R)\sqrt{\frac{1 - R}{R}} + \frac{\pi}{2} + \theta\right] + j\frac{4R}{\pi}(R - 1) \tag{8.32-14}$$

A plot of the negative reciprocal of the describing function for backlash is shown in Fig. 8.32-2.

In Fig. 8.32-3 is shown the Nyquist plot for a typical control system. For illustration $G(-0.1 + j\omega)$, $G(j\omega)$, and $G(0.1 + j\omega)$ are shown. Since this system has open loop poles in the right half plane, the Nyquist plot encircles the $-1 + j0$ point.

This plot shows that as the amplitude of the input signal to the system increases, the intersection of $-1/N(A)$ and the Nyquist plot $G(s)$ moves

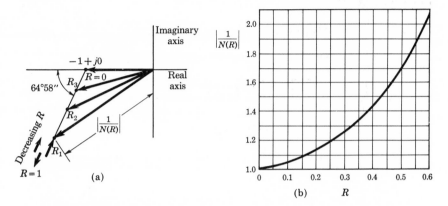

Fig. 8.32-2 (a) Complex plot of the negative reciprocal describing function for backlash; (b) Absolute value of reciprocal describing function for backlash.

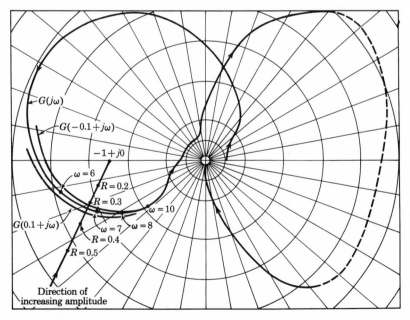

Figure 8.32-3

from a value of $s = +\alpha + j\omega$ to a value of $-\alpha + j\omega$. This means that the output of the system changes from one with terms of $\epsilon^{\alpha t} \sin \omega t$ to one with terms of $\epsilon^{-\alpha t} \sin \omega t$ as the limit cycle builds up. Hence this intersection gives rise to a stable limit cycle.

## 8.40 PROBLEMS

1. Derive the Fourier's series expansion for the square wave of Fig. 8.40-1.

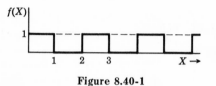

**Figure 8.40-1**

2. Derive the Fourier's series expansion for the 60 cps full-wave rectifier output of Fig. 8.40-2.

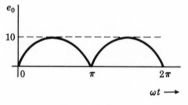

**Figure 8.40-2**

3. Plot the first two terms of the Fourier's series for the square wave of Prob. 1 and then the first three terms. To what value is it converging at $X = 1$?

4. Graphically derive the Fourier's series expansion of Prob. 2.

5. Show that the Fourier's series can be expressed as

$$f(x) = A_0 + \sum_{n=1}^{\infty} A_n \sin (n\omega t - \psi_n).$$

Determine the relationship between $A_n$ and the Fourier coefficients.

6. In Fig. 8.32-2(a) the negative reciprocal of the describing function for backlash is approximated by a straight line at an angle of 64°58″ with the $-1 + j0$ point. Show this analytically by means of Eq. (8.32-14).

# CHAPTER NINE

# ENERGY CONVERSION

## 9.00 INTRODUCTION

One of the basic laws of our engineering science is that of conservation of energy, which states that energy can neither be created nor destroyed. It does not say, however, that energy cannot be changed from one form to another. We change the form of energy in our everyday life when we use electrical energy converted from the potential energy in a height of water behind a dam or from the energy stored in coal or oil. In fact one of the most important parts of any control system is the energy conversion unit. In the Type 1 system discussed in Chap. 6, for instance, the energy conversion unit was a d-c motor which converted electrical energy to mechanical energy for positioning the load of the antenna.

These energy conversion units are designed and rated as to the amount of energy per unit time they can convert. This means, of course, that they are rated as to their power capabilities. The theory of feedback control as developed in Chap. 6 was based on the assumption that the power capabilities of the energy conversion units in the system were unlimited. However we all know this is not true, and it is the purpose of this chapter to examine the relationship between the frequency response of a system and its power capabilities. Some typical power sources will also be examined and their block diagrams developed.

## 9.10 THE TRANSIENT RESPONSE AND ITS EFFECT ON MAXIMUM POWER

As a heuristic example to illustrate the interaction of the transient response of a system and its maximum power demands, consider the system shown in Fig. 9.10-1. This system can be considered as a d-c motor being driven by a current source and driving a load with inertia and viscous friction. The error-producing device can be a synchro and thus the system will be Type 1.

The instantaneous output power of the system is obtained by multiplying torque and speed as

$$p(t) = \omega_0(t)T(t) \tag{9.10-1}$$

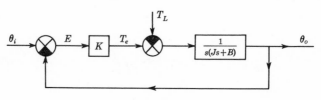

**Figure 9.10-1**

Considering the system of Fig. 9.10-1 as a servomechanism, i.e., $T_L = 0$, the Laplace transform of the output speed for a step function input of $|\theta_i|$ radians is

$$\Omega_0(s) = \frac{K|\theta_i|}{J\left(s^2 + \dfrac{B}{J}s + \dfrac{K}{J}\right)} \tag{9.10-2}$$

Nondimensionalizing Eq. (9.10-2) as in Sec. 2.60 of Chap. 2,

$$\Omega_0(s) = \frac{\omega_n^2|\theta_i|}{s^2 + 2\zeta\omega_n s + \omega_n^2} \tag{9.10-3}$$

where $\omega_n^2 = K/J$ and $2\zeta\omega_n = B/J$. Thus the time response corresponding to Eq. (9.10-3) is

$$\omega_0(t) = \frac{\omega_n}{\sqrt{1-\zeta^2}}|\theta_i|\epsilon^{-\zeta\omega_n t}\sin\left(\omega_n\sqrt{1-\zeta^2}\,t\right) \tag{9.10-4}$$

The torque response of the system can be obtained by first solving for the error $E(s)$ of the system which is

$$E(s) = \theta_i(s) - \theta_0(s) \tag{9.10-5}$$

For a step input $|\theta_i|$ radians, Eq. (9.10-5) becomes

$$E(s) = \frac{|\theta_i|}{s} - \frac{\omega_n^2|\theta_i|}{s(s^2 + 2\zeta\omega_n s + \omega_n^2)} \tag{9.10-6}$$

Rearranging Eq. (9.10-6),

$$E(s) = \frac{|\theta_i|}{s}\left[\frac{s^2 + 2\zeta\omega_n s + \omega_n^2 - \omega_n^2}{s^2 + 2\zeta\omega_n s + \omega_n^2}\right] \tag{9.10-7}$$

and thus

$$E(s) = |\theta_i|\left[\frac{s + 2\zeta\omega_n}{s^2 + 2\zeta\omega_n s + \omega_n^2}\right] \tag{9.10-8}$$

Since $T(s) = KE(s)$, the torque time response becomes

$$T(t) = \frac{K|\theta_i|}{\sqrt{1 - \zeta^2}} \epsilon^{-\zeta\omega_n t}[\zeta \sin (\omega_n \sqrt{1 - \zeta^2}\, t) + \sqrt{1 - \zeta^2} \cos (\omega_n \sqrt{1 - \zeta^2}\, t)]$$

(9.10-9)

Multiplying Eqs. (9.10-9) and (9.10-4), the power time response becomes

$$p(t) =$$
$$\frac{K\omega_n|\theta_i|^2}{(1 - \zeta^2)} \epsilon^{-2\zeta\omega_n t} \left[ \zeta \sin^2 (\omega_n \sqrt{1 - \zeta^2}\, t) + \frac{\sqrt{1 - \zeta^2}}{2} \sin (2\omega_n \sqrt{1 - \zeta^2}\, t) \right]$$

(9.10-10)

To find the peak or maximum power, Eq. (9.10-10) must be differentiated with respect to time and equated to zero. Proceeding thus, the equations reduce to

$$0 = -2\zeta\omega_n \left[ \zeta \sin^2 (\omega_n \sqrt{1 - \zeta^2}\, t) + \frac{\sqrt{1 - \zeta^2}}{2} \sin (2\omega_n \sqrt{1 - \zeta^2}\, t) \right]$$
$$+ 2\omega_n\zeta \sqrt{1 - \zeta^2} \sin (\omega_n \sqrt{1 - \zeta^2}\, t) \cos (\omega_n \sqrt{1 - \zeta^2}\, t)$$
$$+ \omega_n(1 - \zeta^2) \cos (2\omega_n \sqrt{1 - \zeta^2}\, t)$$

(9.10-11)

By making use of the trigonometric identity

$$\sin^2 x = \tfrac{1}{2}(1 - \cos 2x)$$

Eq. (9.10-11) reduces to

$$\cos (2\omega_n \sqrt{1 - \zeta^2}\, t) = \zeta^2$$

(9.10-12)

Hence the maximum power occurs at a time $t_{max}$ given by

$$t_{max} = \frac{1}{2\omega_n \sqrt{1 - \zeta^2}} \cos^{-1} \zeta^2 \quad (9.10\text{-}13)$$

By means of the triangle shown in Fig. 9.10-2 the following relationships are obtained:

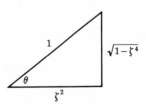

$$\cos \theta = \zeta^2 \qquad (9.10\text{-}14)$$

and

$$\sin \theta = \sqrt{1 - \zeta^4} \qquad (9.10\text{-}15)$$

**Figure 9.10-2**

By substituting Eqs. (9.10-13) to (9.10-15) into Eq. (9.10-10), the expression for the maximum power is obtained and becomes

$$p_{max} = \frac{K\omega_n|\theta_i|^2}{(1 - \zeta^2)} \epsilon^{-(\zeta\cos^{-1}\zeta^2)/\sqrt{1-\zeta^2}} \left[ \frac{\zeta}{2} (1 - \zeta^2) + \frac{\sqrt{1 - \zeta^2}}{2} (\sqrt{1 - \zeta^4}) \right]$$

(9.10-16)

Equation (9.10-16) can be rewritten as

$$p_{max} = K\omega_n|\theta_i|^2 f(\zeta) \tag{9.10-17}$$

where

$$f(\zeta) = \epsilon^{-(\zeta\cos^{-1}\zeta^2)/\sqrt{1-\zeta^2}}\left[\frac{\zeta + \sqrt{1 + \zeta^2}}{2}\right] \tag{9.10-18}$$

In Chap. 2 it was pointed out that the exponential term $\epsilon^{-\zeta\omega_n t}$ is the envelope of the underdamped response. Hence the term $-\zeta\omega_n$ determines how fast the transient response decays. It is convenient to speak then of a term $t_R$ called the *settling time* and defined as

$$t_R = \frac{4}{\zeta\omega_n} \tag{9.10-19}$$

By substituting Eq. (9.10-19) into Eq. (9.10-17) and making use of the relationship

$$\omega_n^2 = K/J \tag{9.10-20}$$

the expression for maximum power becomes

$$p_{max} = \frac{64J|\theta_i|^2}{t_R^3}\frac{f(\zeta)}{\zeta^3} \tag{9.10-21}$$

Now from Eq. (9.10-21) the important fact is seen that if the response of a system, characterized by a second-order response, in terms of the settling time is decreased by a factor of 2:1, the maximum power demand is increased by a factor of exactly 8:1. (It is assumed the damping ratio is not changed.)

The equations for a more complex system would be more involved, of course, and hence the transient response of a system is not a starting point for a thorough examination of its power demands. However, in the frequency-response method of system design it is the signal frequency rather than time which is the critical value, and it seems logical to study the parameters of the power expressions which are frequency sensitive. Before doing this we will now develop some power concepts which are best derived from the electrical engineering viewpoint.

## 9.11  A-C POWER

In the series circuit of Fig. 9.11-1 the voltage and current in the steady state are given by the relationships

$$e = E_M \sin \omega t \tag{9.11-1}$$

$$i = I_M \sin (\omega t + \theta) \tag{9.11-2}$$

$$\theta = \tan^{-1}\left(\frac{1/\omega C - \omega L}{R}\right) \tag{9.11-3}$$

The instantaneous power can be obtained by multiplying Eq. (9.11-1) and (9.11-2) as

$$p = E_M I_M \sin \omega t \sin (\omega t + \theta) \qquad (9.11\text{-}4)$$

By the trigonometric identities

$$\sin^2 \theta = \tfrac{1}{2}(1 - \cos 2\theta) \qquad (9.11\text{-}5)$$

$$\sin (A + B) = \sin A \cos B + \cos A \sin B \qquad (9.11\text{-}6)$$

$$\cos (A + B) = \cos A \cos B - \sin A \sin B \qquad (9.11\text{-}7)$$

Eq. (9.11-4) becomes

$$p = \frac{E_M I_M}{2} [\cos \theta - \cos (2\omega t + \theta)] \qquad (9.11\text{-}8)$$

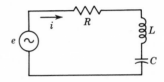

**Fig. 9.11-1**   Series R-L-C circuit.

This equation shows that the power in an a-c circuit consists of two parts—one an average value $(E_M I_M / 2) \cos \theta$ and the other a frequency-dependent part $(-E_M I_M / 2) \cos (2\omega t + \theta)$ which varies at twice the frequency of the voltage or current. This power can be either positive or negative depending on the direction of power flow, i.e. from or to the power source. Energy conversion units are rated by the average power consumed or generated, hence the formula

$$P = \frac{E_M I_M}{2} \cos \theta \qquad (9.11\text{-}9)$$

should be understood as meaning average power.

Using the phasor notation, Eqs. (9.11-1) and (9.11-2) become

$$\bar{E} = \frac{E_M}{\sqrt{2}} \underline{/0} \qquad (9.11\text{-}10)$$

and

$$\bar{I} = \frac{I_M}{\sqrt{2}} \underline{/\theta} \qquad (9.11\text{-}11)$$

where $\theta$ is defined as in Eq. (9.11-3). Thus if Eqs. (9.11-10) and (9.11-11) are multiplied, the result is

$$\bar{E}\bar{I} = \frac{E_M I_M}{2} \underline{/\theta} \qquad (9.11\text{-}12)$$

which can be expressed in rectangular form as

$$\bar{E}\bar{I} = \frac{E_M I_M}{2} \cos \theta + j \frac{E_M I_M}{2} \sin \theta \qquad (9.11\text{-}13)$$

In Eq. (9.11-13) the quantity $EI$ is termed *volt-amps* or *vector power*. The real part of the vector, i.e., $(E_M I_M/2) \cos \theta$, is the power in watts, and the imaginary portion, $(E_M I_M/2) \sin \theta$, is termed either *volt-amps reactive* (*VARS*) or *quadrature power*. These relationships can be shown by a vector diagram as in Fig. 9.11-2. Thus watts represent energy dissipated per unit time in a system and VARS represent energy stored per unit time as in inductances and capacitors.

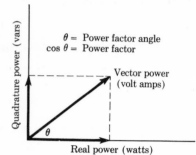

Fig. 9.11-2 Power vector diagram.

From the techniques developed in Chap. 3 this same concept can be applied to systems other than pure electrical. For example, let us consider the separately excited d-c motor of Fig. 9.11-3 and determine the ratio of $e$ to $i$ for a sinusoidal voltage input. Thus we wish to determine the equivalent input impedance of this system. The equations are developed in Chap. 3 and are

$$e_T - i_a R_a = e_c \qquad (9.11\text{-}14)$$

$$e_c = K_c \omega \qquad (9.11\text{-}15)$$

$$K_T i_a = J \frac{d\omega}{dt} + B\omega \qquad (9.11\text{-}16)$$

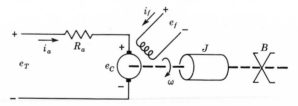

Fig. 9.11-3 Separately excited d-c motor.

Taking the Laplace transform of Eqs. (9.11-14) to (9.11-16) we obtain the set of equations

$$E_T - I_a R_a = E_c \qquad (9.11\text{-}17)$$

$$E_c = K_c \Omega \qquad (9.11\text{-}18)$$

$$K_T I_a = Js\Omega + B\Omega \qquad (9.11\text{-}19)$$

Thus

$$I_a = \frac{1}{K_T} [Js + B]\Omega \qquad (9.11\text{-}20)$$

Substituting Eqs. (9.11-20) and (9.11-18) into (9.11-17) we obtain

$$E_T - I_a R_a = K_c K_T \left[ \frac{1}{Js + B} \right] I_a \tag{9.11-21}$$

Thus, rearranging Eq. (9.11-21),

$$E_T = I_a \left[ \frac{K_c K_T}{Js + B} + R_a \right] \tag{9.11-22}$$

The input impedance of the system becomes

$$\frac{E_T}{I_a}(s) = Z(s) = \frac{K_c K_T}{Js + B} + R_a \tag{9.11-23}$$

The impedance of a parallel $R$-$C$ circuit as shown in Fig. 9.11-4 is

$$Z = \frac{R/Cs}{R + 1/Cs} = \frac{R}{RCs + 1} \tag{9.11-24}$$

Thus if we define

$$R = \frac{K_c K_T}{B} \tag{9.11-25}$$

and

$$RC = \frac{J}{B} \tag{9.11-26}$$

then

$$C = \frac{J}{B} \times \frac{B}{K_c K_T} = \frac{J}{K_c K_T} \tag{9.11-27}$$

The equivalent circuit of Fig. 9.11-3 becomes that of Fig. 9.11-5.

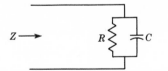
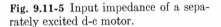

**Fig. 9.11-4** Parallel R-C circuit.       **Fig. 9.11-5** Input impedance of a separately excited d-c motor.

This equivalent circuit will only show the power loss in transmitting a signal and not a steady-state power loss such as that due to the field, i.e., $e_f i_f$. The signal power can now be obtained from the circuit of Fig. 9.11-5 by first obtaining the input impedance $Z(s)$ as in Eq. (9.11-24). Thus

$$Z(s) = \frac{K + K_T/J}{1 + (J/B)s} + R_a \tag{9.11-28}$$

Rearranging Eq. (9.11-28),

$$Z(s) = \frac{R_a + \dfrac{K_T K_c}{J} + \dfrac{R_a J}{B} s}{1 + \dfrac{J}{B} s} \tag{9.11-29}$$

Hence the input current becomes

$$I(s) = \frac{E}{Z}(s) = E(s)\left[\frac{\dfrac{J}{B} s + 1}{R_a + \dfrac{K_T K_c}{J} + \dfrac{R_a J}{B} s}\right] \tag{9.11-30}$$

For sinusoidal inputs we replace $s$ with $j\omega$ and Eq. (9.11-30) becomes

$$\frac{I}{E}(j\omega) = \left[\frac{1 + j\dfrac{J}{B}\omega}{R_a + \dfrac{K_T K_c}{J} + j\dfrac{R_a J}{B}\omega}\right] \tag{9.11-31}$$

Using effective values for current and voltage, i.e.,

$$\sqrt{2}\, E = E_M \tag{9.11-32}$$

and

$$\sqrt{2}\, I = I_M \tag{9.11-33}$$

Eq. (9.11-3) becomes the phasor

$$\frac{I}{E}\underline{/\theta} = \frac{\left(R_a + \dfrac{K_T K_c}{J} + \dfrac{R_a J^2}{B^2}\omega^2\right) + j\,\dfrac{K_c K_T}{B}\omega^2}{\left(R_a + \dfrac{K_c K_T}{J}\right)^2 + \left(\dfrac{R_a J}{B}\right)^2\omega^2} \tag{9.11-34}$$

Now since the input voltage is considered as a phasor of zero angle,

$$EI\underline{/\theta} = E^2\left[\frac{\left(R_a + \dfrac{K_T K_c}{J} + \dfrac{R_a J^2}{B^2}\omega^2\right) + j\,\dfrac{K_c K_T}{B}\omega^2}{\left(R_a + \dfrac{K_c K_T}{J}\right)^2 + \left(\dfrac{R_a J}{B}\right)^2\omega^2}\right] \tag{9.11-35}$$

Hence

$$\text{power} = \frac{E^2\left(R_a + \dfrac{K_T K_c}{J} + \dfrac{R_a J^2 \omega^2}{B^2}\right)}{\left(R_a + \dfrac{K_c K_T}{J}\right)^2 + \left(\dfrac{R_a J}{B}\right)^2\omega^2} \tag{9.11-36}$$

$$\text{and} \qquad \text{quadrature power} = \frac{\dfrac{K_c K_T}{B} \omega^2}{\left(R_a + \dfrac{K_c K_T}{J}\right)^2 + \left(\dfrac{R_a J}{B}\right)^2 \omega^2} \qquad (9.11\text{-}37)$$

## 9.20 OBTAINING THE POWER RESPONSE FROM THE FREQUENCY RESPONSE

In Fig. 9.20-1 is shown the block diagram of a typical control system which can act as a servomechanism or regulator. The servo response $(T_L = 0)$ becomes

$$\frac{\theta_0}{\theta_i}(s) = \frac{K_1 K_2 G_1 G_2(s)}{1 + K_1 K_2 G_1 G_2(s)} \qquad (9.20\text{-}1)$$

or

$$\frac{\Omega_0}{\theta_i}(s) = \frac{s K_1 K_2 G_1 G_2(s)}{1 + K_1 K_2 G_1 G_2(s)} \qquad (9.20\text{-}2)$$

The regulator response $(\theta_i = 0)$ becomes

$$\frac{\theta_0}{T_L}(s) = \frac{K_1 G_1(s)}{1 + K_1 K_2 G_1 G_2(s)} \qquad (9.20\text{-}3)$$

For sinusoidal inputs the vector power can be obtained from these three equations as follows:

For $T_L = 0$,

$$\Omega(j\omega) = |\theta_i| j\omega \frac{K_1 K_2 G_1 G_2(j\omega)}{1 + K_1 K_2 G_1 G_2(j\omega)} \qquad (9.20\text{-}4)$$

($|\theta_i|$ is the effective value of the input sinusoid) and

$$T_0(j\omega) = |\theta_i| \frac{K_1 G_1(j\omega)}{1 + K_1 K_2 G_1 G_2(j\omega)} \qquad (9.20\text{-}5)$$

Let us now define the vector

$$H_T \underline{/\theta_T} = \left| \frac{K_1 K_2 G_1 G_2(j\omega)}{1 + K_1 K_2 G_1 G_2(j\omega)} \right| \underline{/\theta_T} \qquad (9.20\text{-}6)$$

and thus

$$\Omega(j\omega) = |\theta_i| j\omega H_T \underline{/\theta_T} \qquad (9.20\text{-}7)$$

and

$$T_0(j\omega) = |\theta_i| \frac{H_T \underline{/\theta_T}}{K_2 G_2(j\omega)} \qquad (9.20\text{-}8)$$

The vector power now becomes

$$\Omega T_0 = |\theta_i|^2 H_T^2 \underline{/2\theta_T} \; \frac{1}{K_2 G_2(j\omega)} \times \omega \underline{/90°} \qquad (9.20\text{-}9)$$

With the definition

$$H_2 \underline{/\theta_2} = |K_2 G_2(j\omega)| \underline{/\text{ang } G_2(j\omega)} \qquad (9.20\text{-}10)$$

Eq. (9.20-9) becomes

$$\Omega T_0 = |\theta_i|^2 \frac{H_T^2}{H_2} \omega \underline{/2\theta_T + \frac{\pi}{2} - \theta_2} \qquad (9.20\text{-}11)$$

Thus

$$\text{real power} = |\theta_i|^2 \frac{H_T^2}{H_2} \omega \cos\left(2\theta_T - \theta_2 + \frac{\pi}{2}\right) \qquad (9.20\text{-}12)$$

and

$$\text{quadrature power} = |\theta_i|^2 \frac{H_T^2}{H_2} \omega \sin\left(2\theta_T - \theta_2 + \frac{\pi}{2}\right) \qquad (9.20\text{-}13)$$

Returning to Eq. (9.20-9), let us examine the magnitude of the vector power for this system. Thus

$$|\Omega T_0| = |\theta_i|^2 \left|\frac{\theta_0}{\theta_i}\right|^2 \left|\frac{\omega}{K_2 G_2(j\omega)}\right| \qquad (9.20\text{-}14)$$

But from Fig. 9.20-1,

$$\frac{T_0}{\theta_0}(s) = \frac{1}{K_2 G_2(s)} \qquad (9.20\text{-}15)$$

and hence

$$|\Omega T_0| = |\theta_i|^2 \left|\frac{\theta_0}{\theta_i}\right|^2 \left|\frac{T_0}{\theta_0}\right| \omega \qquad (9.20\text{-}16)$$

For the regulator ($\theta_i = 0$) the same procedure can be utilized to obtain the power demands of the system. From Fig. 9.20-1,

$$T_T(s) = T_L(s) - T_0(s) \qquad (9.20\text{-}17)$$

and hence

$$\frac{T_T}{T_L}(s) = \frac{1}{1 + K_1 K_2 G_1 G_2(s)} \qquad (9.20\text{-}18)$$

The torque $T_0$ is actually a control torque which cancels the load torque $T_L$ and hence

$$\frac{T_0}{T_L}(s) = \frac{K_1 K_2 G_1 G_2(s)}{1 + K_1 K_2 G_1 G_2(s)} \qquad (9.20\text{-}19)$$

also,

$$\frac{\Omega}{T_L}(s) = \frac{s K_2 G_2(s)}{1 + K_1 K_2 G_1 G_2(s)} \qquad (9.20\text{-}20)$$

For sinusoidal inputs with $|T_L|$ the effective value of the load torque the vector power becomes

$$T_T\Omega = \frac{|T_L|^2 j\omega[K_2G_2(j\omega)]}{[1 + K_1K_2G_1G_2(j\omega)]^2} \tag{9.20-21}$$

Defining

$$H_{2T}\underline{/\theta_{2T}} = \left|\frac{K_2G_2(j\omega)}{1 + K_1K_2G_1G_2(j\omega)}\right|\underline{/\theta_{2T}} \tag{9.20-22}$$

Eq. (9.20-21) becomes

$$T_T\Omega = |T_L|^2\omega\frac{H_{2T}^2}{H_2}\underline{/\frac{\pi}{2} + 2\theta_{2T} - \theta_2} \tag{9.20-23}$$

and thus

$$\text{real power} = |T_L|^2\omega\frac{H_{2T}^2}{H_2}\cos\left(\frac{\pi}{2} + 2\theta_{2T} - \theta_2\right) \tag{9.20-24}$$

and

$$\text{quadrature power} = |T_L|^2\omega\frac{H_{2T}^2}{H_2}\sin\left(\frac{\pi}{2} + 2\theta_{2T} - \theta_2\right) \tag{9.20-25}$$

The absolute magnitude of the vector power becomes

$$|T_T\Omega| = |T_L|^2\omega\left|\frac{E}{T_L}\right|^2\left|\frac{1}{K_2G_2}\right| \tag{9.20-26}$$

(For the regulator $\theta_i = 0$ and hence $E(s) = -\theta_0(s)$.)

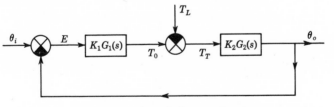

**Fig. 9.20-1** A typical control system.

The important fact that emerges from this development is that an analogous graph to that of the Bode plot can be drawn for the power response and in fact much of the information can be obtained from the Bode plot. Thus the interrelation between speed of response and power demands can be examined. In many military and industrial systems today size and weight limitations play as large a role as the speed of response and, hence, optimization of the system from a frequency-response viewpoint might be limited by the availability of power.

**9.21** EXAMPLE

The system of Fig. 9.10-1 acting as a servomechanism can serve as a simple example of the techniques developed in the preceding section. Thus in Eq. (9.20-14)

$$\frac{\theta_0}{\theta_i}(s) = \frac{\omega_n^2}{s^2 + 2\zeta\omega_n s + \omega_n^2} \tag{9.21-1}$$

where

$$\omega_n^2 = K/J \tag{9.21-2}$$

and

$$2\zeta\omega_n = B/J \tag{9.21-3}$$

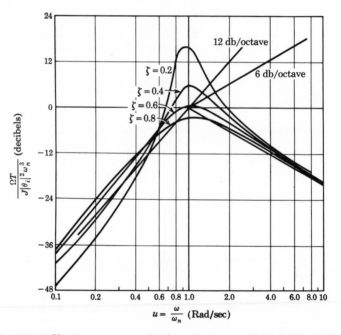

**Fig. 9.21-1** Vector power magnitude *vs.* frequency for Equation 9.21-8.

The absolute magnitude of the frequency response becomes

$$\left|\frac{\theta_0}{\theta_i}(j\omega)\right| = \frac{\omega_n^2}{\sqrt{(\omega_n^2 - \omega^2)^2 + 4\zeta^2\omega_n^2\omega^2}} \tag{9.21-4}$$

and

$$\left|\frac{1}{K_2 G_2(j\omega)}\right| = J\omega\sqrt{4\zeta^2\omega_n^2 + \omega^2} \tag{9.21-5}$$

The absolute magnitude of the vector power now becomes

$$|\Omega T| = \frac{\omega_n^4 |\theta_i|^2 \times J\omega^2 \sqrt{4\zeta^2 \omega_n^2 + \omega^2}}{(\omega_n^2 - \omega^2)^2 + 4\zeta^2 \omega_n^2 \omega^2} \tag{9.21-6}$$

Nondimensionalizing Eq. (9.21-6),

$$|\Omega T| = \frac{J|\theta_i|^2 \omega_n^3 \left(\dfrac{\omega}{\omega_n}\right)^2 \sqrt{\left(\dfrac{\omega}{\omega_n}\right)^2 + 4\zeta^2}}{\left[1 - \left(\dfrac{\omega}{\omega_n}\right)^2\right]^2 + 4\zeta^2 \left(\dfrac{\omega}{\omega_n}\right)^2} \tag{9.21-7}$$

With the substitution $u = \omega/\omega_n$ Eq. (9.21-7) becomes

$$|\Omega T| = \frac{J|\theta_i|^2 \omega_n^3 u^2 \sqrt{u^2 + 4\zeta^2}}{(1 - u^2)^2 + 4\zeta^2 u^2} \tag{9.21-8}$$

In Fig. 9.21-1 is shown a plot of the frequency-dependent portion of Eq. (9.21-8) for various values of $\zeta$. The values obtained from this plot must be added to the scale factor $20 \log [J|\theta_i|^2 \omega_n^3]$ to obtain the vector power magnitude in decibels.

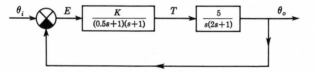

**Fig. 9.21-2** A fourth-order system.

The technique developed in Sec. 6.35 of Chap. 6 is very useful in obtaining a quick approximation to the power demands of a system. For an example consider the simple servomechanism of Fig. 9.21-2 in which there are two lags between the error and the torque. Utilizing the notation of Sec. 9.20,

$$K_1 G_1(s) = \frac{K}{(0.5s + 1)(s + 1)} \tag{9.21-9}$$

and

$$K_2 G_2(s) = \frac{5}{s(2s + 1)} \tag{9.21-10}$$

The next step is to obtain the approximate closed loop response* as shown in Fig. 9.21-3. Now the magnitude of the vector power was given as

$$|\Omega T| = |\theta_i|^2 \left|\frac{\theta_0}{\theta_i}\right|^2 \left|\frac{\omega}{K_2 G_2}\right| \tag{9.21-11}$$

_____

\* See Chap. 6, Sec. 6.35.

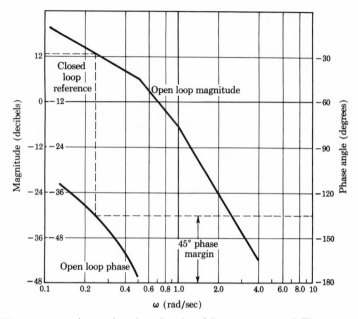

**Figure 9.21-3** Approximating the closed loop response of Fig. 9.21-2.

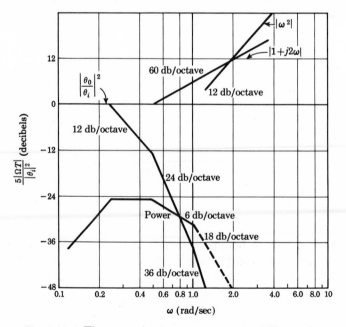

**Fig. 9.21-4** The approximate power response of Fig. 9.21-2.

The term $|\theta_0/\theta_i|^2$ can be obtained from Fig. 9.21-3 by multiplying the approximated closed loop response by a factor of 2 since $\log x^2 = 2 \log x$. The expression $|\omega/K_2 G_2|$ can be obtained from Eq. (9.21-10) and hence Eq. (9.21-11) will appear as shown in Fig. 9.21-4. The nondimensionalized vector power has a maximum of $-24$ db at 0.4 radians/sec.

Suppose that to the torque-producing element is added a compensating network of the form

$$K_c G_c(s) = \frac{2s + 1}{0.25s + 1} \tag{9.21-12}$$

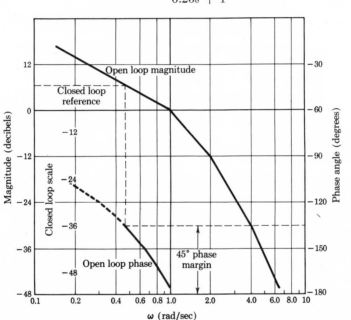

**Fig. 9.21-5** Approximating the compensated closed loop response of Fig. 9.21-2.

The compensated open loop response and approximated closed loop response can now be formed as shown in Fig. 9.21-5. The magnitude of the vector power can now be obtained as shown in Fig. 9.21-6. Thus the peak power occurs at a frequency of 0.48 radians/sec and has a value of $-12$ decibels. The important fact to realize here is not the absolute value of this power but the fact that the compensation network has increased the power demands of the system by a factor of 12 decibels or approximately 4:1. Thus before the engineer inserts a compensating device into a system some thought must be given to the increased power drain.

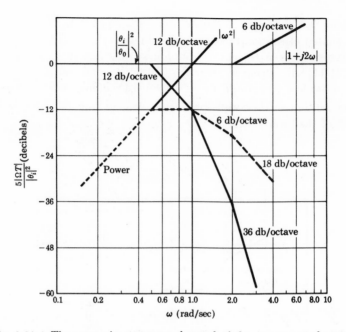

**Fig. 9.21-6** The approximate power demand of the compensated system.

## 9.30 THE D-C MACHINE AS AN ENERGY CONVERSION UNIT

The d-c machine is one of the most versatile electromechanical energy conversion units at the engineer's disposal. This versatility is due to two features of this type of transducer—one, the ease with which its output can be controlled, and the other, the ease with which electric energy can be transmitted from one location to another.

The equations for a d-c machine have previously been developed, but a different approach is not out of place at this point. In Fig. 9.30-1 is shown a very elementary d-c machine which has an armature with only one turn of wire and a commutator with only two segments. The purpose of the poles and their windings is to create a magnetic field. The direction of the flux $\phi$ can be obtained by Fleming's right hand rule which states that if the thumb of the right hand is pointed in the direction of the current, then the fingers encircle the conductor in the same direction as the flux. In Fig. 9.30-1 a cross indicates current is flowing into the paper and a dot the converse.

Electrical energy is put into the field and stored as given by the formula

$$W_{\text{field}} = \tfrac{1}{2}Li_f^2 \tag{9.30-1}$$

where $W_{\text{field}}$ = energy stored in the field,

   $L$ = self-inductance of field windings,

   $i_f$ = field current.

(In this simplified discussion we are neglecting the core losses.) The flux in the field circuit is a function of the magnetomotive force (mmf) and the reluctance or

$$\phi = \frac{Ni_f}{\mathcal{R}} \tag{9.30-2}$$

where $\phi$ = flux in webers,

   $N$ = number of turns,

   $i_f$ = field current in amperes,

   $\mathcal{R}$ = reluctance in ampere-turns per weber.

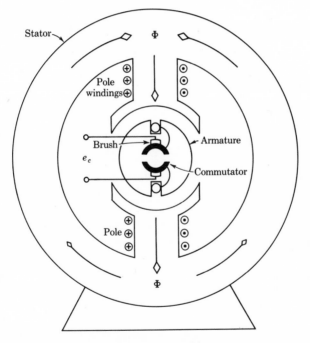

**Fig. 9.30-1** A d-c machine.

The reluctance of any magnetic circuit containing ferromagnetic material is a function of the flux in the circuit. However, for some range of current we can state that

$$\phi = K_f i_f \tag{9.30-3}$$

(Fig. 7.30-2 of Chap. 7 shows the effect of saturation in the field circuit of a d-c machine.)

Suppose now the armature is rotated at an angular frequency $\omega$ radians per sec. Faraday's law states that the instantaneous emf is given by the relationship

$$e = \frac{d\lambda}{dt}$$

where $\lambda$ = flux linkages. But for a simple circuit in which all of the field flux links all $N$ turns of the armature windings,

$$\lambda = N\phi \qquad (9.30\text{-}4)$$

and Eq. (9.30-4) becomes

$$e = N\frac{d\phi}{dt} \qquad (9.30\text{-}5)$$

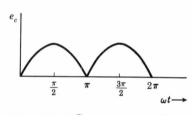

Fig. **9.30-2** Commutator action.

The armature coil can be considered as extending a length $l$ meters into the magnetic field and as having diameter $D$. Suppose we assume the area enclosed by the coil is perpendicular to the flux originally and is then given a constant rotation. The area the coil encloses is

$$A = Dl \cos \theta$$

where $\theta = \omega t$. Now since $\phi = BA$, Eq. (9.30-5) becomes

$$e = -Dl\omega B \sin \omega t \qquad (9.30\text{-}6)$$

where $B$ = flux density in webers/meter$^2$.

Equation (9.30-6) shows that the voltage induced in the armature coil is an a-c voltage. However, the commutator acts as a full-wave rectifier as shown in Fig. 9.30-2. The average value of Eq. (9.30-6), which is called the *counter emf* or *back emf*, is

$$e_c = -\frac{2}{\pi} \int_0^{\pi} BDl\omega \sin (\omega t)\, d\omega t \qquad (9.30\text{-}7)$$

and hence

$$e_c = \frac{4}{\pi} BDl\omega \qquad (9.30\text{-}8)$$

Thus the back emf of a d-c machine is obtained as

$$e_c = K_c \omega \qquad (9.30\text{-}9)$$

(See Fig. 7.30-3 in Chap. 7.) The addition of more turns to the simple machine will merely change the value of $K_c$ in Eq. (9.30-9).

If a resistor is placed across the output of the commutator a current will flow in the armature coils. The force on a conductor of length $l$ carrying a current $i_a$ in a magnetic field $B$ is given by the relationship

$$f = Bli_a \qquad (9.30\text{-}10)$$

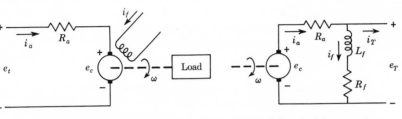

(a) Separately excited d-c motor        (b) Self-excited d-c generator

**Fig. 9.30-3** Equivalent circuits for the d-c machine; (a) Separately excited d-c motor; (b) Self excited d-c generator.

If $r$ is the radius of the armature coil the torque is

$$T = Brli_a \qquad (9.30\text{-}11)$$

If the machine is acting as a generator this is the torque the prime mover must produce to turn the armature. If the machine is acting as a motor this is the torque produced by the motor. The magnetic field produced by the armature coils tends to distort that produced by the pole windings somewhat, but we usually neglect this.

The equivalent circuits are those of Fig. 9.30-3 where $R_a$ is the effective resistance of the armature windings. (See Figs. 5.20-3 and 7.30-1.) It is usual to neglect the inductance of the armature windings.

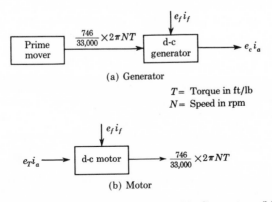

(a) Generator

$T =$ Torque in ft/lb
$N =$ Speed in rpm

(b) Motor

**Fig. 9.30-4** Energy flow for a d-c machine; (a) Generator; (b) Motor.

In general, when the d-c machine is used as a motor in a control system, the armature voltage is varied, and the field is excited from a separate source; such a machine is called a *separately excited shunt wound d-c motor.* (If the motor were series wound, a non-linear equation would result.) When it is used as a generator one can use the generated voltage to supply the field current also. This means the machine must have some residual magnetism. Such a machine is called a *self-excited d-c generator.* The electromechanical conversion process of the d-c machine can be summarized as shown in Fig. 9.30-4.

## 9.40 THE GAS TURBINE

The gas turbine is an engine consisting of a compressor, burner, and turbine which uses a gaseous fluid as the working medium. It converts heat energy obtained from a fuel such as kerosene to mechanical energy in the form of shaft horsepower or jet thrust or both as in the case of a turbo-prop engine. It produces a high power output with a relatively small weight. It is not in general a variable-speed device as is a d-c motor but is used to deliver power at a constant shaft speed.

The operation can best be explained from a simplified diagram such as Fig. 9.40-1 which shows the important thermodynamic stations in a turbo-prop engine. The inlet conditions, which are a function of altitude and atmospheric conditions, exist at station 0. If the turbine has been started by some external source and is in operation, air will be drawn to the compressor suction inlet. There is some loss in the inlet and hence station 1 is the beginning of the operating cycle. Here the air is compressed to a higher pressure, and a higher temperature, of course, follows. The compressor ratio and construction then determine the conditions at station 2. The next step is to inject a petroleum base fuel such as kerosene through an atomizer and ignite it. The heat energy released causes the air to expand. The expanded gases create the conditions at station 3. The gas then passes across the turbine section and is partially converted to mechanical work as the turbine shaft moves. Note that the turbine shaft is also the compressor shaft. After passing across the turbine blades the gas reaches station 4. The gases, still expanding, then pass out the jet nozzle at station 5 imparting a thrust to the engine. Thus by varying the fuel flow to the burner section the energy imparted to the turbine shaft can be varied, and hence the speed at which the shaft rotates is varied. The common method of controlling the speed of gas turbines is by means of fuel flow. A common symbol for the gas turbine is shown in Fig. 9.40-2. The gas turbine can be started by an electric motor operated by a battery, by an external compressor, or by a cartridge which produces compressed air by a chemical reaction (explosion).

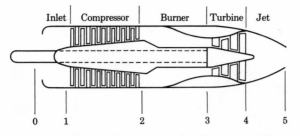

**Fig. 9.40-1** Thermodynamic stations in a gas turbine.

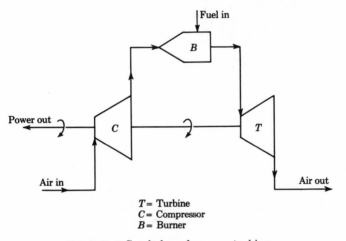

$T=$ Turbine
$C=$ Compressor
$B=$ Burner

**Fig. 9.40-2** Symbology for a gas turbine.

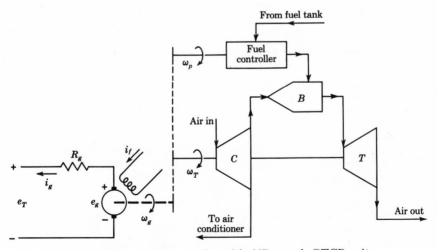

**Fig. 9.41-1** Primary power station with AiResearch GTCP unit.

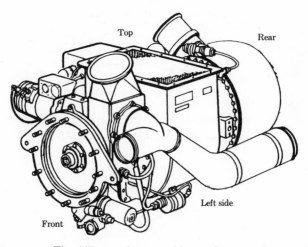

**Fig. 9.41-2** The AiResearch gas turbine. (Courtesy Garrett Corp., AiResearch Manufacturing Division, Phoenix, Arizona)

### 9.41 THE AIRESEARCH* MODEL GTCP GAS TURBINE FOR PNEUMATIC AND SHAFT POWER

For an example of a gas turbine we have chosen the AiResearch GTCP type, designed to deliver both shaft horse power and a pneumatic output. It is especially useful as a primary power station for a missile ground power system. Thus such a station could furnish either d-c or a-c power or both for a guidance and control compartment during the test and checkout phase before launching. A sample schematic of such a system is shown in Fig. 9.41-1. A sketch of this device is shown in Fig. 9.41-2 with a

---

\* The Garrett Corporation, AiResearch Manufacturing Division, Phoenix, Arizona.

---

**TABLE 9.41-1** KEY TO FIG. 9.41-3

| | |
|---|---|
| 1. Pump and Control Unit Assy—Fuel | 16. Actuator |
| 2. Valve—Acceleration limiter | 17. Valve—Dump |
| 3. Valve—Fuel solenoid | 18. Valve—Flow divider |
| 4. Valve—Relief | 19. Atomizer Assy—Fuel |
| 5. Filter—Fuel | 20. Plug—Igniter |
| 6. Pump—Fuel | 21. Chamber—Combustion |
| 7. Connection—Fuel inlet | 22. Thermostat—Acceleration and over-temperature control |
| 8. Tap—Fuel pressure | |
| 9. Drain—Fuel | 23. Thermostat—Bleed—Load control |
| 10. Governor—Fuel | 24. Valve—Turbine drain check |
| 11. Regulator—Differential air pressure | 25. Tap—Compressor air pressure |
| 12. Valve—Unloading air shut-off | 26. Shaft—Output drive |
| 13. Valve—Electromagnetic | 27. Fan—Cooling air |
| 14. Electromagnet | 28. Valve—Acceleration stabilizer solenoid |
| 15. Valve—Rate control | |

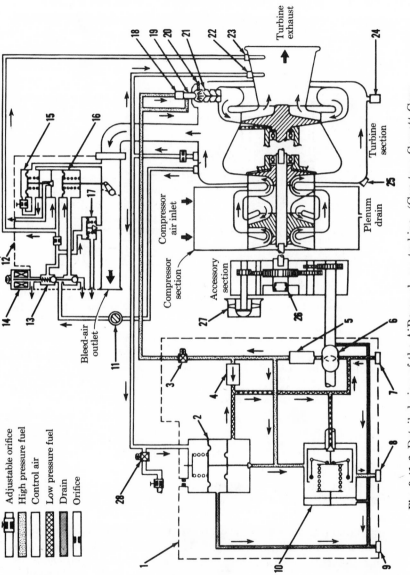

Fig. 9.41-3  Detailed view of the AiResearch gas turbine. (Courtesy Garrett Corp., AiResearch Manufacturing Division, Phoenix, Arizona)

more detailed diagram in Fig. 9.41-3. The thermostats shown by numbers 22 and 23 and valves numbered 15, 12, and 2 form a protective inner system for the turbine and do not contribute to the control action. The speed is maintained constant by the fuel pump and governor assembly which is shown in Fig. 9.41-4.

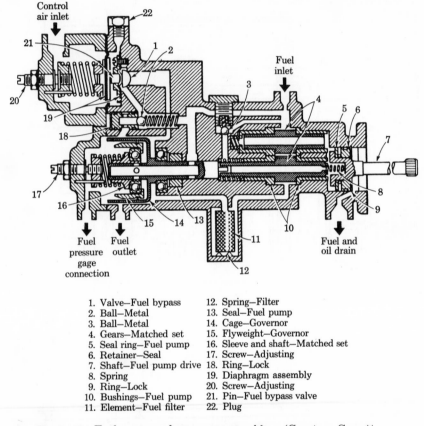

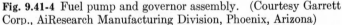

| | |
|---|---|
| 1. Valve—Fuel bypass | 12. Spring—Filter |
| 2. Ball—Metal | 13. Seal—Fuel pump |
| 3. Ball—Metal | 14. Cage—Governor |
| 4. Gears—Matched set | 15. Flyweight—Governor |
| 5. Seal ring—Fuel pump | 16. Sleeve and shaft—Matched set |
| 6. Retainer—Seal | 17. Screw—Adjusting |
| 7. Shaft—Fuel pump drive | 18. Ring—Lock |
| 8. Spring | 19. Diaphragm assembly |
| 9. Ring—Lock | 20. Screw—Adjusting |
| 10. Bushings—Fuel pump | 21. Pin—Fuel bypass valve |
| 11. Element—Fuel filter | 22. Plug |

**Fig. 9.41-4** Fuel pump and governor assembly. (Courtesy Garrett Corp., AiResearch Manufacturing Division, Phoenix, Arizona)

The fuel pump itself is a two-gear, positive-displacement, high-pressure pump. The governor, which is integral with the fuel pump, consists of a hollow input shaft, sleeve cage, flyweights, bearings, spring, and an adjustment shaft and nut. The position of the flyweights acting against the spring controls the amount of fuel that is passed. By tightening the adjustment shaft the speed at which the system will operate is set.

The thermodynamic equations could be derived at each station and then linearization techniques applied. However, a similarity between the

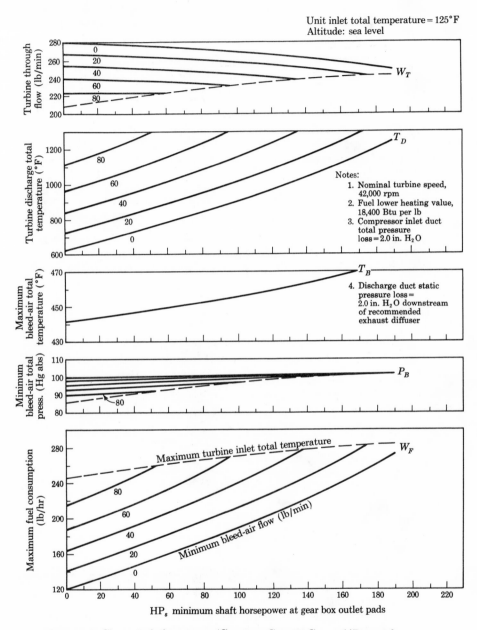

**Fig. 9.41-5** Characteristic curves. (Courtesy Garrett Corp., AiResearch Manufacturing Division, Phoenix, Arizona).

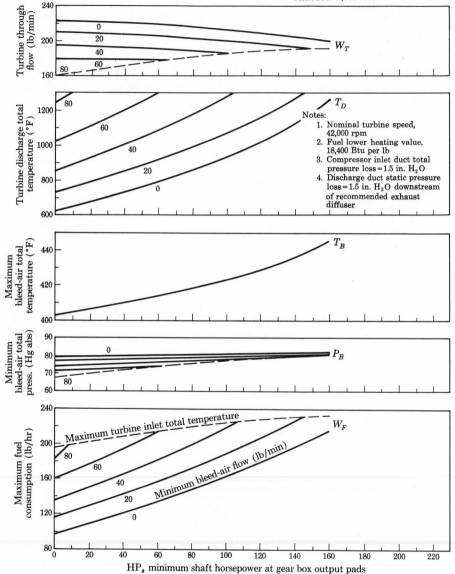

**Fig. 9.41-6** Effect of altitude on the characteristic curves.   (Courtesy Garrett Corp., AiResearch Manufacturing Division, Phoenix, Arizona)

characteristic curves of a triode as shown in Fig. 7.20-2 and the gas turbine can be seen by reference to Fig. 9.41-5. Here the shaft horsepower is analogous to plate voltage, fuel flow to plate current, and the bias is determined by bleed air. Thus

$$\text{hp} = f(\omega_f, \omega_B) \tag{9.41-1}$$

where hp = shaft horsepower,

$\quad \omega_f$ = fuel flow in lb/hour,

$\quad \omega_B$ = bleed air flow in lb/min.

Applying our linearization technique,

$$\Delta \text{hp} = \frac{\partial f}{\partial \omega_f}\bigg]_{\omega_B = c} \Delta \omega_f - \frac{\partial f}{\partial \omega_B}\bigg]_{\omega_f = c} \Delta \omega_B \tag{9.41-2}$$

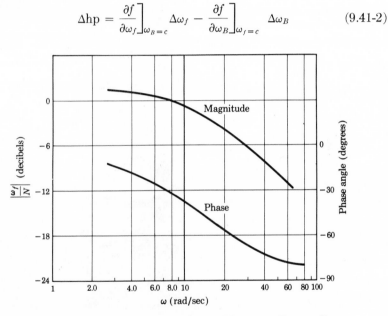

**Fig. 9.41-7** Bode plot for fuel regulator. (Courtesy Garrett Corp., AiResearch Manufacturing Division, Phoenix, Arizona)

It seems reasonable that there would be some time lag in the combustion process; tests show that there is and it is of the form

$$G_c(s) = \frac{\epsilon^{-as}}{(\tau_c s + 1)} \tag{9.41-3}$$

Actual tests with results as shown in Fig. 9.41-7 show that the fuel pump has a time lag of the form

$$K_f G_f(s) = \frac{K_f}{(\tau_f s + 1)} \tag{9.41-4}$$

In general we wish to have our output in terms of torque and speed. Thus we proceed to linearize the horsepower as

$$\text{hp} = \frac{2\pi}{33,000} nT \tag{9.41-5}$$

where $n$ = speed in rpm,

$\quad T$ = torque in ft-lb.

Hence
$$\Delta\text{hp} = \frac{2\pi}{33,000} T_0\,\Delta n + \frac{2\pi}{33,000} N_0\,\Delta T \tag{9.41-6}$$

This simplification is quite good in this case as the turbine will tend to operate over a very small speed range. Now if the system of Fig. 9.41-1 is considered to have inertia and viscous friction, the block diagram becomes as shown in Fig. 9.41-8.

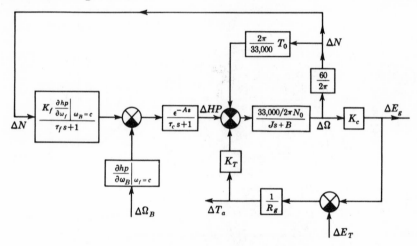

**Fig. 9.41-8** Block diagram of primary power station.

## 9.50 PROBLEMS

1. Derive an expression for the speed at which the power delivered to the load by a separately excited d-c motor is a maximum. (Note that neglecting frictional losses the power delivered to the load is $e_c i_a$).

2. Using Prob. 8 of Chap. 6 compare the power response of the system before and after the tachometric feedback is added.

3. Derive an expression for the vector power of a system as in Fig. 9.10-1 but with an element $K_{fb} G_{fb}(s)$ in the feedback path.

4. Consider the generator of Fig. 9.41-1 as supplying power to a missile heating blanket of resistance $R_H$. Derive the speed response of the system to a change in $\Delta\Omega_B$.

# CHAPTER TEN

# DISTRIBUTED SYSTEMS

## 10.00 INTRODUCTION

Many engineering applications are concerned with the relationship of events that, although they occur at points remote to each other, are related by the physical system between those points. In an electrical transmission system the energy input at the power station is to be delivered to a consumer who may be miles away. A chemical reactor may itself be long, or it may have a long line feeding it some of its raw materials. A long pneumatic line may be used to monitor some function at a missile test stand when the control room is remote to the stand. These physical systems respond to forcing functions or disturbances in such a way that their outputs cannot be predicted by treating them as lumped constant systems. The fact that small amounts of energy are either stored or dissipated in each increment of length must be taken into account.

An analogy in nature of this chipping-away effect is the journey of salmon up a stream to spawn. The number of salmon passing a given point decreases the farther upstream you look because some are caught by fishermen, some cannot negotiate the height of waterfalls, some fall by the wayside for other reasons. A long endurance automobile race is another example of a distributed system where attrition takes place as a function of distance, and both time and distance are the important variables. Neither of these "systems" is uniform (or homogeneous), one of the conditions which we will impose on the distributed systems we examine. For example, the diameter of a hydraulic pipe line or the size of an electric conductor cannot vary with distance. A second restriction is that only those systems which can be characterized by distribution in *one* space dimension will be discussed. This limitation excludes, for example, heat transfer problems in which more than one space dimension is involved, as in the case of a heat source at the center of a large sphere. In these one-dimensional space systems, the distributed-element approach is usually not required unless the length of the system exceeds one-tenth to one-half the wavelength of the highest frequency under consideration. In fact, even when the length is several wavelengths long, the system can be represented effectively by several T or $\pi$ networks in cascade. Such an approximation will be demonstrated in Sec. 10.40.

## 10.10 ELEMENTS OF DISTRIBUTED SYSTEMS

The general case of the one-dimensional distributed system can be represented by four elements per unit length. These are a series energy storage element, a series dissipative element, a shunt energy storage element, and a shunt dissipative element. All four elements do not have to be included in every distributed system. In thermodynamic systems the series energy storage element never exists since it is the inductive type.

## 10.11 BASIC ELEMENTS OF ELECTRIC TRANSMISSION LINES

Electric transmission lines can fulfill the necessary conditions of homogeneity and distribution in one dimension. Provided the separation of the conductors is small compared to the wavelength of the frequencies involved, transmission lines can be analyzed with standard circuit theory.

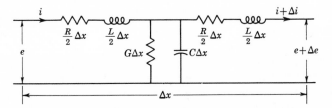

**Fig. 10.11-1** Electrical transmission line element.

They can be characterized by four basic parameters. In each increment of length, energy is stored in the electromagnetic field around the conductors and in the electrostatic field between conductors. The energy storage elements can thus be represented as a series inductance and a shunt capacitance. Also in each increment, energy is dissipated because of the current flow along conductors and leakage current flow between conductors, so both a series and shunt resistance are required to simulate power dissipation elements. For analysis the shunt element is more conveniently treated as a conductance. An incremental length of transmission line can then be represented by the network shown in Fig. 10.11-1, where $R$, $L$, $G$, and $C$ represent respectively the resistance *per unit length,* the inductance *per unit length,* the leakage conductance *per unit length,* and the shunt capacitance *per unit length.* $e$ is the voltage, $i$ the current, and $\Delta x$ the incremental length of the transmission line.

## 10.12 BASIC ELEMENTS OF DISTRIBUTED RECTILINEAL SYSTEMS

A long bar or a long string is an example of a distributed mechanical rectilineal system. Air friction may represent the damping per unit length. The mass per unit length is the series storage element, and the elasticity results in a spring constant per unit length. The shunt dissipative element will be neglected. The equivalent circuit for an incremental length is shown in Fig. 10.12-1.

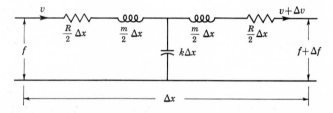

**Fig. 10.12-1** Rectilineal transmission line element.

## 10.13 BASIC ELEMENTS OF DISTRIBUTED FLUID SYSTEMS

Hydraulic and pneumatic distributed systems can be grouped as fluid systems because they behave the same. The only difference is in the calculation of the element values as explained in Chap. 3. In fluid systems there are equivalent energy storage elements for both the inductance and capacitance. The inertance opposes any change in volumetric flow just as the inductance opposes any change in current flow. The capacitance is

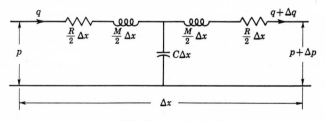

**Fig. 10.13-1** Fluid transmission line element.

associated with the energy stored due to the compressibility of the fluid. The analog of the series resistance is a resistance which represents the heating effect as the fluid particles pass through the fluid line. An analog of the shunt conductance in Fig. 10.11-1 would represent a uniform leakage of fluid from the line. Such leakage, if it occurs, is usually negligible, so this element will be omitted in the fluid line. An elemental length of the fluid line is shown in Fig. 10.13-1. $R$, $M$, and $C$ are respectively the resistance *per unit length*, the inertance *per unit length*, and the capacitance *per unit length*. $p$ stands for the pressure, $q$ for the volumetric flow. $\Delta x$ again is the incremental length.

## 10.14 BASIC ELEMENTS OF DISTRIBUTED THERMODYNAMIC SYSTEMS

Thermodynamic systems have no energy storage element equivalent to inductance but do have the equivalent to capacitance. The flow of heat along a thermal conductor causes a temperature gradient analogous to the voltage gradient due to current flow along an electrical conductor. The heat loss from the surface of a thermal conductor corresponds to the current loss between electrical conductors and can be approximated as a constant under some conditions. The thermal capacitance represents the heat storage in the thermal conductor. The thermodynamic distributed system is then represented by the circuit of Fig. 10.14-1. $R$, $G$, and $C$ are the thermodynamic transmission line properties per unit length. $\theta$ stands for the driving function temperature and $q$ for the heat flow.

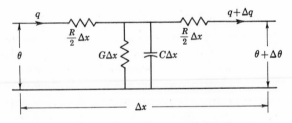

**Fig. 10.14-1** Thermodynamic transmission line element.

## 10.15 MECHANICAL ROTATIONAL SYSTEMS

Although distributed mechanical rotational systems can be devised, their occurrence in everyday practice is more limited than that of some of the others. So mechanical distributed systems will not be discussed here. An extremely long shaft in a rotational system might represent a distributed rotational system.

## 10.20 DERIVATION OF TRANSMISSION LINE EQUATIONS

Since the electrical transmission line element has all effects the other systems have, it can be used as the model to develop the general case. The special cases such as $G$ equal to zero can then be derived from the general case. The basic differential equations describing the behavior of transmission lines can be developed by applying standard analysis techniques to the circuit of Fig. 10.11-1.

$$e - i\frac{R}{2}\,\Delta x - \frac{L}{2}\,\Delta x\,\frac{\partial i}{\partial t} - (i + \Delta i)\frac{R}{2}\,\Delta x$$

$$-\frac{L}{2}\,\Delta x\,\frac{\partial(i + \Delta i)}{\partial t} = e + \Delta e \qquad (10.20\text{-}1)$$

Equation (10.20-1) can be simplified to

$$-\Delta e = iR\,\Delta x + L\,\Delta x\,\frac{\partial i}{\partial t} + \Delta i\,\frac{R}{2}\,\Delta x + \frac{L}{2}\,\Delta x\,\frac{\partial \Delta i}{\partial t} \qquad (10.20\text{-}2)$$

Since the last two terms on the right-hand side of Eq. (10.20-2) contain second-order increments, they can be neglected. If the remaining terms are divided by $\Delta x$, Eq. (10.20-2) reduces to the following form:

$$-\frac{\Delta e}{\Delta x} = iR + L\frac{\partial i}{\partial t} \qquad (10.20\text{-}3)$$

The increment of current $\Delta i$ is the sum of the currents through the two shunt elements $G\,\Delta x$ and $C\,\Delta x$ and is negative with the indicated directions. The voltage across the two shunt elements is

$$e_s = e - i\frac{R}{2}\,\Delta x - \frac{L}{2}\,\Delta x\,\frac{\partial i}{\partial t} \qquad (10.20\text{-}4)$$

The expression for $-\Delta i$ can then be obtained from Eq. (10.20-4) as follows:

$$-\Delta i = G\,\Delta x e_s + C\,\Delta x\,\frac{\partial e_s}{\partial t} \qquad (10.20\text{-}5)$$

$$-\Delta i = G\,\Delta x\left(e - i\frac{R}{2}\,\Delta x - \frac{L}{2}\,\Delta x\,\frac{\partial i}{\partial t}\right)$$

$$+ C\,\Delta x\,\frac{\partial}{\partial t}\left(e - i\frac{R}{2}\,\Delta x - \frac{L}{2}\,\Delta x\,\frac{\partial i}{\partial t}\right) \qquad (10.20\text{-}6)$$

The second-order increments are discarded, and the remaining terms divided by $\Delta x$. Equation (10.20-6) then is simplified to

$$-\frac{\Delta i}{\Delta x} = Ge + C\frac{\partial e}{\partial t} \qquad (10.20\text{-}7)$$

In the limit as $\Delta x$ approaches zero, Eqs. (10.20-3) and (10.20-7) become a pair of simultaneous partial differential equations.

$$-\frac{\partial e}{\partial x} = iR + L\frac{\partial i}{\partial t} \qquad (10.20\text{-}8)$$

$$-\frac{\partial i}{\partial x} = Ge + C\frac{\partial e}{\partial t} \qquad (10.20\text{-}9)$$

At this point the solutions to the transmission line equations will be limited to those resulting from sinusoidal forcing functions, and these further limited to the steady-state response. Under these limitations the solutions can be assumed to be

$$e(x, t) = \mathcal{E}(x)\epsilon^{j\omega t} \qquad (10.20\text{-}10)$$

$$i(x, t) = \mathcal{I}(x)\epsilon^{j\omega t} \qquad (10.20\text{-}11)$$

when the forcing function is sinusoidal. Since

$$\epsilon^{j\omega t} = \cos \omega t + j \sin \omega t \qquad (10.20\text{-}12)$$

the real part of the solution corresponds to a forcing function of the form $\cos \omega t$ and the imaginary part to $\sin \omega t$. If the assumed solutions for $e$ and $i$ as given in Eqs. (10.20-10) and (10.20-11) are used in Eqs. (10.20-8) and (10.20-9) and the indicated operations performed, the equations can be written in terms of total derivatives with respect to $x$.

$$-\frac{d\mathcal{E}(x)}{dx}\,\epsilon^{j\omega t} = \mathcal{I}(x)\epsilon^{j\omega t}R + j\omega L\mathcal{I}(x)\epsilon^{j\omega t} \qquad (10.20\text{-}13)$$

$$-\frac{d\mathcal{I}(x)}{dx}\,\epsilon^{j\omega t} = \mathcal{E}(x)\epsilon^{j\omega t}G + j\omega C\mathcal{E}(x)\epsilon^{j\omega t} \qquad (10.20\text{-}14)$$

$\epsilon^{j\omega t}$ cancels out of Eqs. (10.20-13) and (10.20-14) and they become

$$-\frac{d\mathcal{E}}{dx} = (R + j\omega L)\mathcal{I} \equiv z\mathcal{I} \qquad (10.20\text{-}15)$$

$$-\frac{d\mathcal{I}}{dx} = (G + j\omega C)\mathcal{E} \equiv y\mathcal{E} \qquad (10.20\text{-}16)$$

where $z$ is defined as the series impedance per unit length and $y$ the shunt admittance per unit length.

The solutions to Eqs. (10.20-15) and (10.20-16) can be found conveniently by the application of Laplace transforms. The letter $p$ is used as the transform variable to emphasize that the basic variable is distance $x$, not time $t$. The transformed equations are

$$-pE(p) + \mathcal{E}(0^+) = zI(p) \qquad (10.20\text{-}17)$$

$$-pI(p) + \mathcal{I}(0^+) = yE(p) \qquad (10.20\text{-}18)$$

Equations (10.20-17) and (10.20-18) can be solved for $E(p)$ and $I(p)$ and yield

$$E(p) = \frac{p\mathcal{E}(0^+) - z\mathcal{I}(0^+)}{p^2 - zy} \qquad (10.20\text{-}19)$$

$$I(p) = \frac{p\mathcal{I}(0^+) - y\mathcal{E}(0^+)}{p^2 - zy} \qquad (10.20\text{-}20)$$

The inverse transforms of Eqs. (10.20-19) and (10.20-20) are

$$\mathcal{E}(x) = \mathcal{E}(0^+) \cosh \sqrt{zy}\, x - \sqrt{z/y}\, \mathcal{I}(0^+) \sinh \sqrt{zy}\, x \qquad (10.20\text{-}21)$$

$$\mathcal{I}(x) = \mathcal{I}(0^+) \cosh \sqrt{zy}\, x - \frac{\mathcal{E}(0^+)}{\sqrt{z/y}} \sinh \sqrt{zy}\, x \qquad (10.20\text{-}22)$$

To get the variation of voltage and current with time, $\epsilon^{j\omega t}$ must be reintroduced so that $e(x, t) = \mathcal{E}(x)\epsilon^{j\omega t}$ and $i(x, t) = \mathcal{I}(x)\epsilon^{j\omega t}$. In Eqs. (10.20-21) and (10.20-22) the quantity $\sqrt{z/y}$ is called the *characteristic impedance* and is denoted by $Z_0$. $\sqrt{zy}$ is referred to as the *propagation constant*, $\gamma$, and in general has both a real and imaginary part expressed as $\alpha + j\beta$. The real part, $\alpha$, is associated with a decrease in maximum values of voltage and current from sending end to receiving end and is therefore called the *attenuation constant*. The imaginary part, $\beta$, is related to phase variation with distance and is termed the *phase constant*.

Equations (10.20-21) and (10.20-22) expressed in terms of the characteristic impedance, $Z_0$, and the propagation constant, $\gamma$, are

$$\mathcal{E}(x) = \mathcal{E}(0^+) \cosh \gamma x - Z_0 \mathcal{I}(0^+) \sinh \gamma x \qquad (10.20\text{-}23)$$

$$\mathcal{I}(x) = \mathcal{I}(0^+) \cosh \gamma x - \frac{\mathcal{E}(0^+)}{Z_0} \sinh \gamma x \qquad (10.20\text{-}24)$$

Because the Laplace transform technique was used to derive Eqs. (10.20-23) and (10.20-24), their boundary-value conditions naturally are those at $x$ equal to zero. More usually known conditions in physical problems are either the input voltage or the input current (their analogs in other systems) and the load impedance $Z_L$. To find the expressions for $\mathcal{E}(x)$ and $\mathcal{I}(x)$ in terms of the more usually known quantities, the total line length $l$ must be used. If $l$ is the value assigned to $x$ in Eqs. (10.20-23) and (10.20-24) we can obtain the expression

$$Z_L = \frac{\mathcal{E}(l)}{\mathcal{I}(l)} = \frac{\mathcal{E}(0) \cosh \gamma l - \mathcal{I}(0)Z_0 \sinh \gamma l}{\mathcal{I}(0) \cosh \gamma l - [\mathcal{E}(0)/Z_0] \sinh \gamma l} \qquad (10.20\text{-}25)$$

Equation (10.20-25) can be solved for $\mathcal{I}(0)$ in terms of $Z_L$ and $\mathcal{E}(0)$.

$$\mathcal{I}(0) = \frac{\mathcal{E}(0)}{Z_0} \left[ \frac{Z_0 \cosh \gamma l - Z_L \sinh \gamma l}{Z_L \cosh \gamma l - Z_0 \sinh \gamma l} \right] \qquad (10.20\text{-}26)$$

The expression for $\mathcal{I}(0)$ is now used in Eqs. (10.20-23) and (10.20-24) to develop the equations for $\mathcal{E}(x)$ in terms of the input voltage $\mathcal{E}(0)$ and the terminating impedance, $Z_L$.

$$\mathcal{E}(x) = \mathcal{E}(0)\left[\frac{Z_L \cosh\gamma(x - l) + Z_0 \sinh\gamma(x - l)}{Z_L \cosh\gamma l - Z_0 \sinh\gamma l}\right] \qquad (10.20\text{-}27)$$

or since $\cosh(-A) = \cosh A$ and $\sinh(-A) = -\sinh A$,

$$\mathcal{E}(x) = \mathcal{E}(0)\left[\frac{Z_L \cosh\gamma(l - x) - Z_0 \sinh\gamma(l - x)}{Z_L \cosh\gamma l - Z_0 \sinh\gamma l}\right] \qquad (10.20\text{-}28)$$

$$\mathcal{I}(x) = \frac{\mathcal{E}(0)}{Z_0}\left[\frac{Z_0 \cosh\gamma(x - l) + Z_L \sinh\gamma(x - l)}{Z_L \cosh\gamma l - Z_0 \sinh\gamma l}\right] \qquad (10.20\text{-}29)$$

or

$$\mathcal{I}(x) = \frac{\mathcal{E}(0)}{Z_0}\left[\frac{Z_0 \cosh\gamma(l - x) - Z_L \sinh\gamma(l - x)}{Z_L \cosh\gamma l - Z_0 \sinh\gamma l}\right] \qquad (10.20\text{-}30)$$

In all of the preceding equations, the distance $x$ is measured from the sending end.

In practical problems the internal impedance of the source affects the input voltage $\mathcal{E}(0)$. If the no-load voltage ($\mathcal{E}_i$) of the generator or source and its internal impedance ($Z_i$) are known, the value of $\mathcal{E}(0)$ can be found by solving Eq. (10.20-26) for the input impedance of the line $Z(0)$ and solving for $\mathcal{E}(0)$ in the circuit illustrated in Fig. 10.20-1. The expression for $Z(0)$ is

$$Z(0) = \frac{\mathcal{E}(0)}{\mathcal{I}(0)} = Z_0\left[\frac{Z_L \cosh\gamma l - Z_0 \sinh\gamma l}{Z_0 \cosh\gamma l - Z_L \sinh\gamma l}\right] \qquad (10.20\text{-}31)$$

and from the circuit of Fig. 10.20-1,

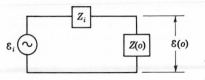

**Fig. 10.20-1** Circuit illustrating calculation of $\mathcal{E}(o)$.

$$\mathcal{E}(0) = \frac{\mathcal{E}_i Z(0)}{Z_i + Z(0)} \qquad (10.30\text{-}32)$$

There are several other forms in which the transmission line equations can be expressed. All quantities are the same as previously defined in this chapter.

$$\mathcal{E}(x) = \mathcal{E}(l) \cosh\gamma(l - x) + Z_0\mathcal{I}(l) \sinh\gamma(l - x) \qquad (10.20\text{-}33)$$

$$\mathcal{I}(x) = \mathcal{I}(l) \cosh\gamma(l - x) + \frac{\mathcal{E}(l)}{Z_0} \sinh\gamma(l - x) \qquad (10.20\text{-}34)$$

## 10.21 STANDING WAVES

The general transmission line when not terminated in its characteristic impedance $Z_0$ shows sinusoidal variations along the line with distance $x$. The variations of $\mathcal{E}(x)$ and $\mathcal{I}(x)$ for a typical case are shown in Fig. 10.21-1. In addition to this variation with distance a time variation is superimposed. So at each point the instantaneous value changes sinusoidally with time.

A special case occurs when the terminating impedance $Z_L$ is equal to the characteristic impedance $Z_0$. If $Z_L$ is made equal to $Z_0$ in Eqs. (10.20-28) and (10.20-30), and the expression for $\mathcal{E}(x)$ divided by that for $\mathcal{I}(x)$, the result is

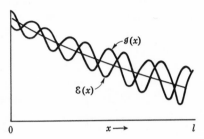

**Fig. 10.21-1** Variation of $\mathcal{E}(x)$ and $\mathcal{I}(x)$ with distance.

$$\frac{\mathcal{E}(x)}{\mathcal{I}(x)} = Z(x) = Z_0 \qquad (10.20\text{-}35)$$

which states that the impedance at any point is independent of $x$ and equal to $Z_0$.

## 10.22 SPECIAL CASES OF $Z_0$ AND $\gamma$

In Sec. 10.10 it was stated that the equivalent of the shunt conductance is usually neglected in mechanical and fluid systems. For these cases

mechanical: $Z_0 = [(R + j\omega m)k/(j\omega)]^{1/2}$          (10.22-1)

fluid:      $Z_0 = [(R + j\omega M)/(j\omega C)]^{1/2}$         (10.22-2)

mechanical:  $\gamma = [(R + j\omega m)j\omega/k]^{1/2}$          (10.22-3)

fluid:        $\gamma = [(R + j\omega M)(j\omega C)]^{1/2}$        (10.22-4)

For the thermodynamic system with no equivalent to inductance,

$$Z_0 = [R/(G + j\omega C)]^{1/2} \qquad (10.22\text{-}5)$$

$$\gamma = [R(G + j\omega C)]^{1/2} \qquad (10.22\text{-}6)$$

## 10.23 TRANSIENT ANALYSIS OF DISTRIBUTED SYSTEMS

Transient analysis of distributed systems becomes complex even for simple forcing functions such as step inputs. Solutions in closed form can be obtained only in a few special cases. The most satisfactory approach usually is to make a model using the information in Chaps. 4 and 10. Then the transient response can actually be measured.

## 10.30 EXAMPLES

Examples of all types of systems will not be given because those involving mechanical and thermodynamic systems are usually more concerned with transient responses. An example of a nonhomogeneous distributed mechanical system in which the transient analysis is important is in the flutter analysis of aircraft or missile wings. Most thermodynamic systems do not have sinusoidal forcing functions. Another point in distributed systems is that electrical transmission lines are designed to transmit energy at a specific frequency or at a band of frequencies. Other systems are more usually concerned with transmitting at zero frequency except as the system may be affected by disturbances or by its position in a control loop. This difference is illustrated by the two examples following. In Sec. 10.31 is given an example of a telephone transmission line. The sample calculation is shown at a single frequency of 1000 cps, although we are actually interested in transmitting the entire spectrum of voice frequencies. The hydraulic example, on the other hand, is concerned with the steady flow except for disturbances such as might originate with a hypercompressor or for the control implications of the transfer function.

## 10.31 ELECTRICAL DISTRIBUTED SYSTEM EXAMPLE*

A telephone system consists of a central office with internal impedance of $(600 - j80)$ ohms at 1000 cps. It feeds a system with five miles of cable which has the following characteristics:

| $R$(ohms/mile) | $L$(mh/mile) | $G$($\mu$mho/mile) | $C$($\mu f$/mile) |
|---|---|---|---|
| 180 | 0.8 | 1.5 | 0.08 |

The load is made up of a nominal 500 telephone set having an impedance of 680 23° ohms at 1000 cps. We would like to know the power available at the load for a 2.5 volt input at 1000 cps.

*Solution:* The first step is to calculate the values of $Z_0$ and $\gamma$ at 1000 cps.

$$Z_0 = \left[ \frac{R + j\omega L}{G + j\omega C} \right]^{1/2} = \left[ \frac{180 + j2\pi \times 1000 \times 0.8 \times 10^{-3}}{1.5 \times 10^{-6} + j2\pi \times 1000 \times 0.08 \times 10^{-6}} \right]^{1/2}$$

$$Z_0 = \left[ \frac{180 + j5.03}{1.5 \times 10^{-6} + j503 \times 10^{-6}} \right]^{1/2} = \left[ \frac{180 \underline{/1.6°}}{503 \times 10^{-6} \underline{/89.8°}} \right]^{1/2}$$

$$Z_0 = 10^3 [0.358 \ \underline{/-88.2°}]^{1/2}$$

$$Z_0 = 598 \ \underline{/-44.2°}$$

---

* Courtesy of Southern Bell Telephone & Telegraph Company.

$$\gamma = [(R + j\omega L)(G + j\omega C)]^{1/2}$$
$$\gamma = [180 \underline{/1.6^\circ} \times 503 \times 10^{-6} \underline{/89.8^\circ}]^{1/2}$$
$$\gamma = [0.0905 \underline{/91.4^\circ}]^{1/2}$$
$$\gamma = 0.301 \underline{/45.7^\circ} = 0.210 + j0.216 = \alpha + j\beta$$

The next quantities required are $\sinh(\gamma l)$ and $\cosh(\gamma l)$. The equations for these hyperbolic functions with complex arguments are

$$\sinh(\alpha l + j\beta l) = \sinh \alpha l \cos \beta l + j \cosh \alpha l \sin \beta l \quad (10.31\text{-}1)$$
$$\cosh(\alpha l + j\beta l) = \cosh \alpha l \cos \beta l + j \sinh \alpha l \sin \beta l \quad (10.31\text{-}2)$$

$$\alpha l = 0.210 \times 5 = 1.05$$
$$\beta l = 0.216 \times 5 = 1.08$$
$$\sinh 1.05 = 1.254$$
$$\sin 1.08 = \sin 61.8^\circ = 0.881$$
$$\cosh 1.05 = 1.604$$
$$\cos 1.08 = \cos 61.8^\circ = 0.473$$

$$\sinh(1.05 + j1.08) = 1.254 \times 0.473 + j1.604 \times 0.881 = 0.594 + j1.413$$
$$= 1.531 \underline{/67.2^\circ}$$
$$\cosh(1.05 + j1.08) = 1.604 \times 0.473 + j1.254 \times 0.881 = 0.758 + j1.105$$
$$= 1.342 \underline{/55.6^\circ}$$

The impedance at the input to the line $Z(0)$ can now be calculated from Eq. (10.20-31).

$$Z(0) = Z_0 \frac{Z_L \cosh \gamma l - Z_0 \sinh \gamma l}{Z_0 \cosh \gamma l - Z_L \sinh \gamma l}$$

$$= 598 \underline{/-44.2^\circ} \frac{680 \underline{/23.0^\circ} \times 1.342 \underline{/55.6^\circ} - 598 \underline{/-44.2^\circ} \times 1.531 \underline{/67.2^\circ}}{598 \underline{/-44.2^\circ} \times 1.342 \underline{/55.6^\circ} - 680 \underline{/23.0^\circ} \times 1.531 \underline{/67.2^\circ}}$$

$$= 598 \underline{/-44.2^\circ} \frac{913 \underline{/78.6^\circ} - 916 \underline{/23.0^\circ}}{803 \underline{/11.4^\circ} - 1040 \underline{/90.2^\circ}}$$

$$= 598 \underline{/-44.2^\circ} \frac{180.5 + j893 + 843 - j358}{787 + j158.8 + 3.6 - j1040}$$

$$= 598 \underline{/-44.2^\circ} \frac{1023 + j535}{791 - j881}$$

$$= 598 \underline{/-44.2^\circ} \frac{1154 \underline{/27.6^\circ}}{1186 \underline{/-48.1^\circ}}$$

$$= 583 \underline{/31.5^\circ} = 497 + j305$$

From Eq. (10.20-32), the input voltage $\mathcal{E}(0)$ is

$$\mathcal{E}(0) = \frac{\mathcal{E}_i Z(0)}{Z_i + Z(0)} = \frac{2.5 \times 583\underline{/31.5^\circ}}{600 - j80 + 497 + j305}$$

$$= \frac{2.5 \times 583\underline{/31.5^\circ}}{1097 + 225}$$

$$= \frac{2.5 \times 583\underline{/31.5^\circ}}{1121\underline{/11.6^\circ}}$$

$$= 1.33\underline{/19.9^\circ}$$

and

$$\mathcal{I}(0) = \frac{\mathcal{E}_i}{Z_i + Z(0)}$$

$$= \frac{2.5}{1121\underline{/11.6^\circ}}$$

$$= 2.23 \times 10^{-3}\,\underline{/-11.6^\circ}$$

Since we have evaluated the denominators of Eqs. (10.20-28) and (10.20-30), we will use them to calculate $\mathcal{E}_L$ and $\mathcal{I}_L$. They become, at $x$ equal to $l$,

$$\mathcal{E}(l) \equiv \mathcal{E}_L = \frac{\mathcal{E}(0)Z_L}{Z_L \cosh \gamma l - Z_0 \sinh \gamma l} \qquad (10.31\text{-}3)$$

and

$$\mathcal{I}(l) \equiv \mathcal{I}_L = \frac{\mathcal{E}(0)}{Z_L \cosh \gamma l - Z_0 \sinh \gamma l} \qquad (10.31\text{-}4)$$

since $\cosh (0) = 1$ and $\sinh (0) = 0$. If the value of the denominator obtained in solving for $Z_0$ is used in the above equations with the calculated values of $\mathcal{E}(0)$ and $Z_L$, the results are

$$\mathcal{E}_L = \frac{1.33\underline{/19.9^\circ} \times 680\underline{/23^\circ}}{1186\,\underline{/-48.1^\circ}}$$

$$= 0.763\underline{/91.0^\circ}$$

and

$$\mathcal{I}_L = \frac{1.33\underline{/19.9^\circ}}{1186\,\underline{/-48.1^\circ}}$$

$$= 1.122 \times 10^{-3}\underline{/68.0^\circ}$$

The current lags the voltage by 23.0°, so the power is

$$\text{power} = |\mathcal{E}_L||\mathcal{I}_L| \cos \theta$$
$$= 0.763 \times 1.122 \times 10^{-3} \cos (-23.0)$$
$$= 0.789 \ mw$$

## 10.32  HYDRAULIC EXAMPLE

A chemical reactor which is characterized by a hydraulic capacitance in parallel with a hydraulic resistance (a let down valve) is fed by a long line. We want to know the variation of reactor pressure with input flow to

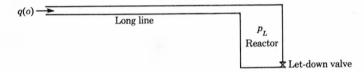

Fig. **10.32-1** Chemical reactor.

the feeder line as a function of frequency. The length of the line precludes treating the line as a lumped parameter system. A diagram of the system is shown in Fig. 10.32-1. The circuit representation is shown in Fig. 10.32-2. In the figure the values are as follows:

$$Ml = 1.01 \times 10^5 \ \text{lb-sec}^2/\text{ft}^5$$
$$Rl = 0.718 \times 10^5 \ \text{lb-sec}/\text{ft}^5$$
$$Cl = 0.972 \times 10^{-6} \ \text{ft}^5/\text{lb}$$
$$R_L = 8.54 \times 10^6 \ \text{lb-sec}/\text{ft}^5$$
$$C_L = 1.39 \times 10^{-6} \ \text{ft}^5/\text{lb}$$

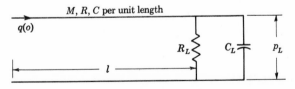

Fig. **10.32-2** Circuit representing chemical reactor.

The values given for the line parameters are total values rather than values per unit length as indicated by the multiplier $l$. The equation for $[p_L/q(0)]$ obtained from Eqs. (10.20-23) and (10.20-24) by letting $x$ equal $l$ and eliminating $\mathcal{E}(0)$ and then substituting equivalent hydraulic parameters is

$$\frac{p_L}{q(0)} = \frac{Z_L Z_0}{Z_L \sinh \gamma l + Z_0 \cosh \gamma l} \tag{10.32-1}$$

An example of the numerical calculations will be shown for $\omega$ equal to 4 radians/second. We will need the values of $Z_L$, $Z_0$, $\gamma l$, $\sinh \gamma l$, and $\cosh \gamma l$ at this frequency. $Z_L$ is the parallel impedance of the resistance $R_L$ and the capacitance $C_L$.

$$Z_L = \frac{R/(j\omega C_L)}{R + 1/(j\omega C_L)}$$

$$= \frac{\dfrac{8.54 \times 10^6}{j4 \times 1.39 \times 10^{-6}}}{8.54 \times 10^6 + \dfrac{1}{j4 \times 1.39 \times 10^{-6}}}$$

$$= 3.79 \times 10^3 - j1.798 \times 10^5$$

$$= 1.798 \times 10^5 \,\underline{/-88.8°}$$

Since $Z_0$ is the square root of the quotient of line elements, the length $l$ cancels out; so either the total values of $Ml$, $Rl$, and $Cl$ or the values per unit length can be used so long as one is consistent.

$$Z_0 = \left[ \frac{Rl + j\omega Ml}{j\omega Cl} \right]^{1/2}$$

$$= \left[ \frac{0.718 \times 10^5 + j4 \times 1.01 \times 10^5}{j4 \times 0.972 \times 10^{-6}} \right]^{1/2}$$

$$= 3.97 \times 10^5 - j2.32 \times 10^5$$

$$= 4.60 \times 10^5 \,\underline{/-30.3°}$$

and

$$\gamma l = [(Rl + j\omega Ml)(j\omega Cl)]^{1/2}$$

$$= [(0.718 \times 10^5 + j4 \times 1.01 \times 10^5)(j4 \times 0.972 \times 10^{-6})]^{1/2}$$

$$= 0.903 + j1.545$$

From Eq. (10.31-1),

$$\sinh(0.903 + j1.545) = \sinh 0.903 \cos 1.545 + j \cosh 0.903 \sin 1.545$$

$$= 0.0266 + j1.436 = 1.436\,\underline{/88.5°}$$

and from Eq. (10.31-2),

$$\cosh(0.903 + j1.545) = \cosh 0.903 \cos 1.545 + j \sinh 0.903 \sin 1.545$$

$$= 0.0371 + j1.031 = 1.031\,\underline{/87.9°}$$

Substituting these calculated values into Eq. (10.32-1),

$$\frac{p_L}{q(0)}$$

$$= \frac{1.798 \times 10^5 \underline{/-88.8°} \times 4.60 \times 10^5 \underline{/-30.3°}}{1.798 \times 10^5 \underline{/-88.8°} \times 1.436 \underline{/88.5°} + 4.60 \times 10^5 \underline{/-30.3°} \times 1.031 \underline{/87.9°}}$$

$$= \frac{8.27 \times 10^{10} \underline{/-119.1°}}{5.13 \times 10^5 + j4.02 \times 10^5}$$

$$= \frac{8.27 \times 10^{10} \underline{/-119.1°}}{6.51 \times 10^5 \underline{/38.1°}}$$

$$= 1.271 \times 10^5 \underline{/-157.2°}$$

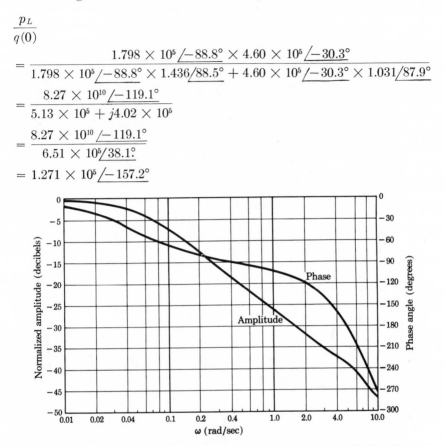

**Fig. 10.32-3** Amplitude and phase response of distributed hydraulic system.

This is the value at $\omega$ equal to 4. At $\omega$ equal to zero the value is simply $R_L$ or $8.54 \times 10^6$. In Fig. 10.32-3 is shown a plot of $p_L/q(0)$ as a function of $\omega$. The magnitude is normalized with respect to the value at $\omega$ equal to zero, or in other words the magnitude is divided by $R_L$, then calculated in db according to

$$\text{db} = 20 \log \frac{p_L/q(0)}{R_L}$$

For example, at $\omega = 4$,

$$\frac{p_L/q(0)}{R_L} = \frac{1.271 \times 10^5}{8.54 \times 10^6} = 0.0149$$

$$20 \log 0.0149 = -36.6$$

The response shown in Fig. 10.32-3 can be approximated with two T networks representing the lines as shown in Fig. 10.32-4(a). The total line values $Rl$, $Ml$, and $Cl$ are divided by 2 to get the values per section. $Rl/2$ and $Ml/2$ are then divided by 2 again to make them the upper arms of the T.

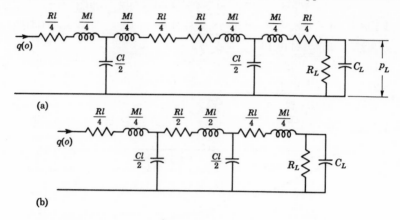

**Fig. 10.32-4** Lumped parameter approximation of hydraulic line.

The resulting network is shown combined in Fig. 10.32-4(b). The transfer function $p_L/q(0)$ for Fig. 10.32-4(b) is

$$\frac{p_L}{q(0)} = \frac{Z_2 Z_4 Z_6}{(Z_2 + Z_3)(Z_4 + Z_5 + Z_6) + Z_4(Z_5 + Z_6)}$$

where $Z_2 = 1/(j\omega Cl/2)$

$\qquad Z_3 = (Rl/2) + (j\omega Ml/2)$

$\qquad Z_4 = 1/(j\omega Cl/2)$

$\qquad Z_5 = (Rl/4) + (j\omega Ml/4)$

$\qquad Z_6 = \dfrac{R_L/(j\omega C_L)}{R_L + 1/(j\omega C_L)}$

To verify the approximation, we will calculate the value of the transfer function $p_L/q(0)$ at $\omega = 0.1$ radians/second. For this frequency the individual impedances have the following values:

$$Z_2 = \frac{1}{j \times 0.1 \times 0.486 \times 10^{-6}}$$
$$= -j206 \times 10^5 = 206 \times 10^5 \underline{/-90°}$$
$$Z_3 = 0.395 \times 10^5 + j \times 0.1 \times 1.01 \times 10^5$$
$$= (0.359 + j0.101) \times 10^5$$
$$= 0.373 \times 10^5 \underline{/15.7°}$$

$$Z_4 = Z_2 = -j206 \times 10^5 = 206 \times 10^5 \underline{/-90°}$$

$$Z_5 = Z_3/2 = (0.1795 + j0.0505) \times 10^5$$
$$= 0.1865 \times 10^5 \underline{/15.7°}$$

$$Z_6 = \frac{8.54 \times 10^6/(j \times 0.1 \times 1.39 \times 10^{-6})}{8.54 \times 10^6 + 1/(j \times 0.1 \times 1.39 \times 10^{-6})}$$
$$= 35.4 \times 10^6 - j42.1 \times 10^5$$
$$= 55.0 \times 10^5 \underline{/-50.0°}$$

$$Z_2 + Z_3 = 0.359 \times 10^5 + j0.101 \times 10^5 - j206 \times 10^5$$
$$\cong -j206 \times 10^5 = 206 \times 10^5 \underline{/-90°}$$

$$Z_4 + Z_5 + Z_6 = -j206 \times 10^5 + 0.1795 \times 10^5 + j0.0505$$
$$\times 10^5 + 35.4 \times 10^5 - j42.1 \times 10^5$$
$$= 35.6 \times 10^5 - j248 \times 10^5$$
$$= 251 \times 10^5 \underline{/-81.8°}$$

$$(Z_2 + Z_3)(Z_4 + Z_5 + Z_6) = 206 \times 10^5 \underline{/-90°} \times 251 \times 10^5 \underline{/-81.8°}$$
$$= 5.17 \times 10^{14} \underline{/-171.8°}$$
$$= -5.13 \times 10^{14} - j0.737 \times 10^{14}$$

$$Z_5 + Z_6 = 0.1795 \times 10^5 + j0.0505 \times 10^5 + 35.4 \times 10^5$$
$$- j42.1 \times 10^5$$
$$= 35.6 \times 10^5 - j42.0 \times 10^5$$
$$= 55.1 \times 10^5 \underline{/-49.7°}$$

$$Z_4(Z_5 + Z_6) = 206 \times 10^5 \underline{/-90°} \times 55.1 \times 10^5 \underline{/-49.7°}$$
$$= 1.135 \times 10^{14} \underline{/-139.7°}$$
$$= -0.867 \times 10^{14} - j0.734 \times 10^{14}$$

The denominator is then

$$(Z_2 + Z_3)(Z_4 + Z_5 + Z_6) + Z_4(Z_5 + Z_6) = -5.13 \times 10^{14} - j0.737 \times 10^{14}$$
$$- 0.867 \times 10^{14}$$
$$- j0.734 \times 10^{14}$$
$$= -6.00 \times 10^{14} - j1.571 \times 10^{14}$$
$$= 6.21 \times 10^{14} \underline{/-165.3°}$$

Then

$$\frac{p_L}{q(0)} = \frac{206 \times 10^5 \underline{/-90°} \times 206 \times 10^5 \underline{/-90°} \times 55.0 \times 10^5 \underline{/-50.0°}}{6.21 \times 10^{14} \underline{/-165.3°}}$$

or

$$\frac{p_L}{q(0)} = 3.76 \times 10^6 \underline{/-64.7°}$$

The value calculated for the distributed system was $3.78 \times 10^6 \,\underline{/-65.2°}$. The two results are within slide-rule accuracy, so the lumped network is a good approximation at $\omega = 0.1$ radians/second. At $\omega = 4.0$ radians/second the lumped network yields a value of $4.28 \times 10^5 \,\underline{/-107.1°}$ compared to the distributed system value of $1.271 \times 10^5 \,\underline{/-157.2°}$. So if we were interested in the response at 4 radians/second, we would have to divide the line into more than two T networks for a lumped constant approximation. However, there is little advantage in increasing the number of T networks for an analytical solution because the lumped network solution becomes more complicated than the distributed system solution. An easier approach is to design an electric analog and test it in the lab. The next section illustrates the design of an electric model of the distributed hydraulic system.

## 10.40 ELECTRIC ANALOG OF DISTRIBUTED HYDRAULIC SYSTEM

Let us assume that we want to make an electric model of the hydraulic system discussed in Sec. 10.32. Furthermore, we are interested in the response of the hydraulic system from 0.01 radians/second to 40 radians/-second. An audio oscillator is available that covers a range from 10 cps to 100,000 cps. Since time is stretched by the factor $\beta$, as shown in Table 4.11-1, frequency is stretched by the reciprocal of $\beta$. 0.01 radians/second corresponds to 0.00159 cps and 40 radians/second to 6.36 cps. If we let $\beta = 10^4$ then the range in the electrical analog will be from 15.9 cps to 63,600 cps which is within the range of the oscillator.

The inductance from Table 4.11-1 is

$$L_j = \gamma_e M_j$$

To keep the inductance in the millihenry region, we let $\gamma_e = 10^{-8}$ since the inertance in the hydraulic system is of the order of magnitude $10^5$. The values in the electrical system are then

$$Ll = \gamma_e(Ml) = 10^{-8} \times 1.01 \times 10^5 = 1.01 \text{ mh}$$

$$R_el = \beta_e\gamma_e(Rl) = 10^4 \times 10^{-8} \times 0.718 \times 10^5 = 7.18 \ \Omega$$

$$C_el = Cl/(\beta_e^2\gamma_e) = 0.972 \times 10^{-6}/(10^8 \times 10^{-8}) = 0.972 \ \mu\text{f}$$

$$R_{eL} = \beta_e\gamma_e R_L = 10^4 \times 10^{-8} \times 8.54 \times 10^6 = 854 \ \Omega$$

$$C_{eL} = C_L/(\beta_e^2\gamma_e) = 1.39 \times 10^{-6}/(10^8 \times 10^{-8}) = 1.39 \ \mu\text{f}$$

$$t_e = t_L/\beta_e = t_L/10^4 = 10^{-4}t_L$$

$$\omega t_L = 10^4\omega t_e$$

If ten T sections are used to represent the line, the values per section are

$$L/\text{unit length} = 0.101 \text{ mh}$$

$$R_e/\text{unit length} = 0.718 \ \Omega$$

$$C_e/\text{unit length} = 0.0972 \ \mu\text{f}$$

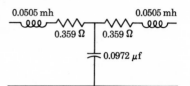

The electrical analog will then consist of ten T's with the values of Fig. 10.40-1 in cascade. The complete network is shown in Fig. 10.40-2. Notice that T elements are combined where possible. To interpret results $e_L$ is divided by $i(0)$. Then

**Fig. 10.40-1** T element of electric analog.

$$\frac{p_L}{q(0)} = \frac{e_L}{i(0)} \frac{1}{\beta_e \gamma_e} = 10^4 \frac{e_L}{i(0)}$$

and $\omega_H = 10^{-4} \omega_e$

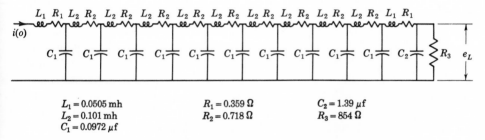

$$L_1 = 0.0505 \text{ mh}$$
$$L_2 = 0.101 \text{ mh}$$
$$C_1 = 0.0972 \ \mu\text{f}$$

$$R_1 = 0.359 \ \Omega$$
$$R_2 = 0.718 \ \Omega$$

$$C_2 = 1.39 \ \mu\text{f}$$
$$R_3 = 854 \ \Omega$$

**Fig. 10.40-2** Electric analog of distributed hydraulic system.

## 10.50 PROBLEMS

1. Derive the transmission line equations for $\mathcal{E}(x)$ and $\mathcal{I}(x)$ in terms of (a) $\mathcal{E}(0)$ and $\mathcal{I}_L$, (b) $\mathcal{I}(0)$ and $\mathcal{E}_L$.

2. A 150-mile transmission line has the following parameters per loop mile:

$$R = 5 \ \Omega/\text{mile}$$

$$L = 3 \text{ mh/mile}$$

$$C = 0.008 \ \mu\text{f/mile}$$

$$G = 5 \times 10^{-6} \text{ mho/mile}$$

Calculate $\mathcal{E}_L/\mathcal{E}(0)$ for $\omega = 5000$ radians/second when $Z_L$ is $(500 + j250)\Omega$.

3. A chemical process is terminated with a let down valve of resistance $5 \times 10^5$ lb-sec/ft$^5$. The reactor itself is a distributed system and has the following total values:

$$Rl = 1.5 \times 10^5 \text{ lb-sec/ft}^5$$
$$Ml = 1.0 \times 10^5 \text{ lb-sec}^2/\text{ft}^5$$
$$Cl = 0.5 \times 10^{-6} \text{ ft}^5/\text{lb}$$

Calculate $p_L/p(0)$ for $\omega = 0.1$ and $\omega = 5.0$ radians per second.

4. Design an electric analog of sufficient T sections to reproduce the response of the hydraulic system of Prob. 3 at $\omega = 1.0$ radians/second.

# CHAPTER ELEVEN

# SUMMARY PROBLEM

## 11.00 INTRODUCTION

In Chaps. 2 through 10 the reader has derived some basic tools which are necessary for a systems engineer. The obvious procedure now is to present typical problems which face the student so he can use all these tools. However, from a textbook standpoint the problem must be somewhat

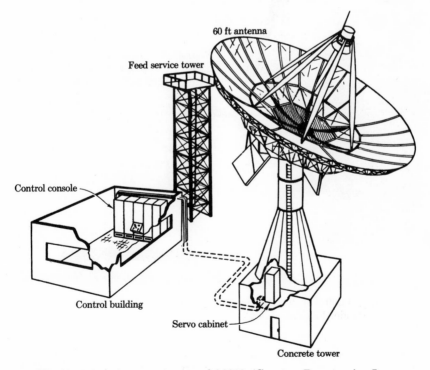

**Fig. 11.00-1** Antenna systems model 3013. (Courtesy Dynatronics, Inc., Orlando, Florida)

**Fig. 11.00-2** Antenna, front view. (Courtesy Dynatronics, Inc., Orlando, Florida)

simplified and idealized so that the application of these tools is not lost in a maze of details that contribute little to professional understanding. It is very rare that there exists a "black and white" solution to any problem; rather, several solutions are available and it is usually the system engineer who must choose the approach to be taken. With these facts in mind, a very simplified problem will be presented based on the work that Dynatronics, Inc., under contract with the United States Navy undertook in the development of an automatic telemetry tracking system. This tracking system was designed to be used on the Pacific Missile Range or the Atlantic Missile Range.

A sketch of the system is shown in Fig. 11.00-1 with a photograph of the antenna itself shown in Fig. 11.00-2. Dynatronics, Inc., itself acted as a system engineer in the development of this system, for the antenna was built by one company and the power sources by another. Dynatronics designed and built the connecting equipment that insured the operation of the system as a whole.

## 11.10  SYSTEM OPERATION

Automatic tracking is defined as the act of automatically following a moving target as the result of r-f signals received from that target. Automatic tracking of this type requires generation of an error signal and a reference voltage, comparison of error and reference, the conversion of the result of this comparison to a d-c drive voltage, and finally the application of the drive voltage to move the antenna. Conical scan of the antenna beam is frequently employed as the means of generating the error signal. This antenna system initiates its automatic tracking by scanning the beam for incoming r-f signals in the 215–260 mc telemetry band. Presence of a target within the cone of acquisition, which is transmitting in this band, will generate an error signal that enables the antenna system to position on the target and automatically track the target movement. In the automatic tracking process the antenna system also provides azimuth and elevation information concerning the location of the target.

The function of the r-f system is to acquire an r-f signal from the target, amplify the signal and then distribute it to eight channels. Also, the r-f system provides a 10 cps amplitude modulation of the incoming r-f signal from which the control installation derives the error signal employed to initiate automatic tracking. An r-f signal propagated from a target in unobstructed space is considered to be in the form of a spherical wave, with the target at the center of the sphere. As all points on the wavefront (the surface of the sphere) are equidistant from the center or target they are of uniform and identical phase.

When a paraboloid reflector is receiving a signal from a target which is located on the boresight axis, the energy in the wavefront is of uniform phase (see Fig. 11.10-1(a)). This wavefront will be reflected in accordance with the laws of optics to a point on the boresight axis in front of the reflector. This focal point is also termed the *phase center*, as all energy reflected to it is identical in phase. Referring to Fig. 11.10-1(b) and con-

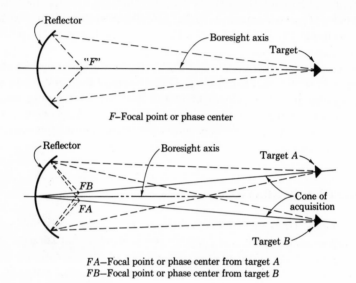

F–Focal point or phase center

FA–Focal point or phase center from target A
FB–Focal point or phase center from target B

**Fig. 11.10-1** (a) Target on boresight axis; (b) Target off boresight axis.

sidering the case of signals from a target in space located off the boresight axis, it is seen that the planes of the incoming wavefronts are not normal to the boresight axis. This results in a phase difference in the energy received by various sections of the reflector surface. The degree of phase difference will be proportional to the angular relationship between the plane of the incoming wavefront and a plane normal to the boresight axis. By applying optics (the angle of reflection equals the angle of incidence), it may be seen that the incoming wavefront is reflected to a focal point not on the boresight axis. A logical extension of this thinking indicates that for every target position of boresight axis in space there is a focal point off boresight axis in front of the reflector. Note that the distance from boresight axis to given focal point is a function of the distance between the target and boresight axis in space.

Consider the intersection of the boresight axis and the reflector to be the vertex of a horizontal cone looking out into space; this is the *cone of acquisition*. In this antenna system the vertex angle of the cone of acquisition is approximately 7°. The circular base of the cone in space will be reflected in the form of a circle of greatly reduced radius in front of the reflector. Also signals from a target within the cone of acquisition will be reflected to a focal point within the circle of reduced radius. This circle is termed the *phase circle*, as any focal point within it is the phase center of signals from a corresponding target position within the cone of acquisition. Thus the phase circle is a reduced reflection of the base of the cone of acquisition in space, and the location of a transmitting target within the cone of acquisition will be indicated by a phase center of maximum energy within the phase circle.

In this antenna system, information concerning target position is derived by scanning the phase circle. This is done by revolving the nutator at 600 rpm. The nutator is offset sufficiently to cover the phase circle once in each revolution and it is so mounted that the plane of the phase circle is within the nutator. Consequently, revolving the nutator is in essence the same as moving the waveguide center around the phase circle. In this manner the phase center of the signal from any target within the cone of acquisition is periodically scanned at 10 cps by the effective lobe of the antenna pattern. The scanning operation results in an amplitude modulation of the incoming r-f signals. The percentage of modulation is dependent upon the radius from the scan axis to the phase center representing the target.

The reference generator, which is direct-coupled to the nutator shaft, provides a rotational time base for the scanning process. The reference generator has two 10 cps outputs in phase quadrature; one output is for azimuth reference and the other is for elevation reference. These outputs are connected to the phase demodulator. Also, the amplitude-modulated r-f signals are applied through the r-f feed assembly to the error signal detection group, where, in the postamplifier, the degree of modulation is detected and delivered as an a-c error signal to the phase demodulator. The phase and magnitude of the a-c error signal are referred to the reference generator outputs in the phase demodulator and resolved into d-c azimuth and elevator voltages. These voltages represent the difference existing between the target position in space and the antenna heading. It is these d-c error voltages which, when applied to the servo system, enable the antenna to track. The antenna will then rotate until the target is aligned with the boresight axis. Thus, if an error exists, the drive motor will rotate and we have a Type 1 system where the nutator acts then to produce an error signal. Thus if the missile to be tracked has the proper signal generator aboard and is within the cone of acquisition, the antenna will point to the target. It is then a simple trigonometric problem to determine its angular position in space relative to the antenna location. The angular time history of the missile is usually recorded by the telemetering system to allow an exact trajectory to be determined after the flight is terminated.

## 11.20 THE PROBLEM

In Fig. 11.20-1 is shown a functional diagram of the system and in Table 11.20-1 some desired characteristics of the system. The problem to be discussed is the design of the position amplifier which takes the d-c error

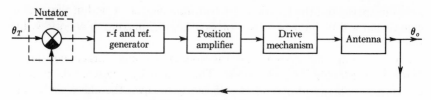

**Fig. 11.20-1** Functional block diagram of the system.

voltage from the r-f system and drives the antenna. The system will also be examined to insure that the desired operating characteristics can be met. The way that this can be accomplished is to derive the transfer functions of each block and then produce the Bode plot of the system. Since this is a Type 1 system with a velocity input, the velocity constant $K_v$ will be the important parameter and its value is determined by the desired accuracy of the system.

**TABLE 11.20-1** DESIRED CHARACTERISTICS OF THE SYSTEM

*Limits*

| | |
|---|---|
| Servo.......................... | $-\frac{1}{4}°$ and 86.5° |
| Electrical..................... | $-\frac{1}{2}°$ and 92° |
| Mechanical.................... | $-2.6°$ and 106° |
| Tracking and slewing acceleration.................... | 5°/sec² maximum |

*Tracking Accuracy*

| | |
|---|---|
| Below 1°/sec................. | 0.12° |
| 6°/sec................. | 0.75° |
| Max wind loading with listed characteristics............. | 30 knots |

*Power Requirements*

| | |
|---|---|
| Motor-generator installation... | Three phase, 4 wire 120/208 volt |
| Control installation.......... | Single phase, 60 cps, 120 volts, 35 amperes |

The equations of motion for the system can best be derived by considering the system as comprised of three basic sections. These sections are:

1. antenna, r-f section, and demodulator
2. velocity servo
3. mechanical load

These sections will be considered as operating in a linear mode. The equations are now derived in the following section.

## 11.30 EQUATIONS OF MOTION

With any lag in the r-f section neglected, the antenna, r-f section, and conical scan act as an error-producing device. The gain of the r-f

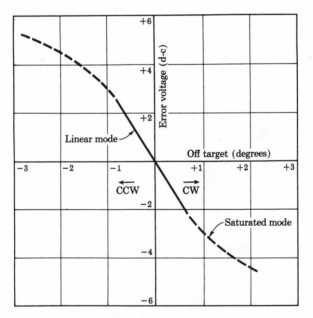

**Fig. 11.30-1** R-F and demodulator steady state gain.

section can be determined from Fig. 11.30-1 and the phase shift of the demodulator from Fig. 11.30-2. Thus, where

$\theta_T$ = target angle in radians,

$K_A$ = antenna gain,

$\theta_A$ = antenna position in radians,

the block diagram becomes that shown in Fig. 11.30-3.

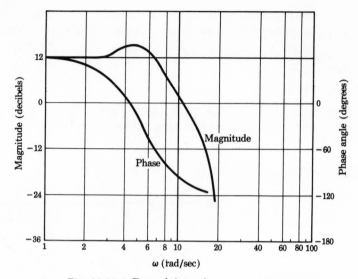

**Fig. 11.30-2** Demodulator frequency response.

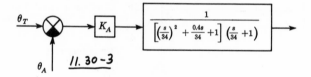

**Fig. 11.30-3** R-F section, antenna conical scan and demodulator block.

## 11.31 THE VELOCITY SERVO

The velocity servo consists of a magnetic amplifier which drives the field of a d-c generator. The d-c generator itself supplies a 20 hp d-c servo motor which is coupled through a torque-limit coupling to a gear reducer. The pinion on the output shaft of the gear reducer engages the ring gear of the turret. For this simplified problem only the azimuth servo loop is shown. This servo motor is equipped with a rate generator and has some parallel compensation. The d-c generator is driven by an a-c induction motor and for this simplified example its speed is considered constant. Fig. 11.31-1 shows a schematic of the azimuth and elevation drive assembly. Fig. 11.31-2 shows the diagram of the velocity servo. The block diagram can now be developed.

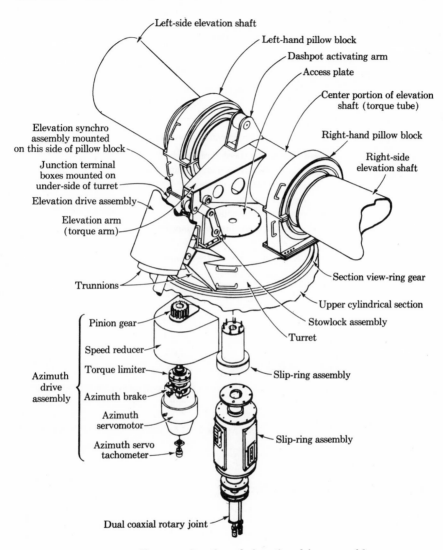

Left-side elevation shaft

Left-hand pillow block

Dashpot activating arm

Access plate

Center portion of elevation
shaft (torque tube)

Elevation synchro
assembly mounted
on this side of pillow block

Right-hand pillow block

Right-side
elevation shaft

Junction terminal
boxes mounted on
under-side of turret

Elevation drive assembly

Elevation arm
(torque arm)

Trunnions

Section view-ring gear

Upper cylindrical section

Pinion gear

Stowlock assembly

Speed reducer

Turret

Azimuth
drive
assembly

Torque limiter

Slip-ring assembly

Azimuth brake

Azimuth
servomotor

Azimuth servo
tachometer

Slip-ring assembly

Dual coaxial rotary joint

**Fig. 11.31-1** Turret, azimuth and elevation drive assembly.

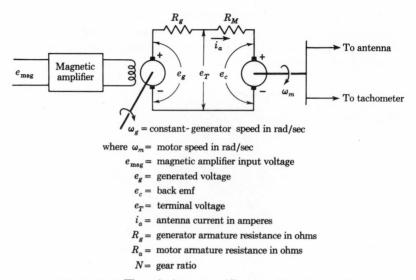

$\omega_g$ = constant-generator speed in rad/sec

where $\omega_m$ = motor speed in rad/sec

$e_{mag}$ = magnetic amplifier input voltage

$e_g$ = generated voltage

$e_c$ = back emf

$e_T$ = terminal voltage

$i_a$ = antenna current in amperes

$R_g$ = generator armature resistance in ohms

$R_a$ = motor armature resistance in ohms

$N$ = gear ratio

**Fig. 11.31-2** The velocity servo. (Courtesy Dynatronics, Inc., Orlando, Florida)

For the motor,

$$T_e = \text{torque developed} = K_T i_a \qquad (K_T = \text{lb-ft/amp}) \qquad (11.31\text{-}1)$$

$$e_c = K_c \omega_m \qquad\qquad\qquad\qquad (K_c = \text{volts/rad/sec}) \qquad (11.31\text{-}2)$$

and

$$e_T - i_a R_a = e_c \qquad\qquad\qquad\qquad\qquad\qquad\qquad\qquad (11.31\text{-}3)$$

For the generator,

$$e_g - i_a R_g = e_T \qquad\qquad\qquad\qquad\qquad\qquad (11.31\text{-}4)$$

Tests on the magnetic amplifier show that

$$\frac{E_g(s)}{E_{mag}(s)} = \frac{2000}{(0.1s + 1)^2} \qquad\qquad\qquad (11.31\text{-}5)$$

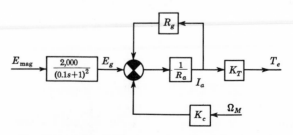

**Fig. 11.31-3** Block diagram of motor-generator set.

The block diagram can now be represented as shown in Fig. 11.31-3. The high gain (2000) present in the magnetic amplifier would tend to cause the servo system to oscillate, so a feedback path is present around the speed of the motor-generator set as shown in Fig. 11.31-4.

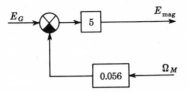

**Fig. 11.31-4**  Parallel compensation of the velocity servo.

## 11.32  MECHANICAL LOAD

While a value of total inertia $J_A$ and compliance $1/c_A$ for the antenna can be obtained from the manufacturer, the load can be considered as consisting of two inertia sections with viscous damping $B/2$ as shown in Fig. 11.32-1. The electrical analog of this circuit can be shown in Fig. 11.32-2.

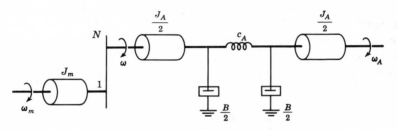

**Fig. 11.32-1**  The mechanical load.

Writing loop equations

$$T_L = T_E - J_m s \Omega_M \tag{11.32-1}$$

$$T_H = N T_L \tag{11.32-2}$$

$$\Omega_H = \frac{\Omega_M}{N} \tag{11.32-3}$$

$$T_H = \left(\frac{J_A}{2} s + \frac{c_A}{s} + \frac{B}{2}\right) \Omega_H - \frac{c_A}{s} \Omega_A \tag{11.32-4}$$

and

$$0 = \frac{-c_A}{s} \Omega_H + \left(\frac{J_A}{2} s + \frac{c_A}{s} + \frac{B}{2}\right) \Omega_A \tag{11.32-5}$$

The torque $T_H$ can be considered as consisting of the mechanical torque of the motor and the wind torque on the antenna.

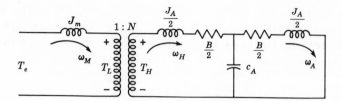

**Fig. 11.32-2** Electrical analog of the mechanical load.

From Eq. (11.32-1) one obtains Fig. 11.32-3; from Eq. (11.32-2) and (11.32-3) one obtains Fig. 11.32-4; from Eq. (11.32-4) one obtains Fig. 11.32-5. The object of this study is to determine a suitable equalizing circuit $G(s)$ to be inserted before the velocity servo. The position servo block diagram would then be as shown in Fig. 11.32-6.

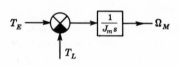

**Figure 11.32-3**

To complete this section Fig. 11.32-7 shows the block diagram of the complete system while Table 11.32-1 shows the values used for the system parameters. In this simplified problem only the azimuth servo loop is considered. The elevation servo loop would have the same block diagram but different parameters owing to the presence of a balljack instead of a gear box as a connecting device between the drive motor and the antenna.

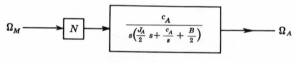

**Figure 11.32-4**

**TABLE 11.32-1** AZIMUTH CONSTANTS

| | | |
|---|---|---|
| $J_A$ | Antenna inertia | $0.242 \times 10^6$ lb-ft-sec$^2$ |
| $1/c_A$ | Compliance | $0.84 \times 10^{-8}$ rad/lb-ft |
| $N$ | Gear ratio | 530:1 |
| $K_c$ | Motor back emf constant | 2.41 volts/rad/sec |
| $K_T$ | Motor torque constant | 1.63 lb-ft/amp |
| | Armature resistance of | |
| $R_a$ | Motor | 0.441 ohms |
| $R_g$ | Generator | 0.441 ohms |
| $J_m$ | Motor inertia | 0.718 lb-ft-sec$^2$ |
| $B$ | Viscous damping (motor speed) | 31 lb-ft/rad/sec |
| $K_A$ | R-F system gain | 183.4 volts/rad |

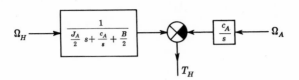

**Figure 11.32-5**

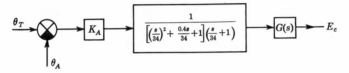

**Figure 11.32-6**

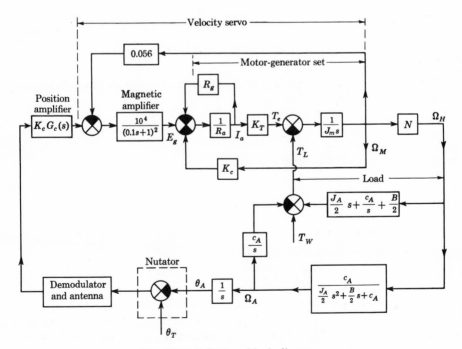

**Fig. 11.32-7** System block diagram.

## 11.33 CHOOSING THE VELOCITY CONSTANT $K_v$

In Table 11.20-1 it is seen that there are two desired tracking accuracies for this system. Thus

$$K_v = \frac{1°/\text{sec}}{0.12°} = 8.3 \text{ sec}^{-1} \qquad (11.33\text{-}1)$$

as in the other case

$$K_v = \frac{6°/\text{sec}}{0.75°} = 8.0 \text{ sec}^{-1} \qquad (11.33\text{-}2)$$

Even in a simplified problem as we have here some decision must be made based on past experience. If the system were perfect a $K_v$ of 8 or 9 would suffice to meet the desired accuracy. However, two additional factors must be considered: one, the acceleration requirements of the system, and the other, the nonlinearities such as brush friction.

The motor inertia is given in Table 11.32-1 and is

$$J_m = 0.718 \text{ lb-ft-sec}^2 \qquad (11.33\text{-}3)$$

and the desired acceleration is

$$\dot{\omega} = 5°/\text{sec}^2 \qquad (11.33\text{-}4)$$

Thus the required torque to overcome the motor inertia is

$$T_m = \frac{0.718}{57.3} \times 5 \text{ lb-ft} \qquad (11.33\text{-}5)$$

The antenna inertia reflected to the motor side through the 530:1 gear ratio is

$$J_R = \frac{0.242}{(530)^2} \times 10^6 = 0.845 \text{ lb-ft-sec}^2 \qquad (11.33\text{-}6)$$

The total acceleration torque is then

$$T_T = \left(\frac{1.563}{57.3}\right) \times 5 = 0.136 \text{ ft-lb} \qquad (11.33\text{-}7)$$

Since the motor is rated at 20 hp and 1100 rpm the rated torque is

$$T_R = \frac{(20)(33,000)}{2\pi \times 1100} = 95.5 \text{ ft-lb} \qquad (11.33\text{-}8)$$

Although this torque seems more than adequate for the acceleration requirements we must remember that most of it is required to move the antenna in a 35 mph wind. There is, of course, some viscous friction in the system and hence an acceleration time constant.

The nonlinearities are due to brush friction and gear box efficiencies which require a finite signal to the velocity servo before the antenna will move. Thus a small dead zone as discussed in Chap. 7 is present. The velocity constant must be large enough then so that $0.12°$ error will generate enough voltage to overcome such effects.

However as the velocity constant is increased and the bandwidth of the system is increased, other troubles arise. The nonlinearities can then give rise to the limit cycles. In particular the backlash in the gears becomes critical. The antenna structure is designed for a certain acceleration, and its structural resonant frequency should be higher than the resonant frequency of the system by a factor between six to ten.

With these facts in mind we will choose a $K_v$ of 20 as the design goal for designing the position amplifier.

## 11.40  DEVELOPING THE BODE PLOT

With the value of the velocity constant determined, the next step is to develop the Bode plot and determine what the type of compensation, if any, is necessary. It is now necessary to reduce the block diagram to the basic form. The rules developed in Chap. 5 can be put to good use in this section. Only the servo response of the system will be examined here, but the regulator response is just as important and must be examined in actual practice.

The first step is to simplify the load dynamics. From Fig. 11.32-7,

$$\frac{T_L}{\Omega_H}(s) = \left(\frac{J_A}{2}s + \frac{c_A}{s} + \frac{B}{2}\right) - \frac{c_A^2}{s}\left(\frac{1}{\dfrac{J_A}{2}s^2 + \dfrac{B}{2}s + c_A}\right) \qquad (11.40\text{-}1)$$

This equation can be written as

$$\frac{T_L}{\Omega_H}(s)$$

$$= \frac{c_A}{s}\left[\left(\frac{s}{\omega_n}\right)^2 + 2\zeta\left(\frac{s}{\omega_n}\right) + 1\right] = \left(\frac{c_A}{s\left[\left(\dfrac{s}{\omega_n}\right)^2 + 2\zeta\left(\dfrac{s}{\omega_n}\right) + 1\right]}\right) \qquad (11.40\text{-}2)$$

where

$$\omega_n = \sqrt{\frac{2c_A}{J_A}} = 31.6 \text{ radians/sec} \qquad (11.40\text{-}3)$$

$$\zeta = 0.566 \qquad (11.40\text{-}4)$$

From Fig. 2.80-2 it is seen that for frequencies less than one-tenth the natural frequencies, a second-order transfer function has unity gain and negligible phase shift. Thus for frequencies less than 3 radians/sec the load dynamics can be neglected.

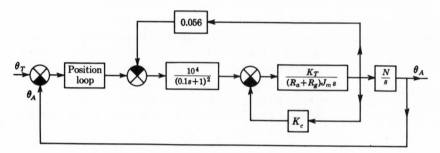

**Fig. 11.40-1** First reduction ($\omega \leq 3$ rad/sec).

The first reduction of the system block diagram then consists of neglecting the load dynamics and closing the loop in the motor-generator diagram due to armature resistances. This reduction is shown in Fig. 11.40-1.

The second reduction consists of closing the loop in the motor diagram due to the back emf constant $K_c$. This step is shown in Fig. 11.40-2. The final step consists of closing the loop around the velocity servo due to the tachometric feedback. The reduced system diagram is shown in Fig. 11.40-3 and has the open loop transfer function

$$KG(s) = \frac{183.4}{(530)(0.056)s} = \frac{6.18}{s} \tag{11.40-5}$$

written in vector form

$$|KG| = 15.85 \text{ db} - 20 \log \omega \tag{11.40-6}$$

$$\angle KG = \angle{-90°} \tag{11.40-7}$$

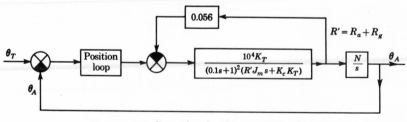

**Fig. 11.40-2** Second reduction ($\omega \leq 3$ rad/sec).

Thus the system has a velocity constant $K_v = 6.18$. The Bode plot shown in Fig. 11.40-4 should be quite good in this region. The large gain in the magnetic amplifier insures a gain of $1/0.056$ in the velocity servo over a

**Fig. 11.40-3** Final reduction ($\omega \leq 3$ rad/sec).

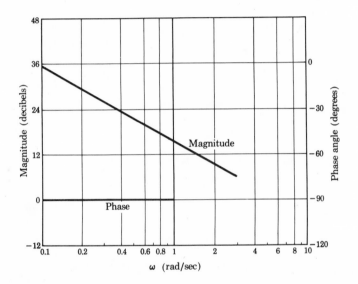

**Fig. 11.40-4** Bode plot for the system in the region $\omega \leq 3$ rad/sec.

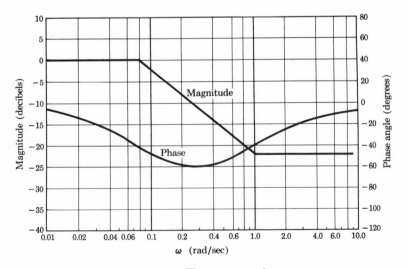

**Fig. 11.40-5** The compensation.

large range of frequencies. Hence the only region in doubt is the structure transfer function. The Bode plot shows the effect of the phase lag in the structure. If the structure has negligible phase shift for 3 radians/second or less, a lag-lead compensating network as shown in Fig. 11.40-5 can be used. The compensated Bode plot is shown in Fig. 11.40-6.

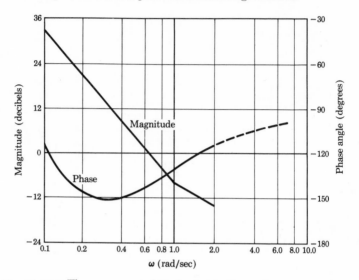

**Fig. 11.40-6** The compensated Bode plot in the region $\omega \leq 3$ rad/sec.

If the gain of the system is increased by a factor of 10 db (3.14) the zero db crossing will occur at 122°. This allows 58° phase margin without considering the structure effect. The compensation item will have the form

$$K_c G_c(s) = \frac{3.14(s+1)}{(12.25s+1)} \tag{11.40-8}$$

and the velocity constant will be

$$K_v = 19.5 \tag{11.40-9}$$

Although the problem developed here has been simplified from the actual system as shown in Fig. 11.40-7, the results should still be valid. The actual open loop frequency response of the Model 3013 antenna system is shown in Fig. 11.40-8.

The point to remember from this problem is not that the results closely approximated actual field test, but that by using these techniques the magnitude of the problem was quickly determined. It was seen that a velocity constant of 20 could be gained with few complications. The region in which the structure would predominate was determined and it was found

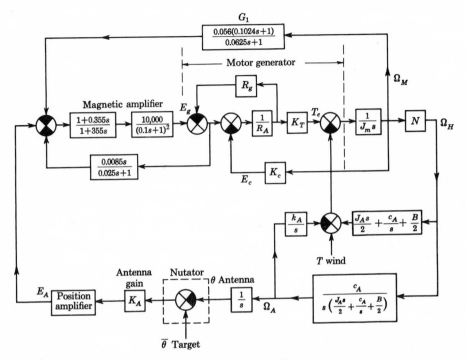

Fig. 11.40-7 System block diagram

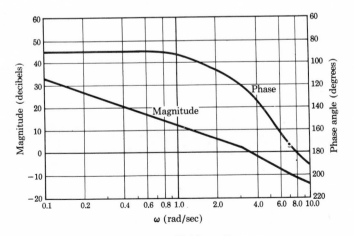

Fig. 11.40-8 Field results

the bandwidth of the system would be determined by this structure. It was also found that owing to the high gain in the velocity servo the theoretical frequency response should correspond quite closely to the actual.

The problem as shown in Fig. 11.40-7 was actually analyzed on an analog computer, but the results of the simplified problem served as a guide to the proper compensation and also as a check on the computer.

## 11.50 CONCLUSIONS

Although this chapter has stressed the control aspects of systems engineering we must not forget that this is only one phase of a system study. The next step would be to study the effect of nonlinearities. A very important facet is that of error analysis, which studies the contributions of each unit of the system to the overall system error, and finally the reliability of the system must be ascertained.

# BIBLIOGRAPHY

CHAPTER ONE

Goode, Harry H., and Machol, Robert E., *Systems Engineering* (New York: McGraw-Hill Book Company, Inc., 1957).

Spiegel, Murray R., *Applied Differential Equations* (Englewood Cliffs, N. J.: Prentice-Hall, Inc., 1958).

CHAPTER TWO

Churchill, R. V., *Operational Mathematics* (New York: McGraw-Hill Book Company, Inc., 1958).

Nixon, F. E., *Handbook of Laplace Transformation* (Englewood Cliffs, N. J.: Prentice-Hall, Inc., 1960).

Thomson, W. T., *Laplace Transformation* (Englewood Cliffs, N. J.: Prentice-Hall, Inc., 1960).

Wylie, C. R., Jr., *Advanced Engineering Mathematics* (New York: McGraw-Hill Book Company, Inc., 1951).

CHAPTER THREE

Campbell, Donald P., *Process Dynamics* (New York: John Wiley & Sons, Inc., 1958).

Hausmann, Erich, and Slack, Edgar P., *Physics* (Princeton, N. J.: D. Van Nostrand Company, Inc., 1957).

King, Horace W., Wisler, Chester O., and Woodburn, James G., *Hydraulics* (New York: John Wiley & Sons, Inc., 1958).

Olson, Harry F., *Dynamical Analogies* (Princeton, N. J.: D. Van Nostrand Company, Inc., 1958).

CHAPTER FOUR

Eshbach, Ovid W., *Handbook of Engineering Fundamentals* (New York: John Wiley & Sons, Inc., 1952).

Firestone, Floyd A., "Twixt Earth and Sky with Rod and Tube; the Mobility and Classical Impedance Analogies," *Journal of the Acoustical Society of America*, **28**:6 (Nov. 1956).

Olson, Harry F., *Dynamical Analogies* (Princeton, N. J.: D. Van Nostrand Company, Inc., 1958).

CHAPTER FIVE

Graybeal, T. D., "Transformation of Block Diagram Networks," AIEE Paper No. 51-298.

CHAPTER SIX

Nixon, Floyd E., *Principles of Automatic Controls* (Englewood Cliffs, N. J.: Prentice-Hall, Inc., 1953).

Brown, G. S., and Campbell, D. P., *Principles of Servo-Mechanisms* (New York: John Wiley & Sons, 1948).

Ahrendt, W. R., and Taplin, J. F., *Automatic Feedback Control* (New York: McGraw-Hill Book Company, Inc., 1951).

CHAPTER SEVEN

Baring, J. A., "Vacuum Tube Techniques Applied to a Hydraulic Motor," AIEE Paper No. 52-298.

Shearer, J. A., "Dynamic Characteristics of Valve-Controlled Hydraulic Servo-motors," ASME Paper No. 53-A-147.

Gould, L. A., and Smith, P. E., "Dynamic Behavior of Pneumatic Devices," presented at 1952 National ISA Conference.

CHAPTER EIGHT

Carslaw, H. S., *Introduction to the Theory of Fourier's Series and Integrals* (New York: Dover Publications Inc., 1952).

Kochenburger, R. J., "A Frequency Response Method of Analyzing and Synthesizing Contactor Servo Mechanisms," *Trans. AIEE*, **69**, pt. I, pp. 270–284 (1950).

Chestnut, H., "Approximate Frequency-Response Methods for Representing Saturation and Dead Band," ASME Paper No. 53-A-25.

CHAPTER NINE

Smith, Otto J. M., *Feedback Control Systems* (New York: McGraw-Hill Book Company, Inc., 1958).

Campbell, D. P., "Power Consumption in Linear Feedback Control Systems," Sc.D. Thesis, Dept. of Electrical Engineering, M.I.T., 1948.

CHAPTER TEN

Karakash, J. J., *Transmission Lines and Filter Networks* (New York: The Macmillan Company, 1950).

Johnson, Walter C., *Transmission Lines and Networks* (New York: McGraw-Hill Book Company, Inc., 1950).

Goldman, Stanford, *Transformation Calculus and Electrical Transients* (Englewood Cliffs, N. J.: Prentice-Hall, Inc., 1949).

# INDEX